SUPER EFFICIENT HOUSES

MANUFACTURED AND DO-IT-YOURSELF KIT HOUSES

Published by
Starcott Media Services
6906 Royalgreen Drive
Cincinnati, Ohio 45244

Printed in the United States of America
Third Edition
Copyright © 1995, 1997 by James T. Dulley
All rights reserved
9, 8, 7, 6, 5, 4, 3, 2

ISBN 0-9625583-5-4

We recommend care and adherence to standard construction safety procedures. Wear adequate protective clothing and safety gear (approved safety eyeglasses, work gloves, breathing filter mask) when working with power and hand tools, and with building and insulation materials. If you have questions about proper safety procedures or protective clothing to wear, contact your local health department, Occupational Safety and Health Administration, or Environmental Protection Agency. Neither the author nor the publisher takes responsibility for accidents that may occur during the building or use of any of the projects or products described in this book.

TABLE OF CONTENTS

INTRODUCTION

Many of my readers have asked me to compile a listing of manufacturers of super-high-efficiency housing and do-it-yourself housing kits including sample floor plan layouts and exterior diagrams.

This book includes floor plan layouts of seven types of super-efficient housing. Each of the floor plans includes the Plan No. or Plan Name so you can identify it when contacting the manufacturer. Most of the floor plan layouts also include an exterior diagram. For some of the types of housing, only one or two sample exterior diagrams are shown. The appearance of these types of houses is basically similar from the outside and, based on the floor plan layout, you can visualize the exterior appearance.

This book is divided into nine general topic sections. Each housing section begins with a background description of the housing type covered. This is followed by a list of the addresses and telephone numbers of the manufacturers of this type of housing. Many of these housing manufacturers have local dealers and builders throughout the U.S. Contact the manufacturer to find its nearest dealer or how you can order directly from the manufacturer. A sample specification sheet for one of the listed manufacturer's housing is included at the begin of the sections.

Section eight shows detailed diagrams and instructions for building a panelized house yourself. The final section includes a listing of the manufacturers of "earth-friendly" building products, many of which are made from recycled materials and can be later recycled themselves. The manufacturers are listed by product type.

Many of the types of housing shown in this book are ideal for the do-it-yourself builder. Depending on your level of skill and the type of equipment you have, you can determine how much of the work you will have to contract out to others. When evaluating the cost of building one of these houses, carefully study all the building plans and processes. You don't want to determine your budget and make your loan, only to find that you will have to contract more of the work outside than you expected.

The lists of manufacturers and product information shown are for your information only and are not an endorsement of these types of products or a specific manufacturer or model. The sample floor plan layouts and exterior diagrams were selected based on how well they described the particular type of housing.

If you choose a particular type of housing, contact all the manufacturers listed for detailed information on their housing. Make a careful comparison of the designs based on your needs. Check with local builders and city or state building codes inspectors to be sure your selected housing meets codes. There may be some unique characteristics of your area that make one type of housing more or less feasible for your area.

Timber-frame house construction is a very old building technique utilizing heavy timbers for the basic structure. All of the beautiful, finely-finished heavy wood beams and posts are exposed in the interior when the house is completed. Many have cathedral ceilings and lofts providing a spacious and open feeling.

A true timber-frame house uses no nails or screws for the framing. All joints between the beams and posts are carefully hand-cut and fitted by experienced craftsmen. This forms an extremely-strong and rigid structure that should last for hundreds of years. Many of the cathedrals in Europe were built using this method.

You can either choose one of many standard models or modify one per your needs. Designing and building the basic timber frame is not a do-it-yourself job. It requires experienced craftsmen building and fitting it by hand. Building the timber frame usually takes about two weeks. Once the timber frame is completed, you can do the finish work yourself.

Upon approval of your preliminary plans, the timber framer will usually develop a complete set of detailed drawings including - site plan, foundation plan, floor plans, elevations, building sections, exterior and interior trim details, electrical plan, plumbing plan, and HVAC plan.

After the framing has been cut and bored to accept the assembly pegs, each timber is planed smooth. Each one is hand-rubbed with a mixture of tung oil and linseed oil. You can also request coloration and a finish with luster.

When the timber-framing is erected, the exterior walls and roof are usually covered with super-efficient foam core stress-skin insulating panels. These provide insulating R-values as high as R-40 and are very soundproof.

These panels, with drywall on the interior surface and exterior-grade sheathing on the outside, are delivered to your building site. You can finish the exterior of the house with any material - brick, siding, stucco, stone, etc.. They look conventional when completed.

Many of the stress-skin panels also have interlocking tongue-and-groove edges. This makes them easy to assemble and very airtight. With this type of home, it is a good idea to install a powered heat recovery ventilation system. This brings outdoor air into your home and reclaims some of the heat before the stale air is exhausted outdoors.

Another energy advantage of timber-framing is that there are no interior supporting walls. This allows you to locate interior walls wherever you wish and as high as you wish. When utilizing solar, wood, or other alternative heating, an open floor plan improves the distribution of heat.

The heavy exposed timbers are on the interior side of the wall insulation, so they stay the same temperature as your room air. This heavy mass can help to moderate temperature swings in your house. Particularly in the summer, this can help to lower your air-conditioning costs.

The foam core panels already have the holes cut for the windows and doors. Since these houses are extremely efficient and airtight, you should consider installing a mechanical fresh-air ventilating systems. A heat recovery ventilator is most effective.

You can order many standard house designs and floor plans or have one made to your architect's drawings. The timber-frame builder sends out an experienced crew to assemble the framing and usually install the foam core wall and roof panels. It takes about two weeks to complete this phase. Then you or your contractor can finish the interior.

MANUFACTURERS OF TIMBER-FRAMED HOUSES

BLUE RIDGE TIMBER FRAME, 2030 Redwood Dr., Christiansburg, VA 24073
(540) 382-1102 (540) 382-8039 FAX

DAVIS FRAME CO., P.O. Box 1079, Claremont, NH 03743
(603) 543-0993

DE CELLE POST & BEAM, P.O. Box 1007, Elkin, NC 28621
(910) 835-1494

G A COOK CO., 12719 Roepke Rd., Gregory, MI 48137
(313) 498-2378

HEARTHSTONE TIMBER FRAMES, Rt. 2, Box 434, Dandridge, TN 37725
(423) 397-9425

HUGH LOFTING TIMBER FRAMING, 339 Lamborntown Rd., West Grove, PA 19390
(610) 444-5382

INTERNATIONAL HOMES OF CEDAR, PO Box 886, Woodinville, WA 98072
(800) 767-7674 (360) 668-8511

KONDOR POST & BEAM, RR. 2, Box 2794, Cambridge, VT 05444
(802) 644-5598

OAKBRIDGE TIMBER FRAMING, 20857 Earnest Rd., Howard, OH 43028
(614) 694-1230

PACIFIC POST & BEAM, P.O. Box 13708, San Luis Obispo, CA 93406
(805) 543-7565

RIVERBEND TIMBER FRAMING, P.O. Box 26, Blissfield, MI 49228
(517) 486-4355

TIMBERCRAFT HOMES, 85 Martin Rd., Port Townsend, WA 98368
(206) 385-3051

TIMBER FRAME SYSTEMS, P.O. Box 458, Frankford, DE 19945
(302) 732-9428

TIMBERHOUSE, 150 Sheafman Creek Rd., Victor, MT 59875
(406) 961-3276 (406) 961-4643 FAX

TIMBERPEG, PO Box 474, W. Lebanon, NH 03784
(603) 298-8820

UPPER LOFT DESIGN, Route 1, Box 2901, Lakemont, GA 30552
(706) 782-5246

VERMONT FRAMES, P.O. Box 100, Hinesburg, VT 05461
(802) 453-3727

WOODHOUSE, P.O. Box 219, Mansfield, PA 16933
(717) 549-6232

HEARTHSTONE, INC.

MATERIALS INCLUDED IN MODELS

1. Complete Structural Oak Frame consisting of: Rafters, Purlins at 4' OC, Posts, Girts, Joists at 4' OC, Braces and Struts, Ridge Pole, Collar Ties, and Closure Plates.

2. Joinery Specification:

Rafters to Post	Bird's mouth - mortise and tenon
Closure Plate to Rafter	Houses mortise and tenon-plate bevelled to carry roof decking
Girt to Post	Shouldered mortise and tenon
Purlin to Rafter	Housed dove tail
Rafter to Rafter	Tongue and fork at ridge pole
Braces and Struts	Mortise and Tenon
Ridge Pole to Rafter	Housed Pocket

    NOTE 1 -   Bottom edges of wind braces are curved
    NOTE 2 -   Exposed edges timbers are chamfered. All other edges rounded.
    NOTE 3 -   All timbers are planed, sanded, and oiled.

3. Windows - Anderson Windows™: High Performance insulating glass - Perma Shield narroline double hung windows that are rigid vinyl clad or polyester urethane finished in terratone color on the exterior. Natural wood interior. Sash lock and fingerlifts applied, molded divided light colonial grilles and aluminum screens to match. Jambs are 4 1/2". Service backing 5 years, glass backing 20 years.

4. Peases™ Entry Doors: the entry door comes as a complete system comprised of the insulated steel door weather stripped frame and sill. Components are shipped to the job site pre-hung.

5. Foam Core Panels - A typical panel is composed of chipboard, polyurethane foam and sheetrock bonded into a single building component. Panel comes in sizes 4' x 8', 4' x 9', 4' x 10', 4' x 12', 4' x 14', and 4' x 16'. The R-Value is 28, thickness is 4 1/2 inches. Stress skin panels cover the exterior of the frame including roof.

6. On Site Erection - The Frame, panels, and exterior doors and windows are erected and/or installed on the client's foundation and subfloor. Erection and pricing is subject to minimum site standards.

7. Asphalt Shingles - Architectural Grade, choice of colors (unerected).

8. Western Red Cedar Siding: Clear V.G. Heart, 1 x 6 Bevel siding, K.D. Including Exterior-Trim Package (unerected).

9. 2 x 6 Spruce Decking - Tongue and Groove, V edged, Kiln dried for 2nd floor only (unerected).

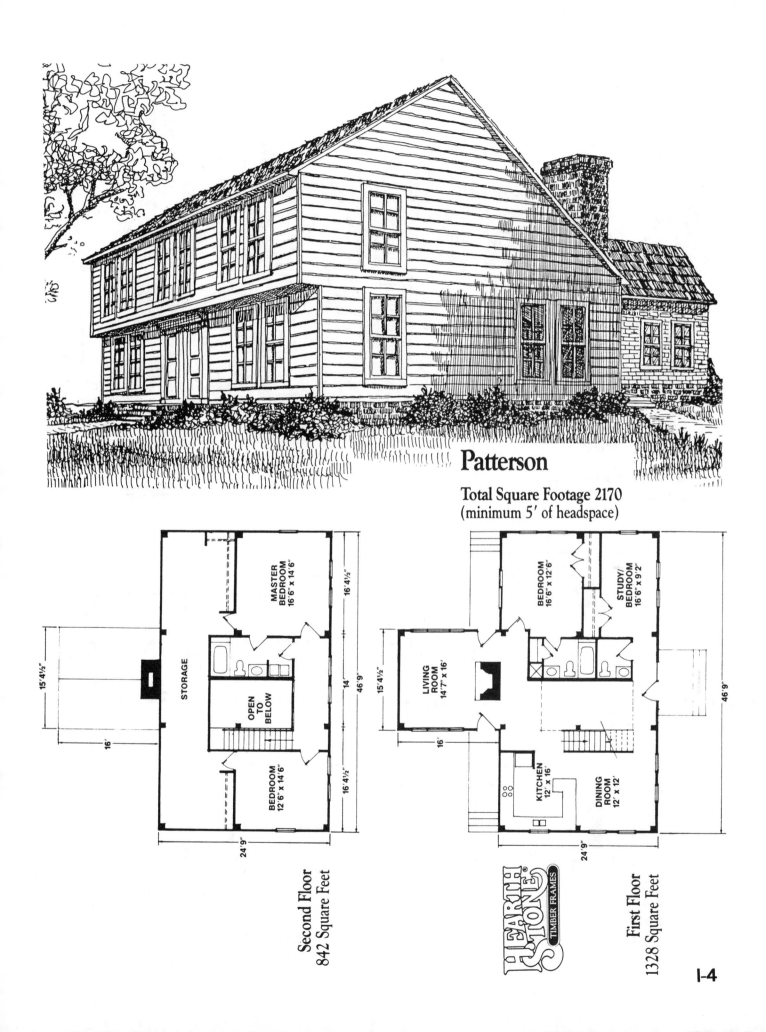

Patterson

Total Square Footage 2170
(minimum 5' of headspace)

MASTER
BEDROOM
16'6" x 14'6"

STORAGE

OPEN
TO
BELOW

BEDROOM
12'6" x 14'6"

16'4½"
14
15'4½"
16'
16'4½"
46'9"
24'9"

Second Floor
842 Square Feet

BEDROOM
16'6" x 12'6"

STUDY/
BEDROOM
16'6" x 9'2"

LIVING
ROOM
14'7" x 16'

KITCHEN
12' x 16'

DINING
ROOM
12' x 12'

15'4½"
16'
46'9"
24'9"

First Floor
1328 Square Feet

HEARTH STONE® TIMBER FRAMES

I-4

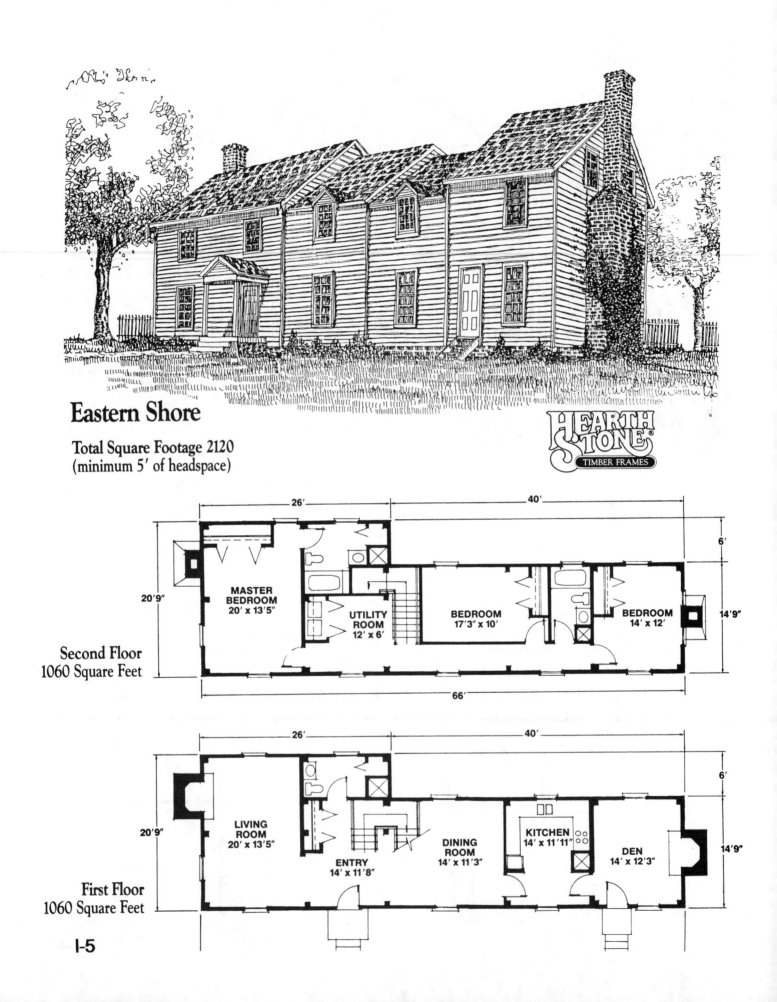

Eastern Shore

Total Square Footage 2120
(minimum 5' of headspace)

HEARTH STONE®
TIMBER FRAMES

Second Floor
1060 Square Feet

26'   40'   6'

20'9"

14'9"

66'

MASTER
BEDROOM
20' x 13'5"

UTILITY
ROOM
12' x 6'

BEDROOM
17'3" x 10'

BEDROOM
14' x 12'

First Floor
1060 Square Feet

26'   40'   6'

20'9"

14'9"

LIVING
ROOM
20' x 13'5"

ENTRY
14' x 11'8"

DINING
ROOM
14' x 11'3"

KITCHEN
14' x 11'11"

DEN
14' x 12'3"

I-5

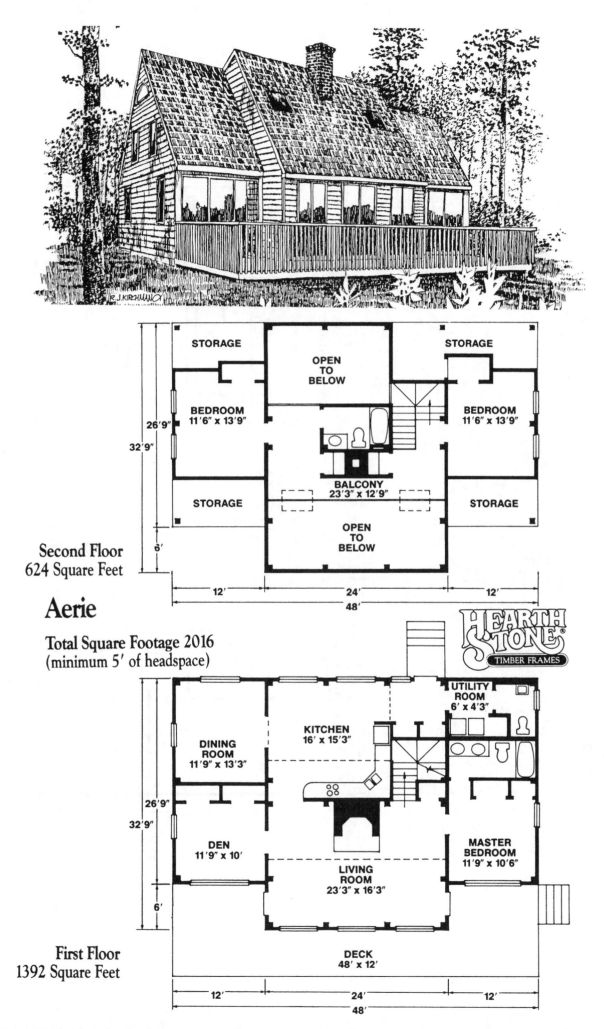

R.J.KIRCHMANN

STORAGE

OPEN
TO
BELOW

STORAGE

BEDROOM
11'6" x 13'9"

BEDROOM
11'6" x 13'9"

STORAGE

BALCONY
23'3" x 12'9"

STORAGE

OPEN
TO
BELOW

26'9"

32'9"

Second Floor
624 Square Feet

8'

12'   24'   12'

48'

Aerie

Total Square Footage 2016
(minimum 5' of headspace)

HEARTH STONE®
TIMBER FRAMES

UTILITY
ROOM
6' x 4'3"

DINING
ROOM
11'9" x 13'3"

KITCHEN
16' x 15'3"

DEN
11'9" x 10'

MASTER
BEDROOM
11'9" x 10'6"

LIVING
ROOM
23'3" x 16'3"

26'9"

32'9"

6'

First Floor
1392 Square Feet

DECK
48' x 12'

12'   24'   12'

48'

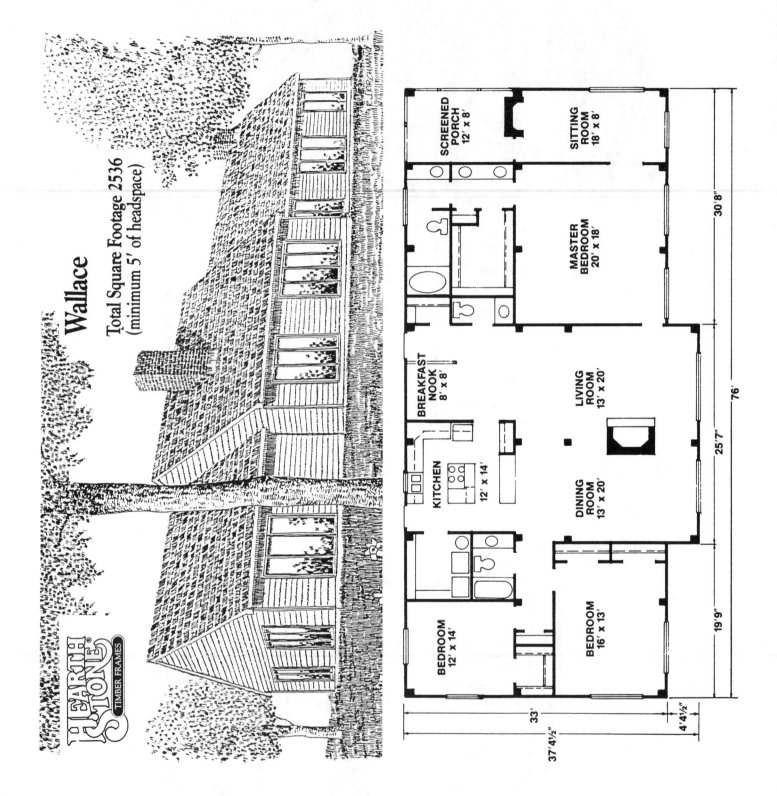

Wallace

Total Square Footage 2536
(minimum 5' of headspace)

SCREENED PORCH
12' x 8'

SITTING ROOM
18' x 8'

MASTER BEDROOM
20' x 18'

BREAKFAST NOOK
8' x 8'

KITCHEN
12' x 14'

LIVING ROOM
13' x 20'

DINING ROOM
13' x 20'

BEDROOM
12' x 14'

BEDROOM
16' x 13'

30'8"

76'

25'7"

19'9"

33'

37'4½'

4'4½"

HEARTH STONE® TIMBER FRAMES

K.J. RICHMAND

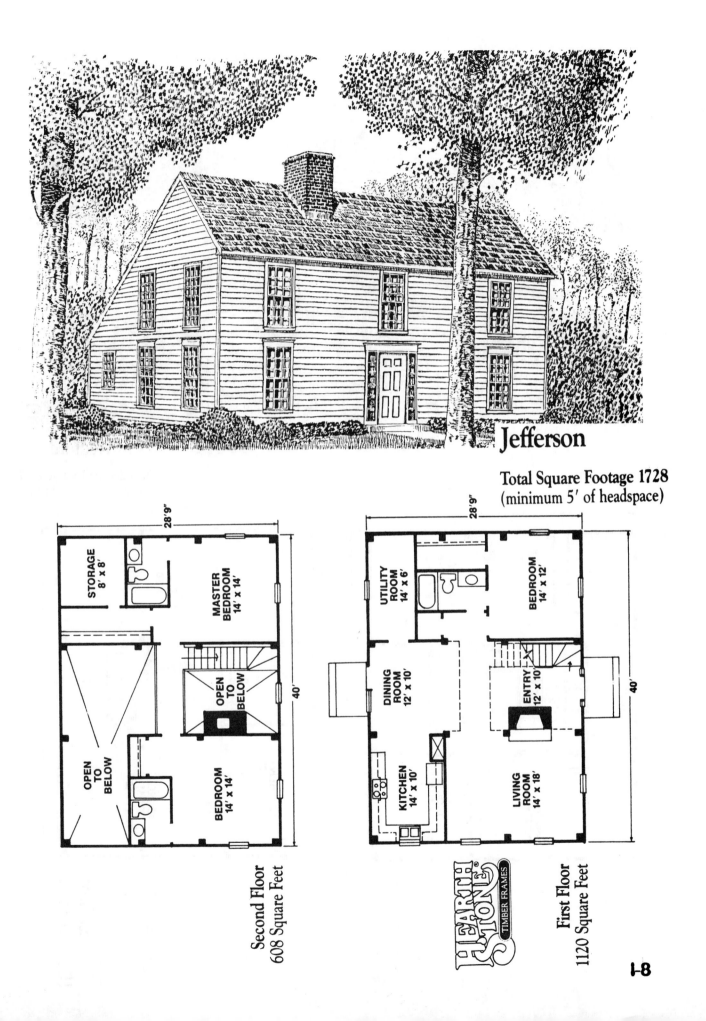

Jefferson

Total Square Footage 1728
(minimum 5' of headspace)

28'9"

STORAGE
8' x 8'

MASTER
BEDROOM
14' x 14'

OPEN
TO
BELOW

OPEN
TO
BELOW

BEDROOM
14' x 14'

40'

Second Floor
608 Square Feet

28'9"

UTILITY
ROOM
14' x 6'

BEDROOM
14' x 12'

DINING
ROOM
12' x 10'

ENTRY
12' x 10'

KITCHEN
14' x 10'

LIVING
ROOM
14' x 18'

40'

First Floor
1120 Square Feet

HEARTHSTONE
TIMBER FRAMES

I-8

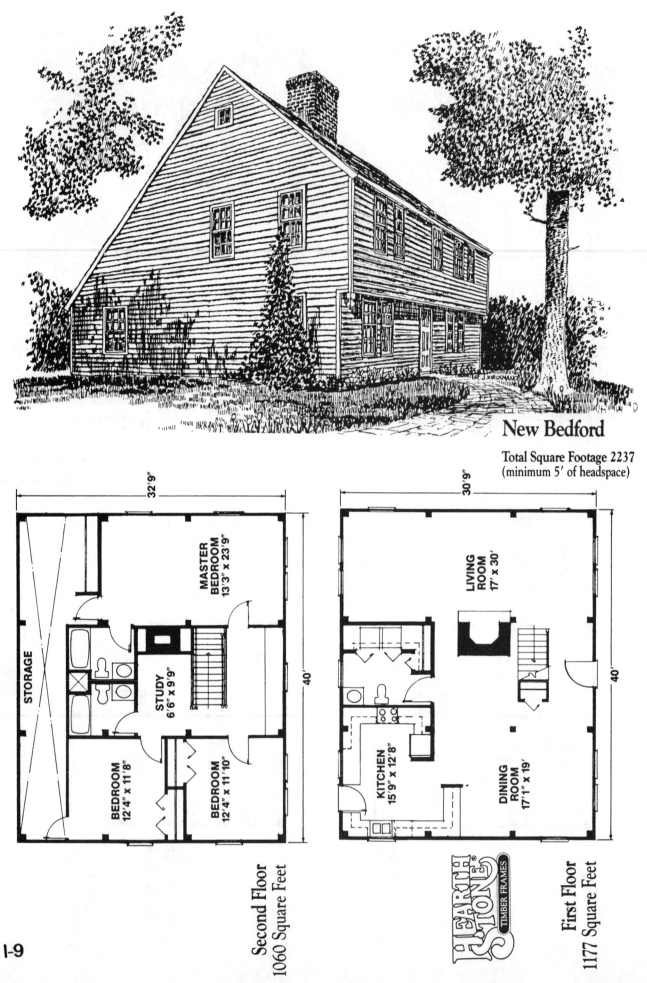

New Bedford

Total Square Footage 2237
(minimum 5' of headspace)

32'9"

STORAGE

MASTER BEDROOM
13'3" x 23'9"

STUDY
6'6" x 9'9"

BEDROOM
12'4" x 11'8"

BEDROOM
12'4" x 11'10"

40'

Second Floor
1060 Square Feet

30'9"

LIVING ROOM
17' x 30'

KITCHEN
15'9" x 12'8"

DINING ROOM
17'1" x 19'

40'

HEARTH STONE
TIMBER FRAMES

First Floor
1177 Square Feet

I-9

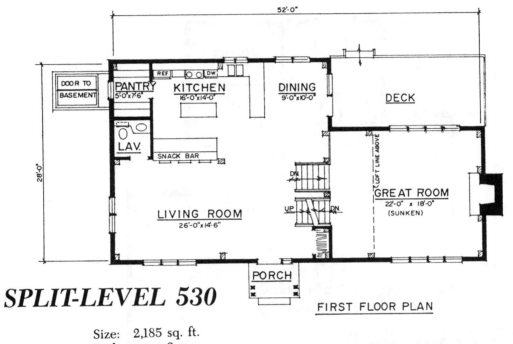

SPLIT-LEVEL 530

FIRST FLOOR PLAN

Size: 2,185 sq. ft.
Bedrooms: 3
Bathrooms: 2 1/2

RIVERBEND
TIMBER FRAMING INC.

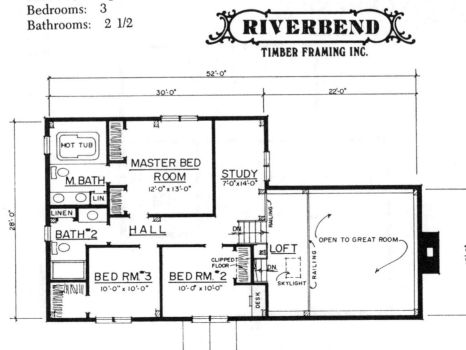

SECOND FLOOR PLAN

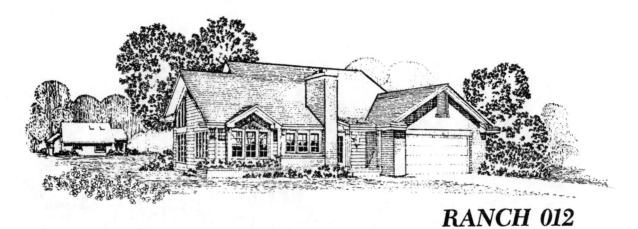

RANCH 012

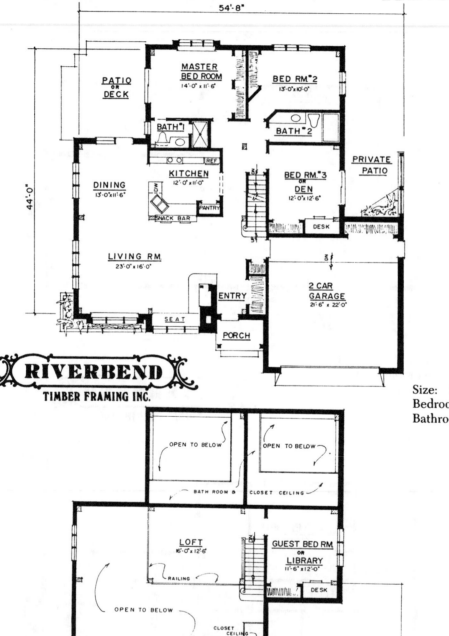

54'-8"

44'-0"

PATIO OR DECK

MASTER BED ROOM
14'-0" x 11'-6"

BED RM. 2
13'-0" x 10'-0"

BATH 1

BATH 2

REF

DINING
13'-0" x 11'-6"

KITCHEN
12'-0" x 11'-0"

DW

SNACK BAR

PANTRY

BED RM. 3 OR DEN
12'-0" x 12'-6"

PRIVATE PATIO

DESK

LIVING RM.
23'-0" x 16'-0"

ENTRY

2 CAR GARAGE
21'-6" x 22'-0"

SEAT

PORCH

RIVERBEND
TIMBER FRAMING INC.

Size: 2,050 sq. ft.
Bedrooms: 2 to 4
Bathrooms: 2

OPEN TO BELOW

OPEN TO BELOW

BATH ROOM &

CLOSET CEILING

LOFT
16'-0" x 12'-6"

RAILING

GUEST BED RM. OR LIBRARY
11'-6" x 12'-0"

DESK

OPEN TO BELOW

CLOSET CEILING

OPTIONAL LOFT PLAN

GAMBREL 649

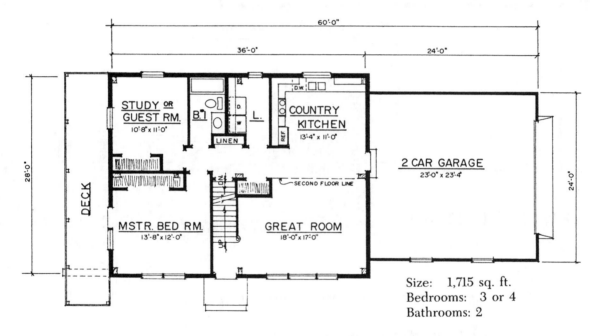

STUDY OR GUEST RM.
10'-8" x 11'-0"

B.

D
W

L.

LINEN

COUNTRY KITCHEN
13'-4" x 11'-0"

D.W.

REF.

2 CAR GARAGE
23'-0" x 23'-4"

SECOND FLOOR LINE

DECK

MSTR. BED RM.
13'-8" x 12'-0"

DN

GREAT ROOM
18'-0" x 17'-0"

60'-0"

36'-0"

24'-0"

28'-0"

24'-0"

Size: 1,715 sq. ft.
Bedrooms: 3 or 4
Bathrooms: 2

FIRST FLOOR PLAN

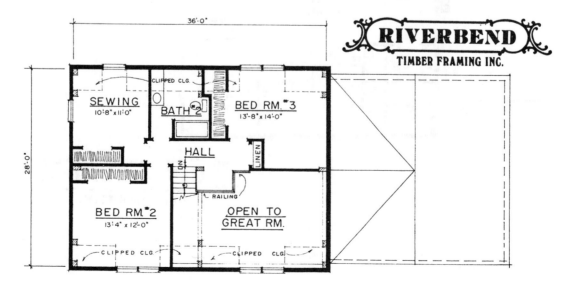

SEWING
10'-8" x 11'-0"

CLIPPED CLG.

BATH #2

BED RM. #3
13'-8" x 14'-0"

HALL

LINEN

DN

BED RM. #2
13'-4" x 12'-0"

RAILING

OPEN TO GREAT RM.

CLIPPED CLG.

CLIPPED CLG.

36'-0"

28'-0"

RIVERBEND
TIMBER FRAMING INC.

SECOND FLOOR PLAN

I-12

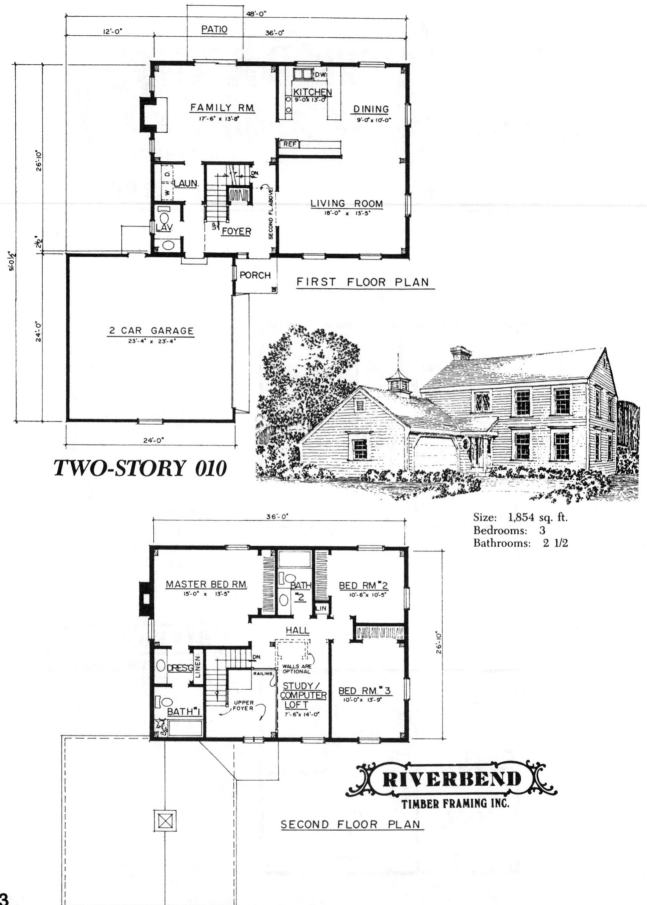

48'-0"

12'-0" PATIO 36'-0"

FAMILY RM.
17'-6" x 13'-8"

KITCHEN
9'-0 x 13'-0"

DW

DINING
9'-0" x 10'-0"

26'-10"

REF

LAUN.
W D

LIVING ROOM
18'-0" x 13'-5"

2½"

LAV

FOYER

SECOND FL. ABOVE

51'-0½"

PORCH

FIRST FLOOR PLAN

24'-0"

2 CAR GARAGE
23'-4" x 23'-4"

24'-0"

TWO-STORY 010

Size: 1,854 sq. ft.
Bedrooms: 3
Bathrooms: 2 1/2

36'-0"

MASTER BED RM.
15'-0" x 13'-5"

BATH
#2

LIN

BED RM. #2
10'-6" x 10'-5"

HALL

26'-10"

DRES'G

LINEN

DN

RAILING

WALLS ARE
OPTIONAL

BATH #1

UPPER
FOYER

STUDY/
COMPUTER
LOFT
7'-6"x 14'-0"

BED RM. #3
10'-0"x 13'-9"

RIVERBEND
TIMBER FRAMING INC.

SECOND FLOOR PLAN

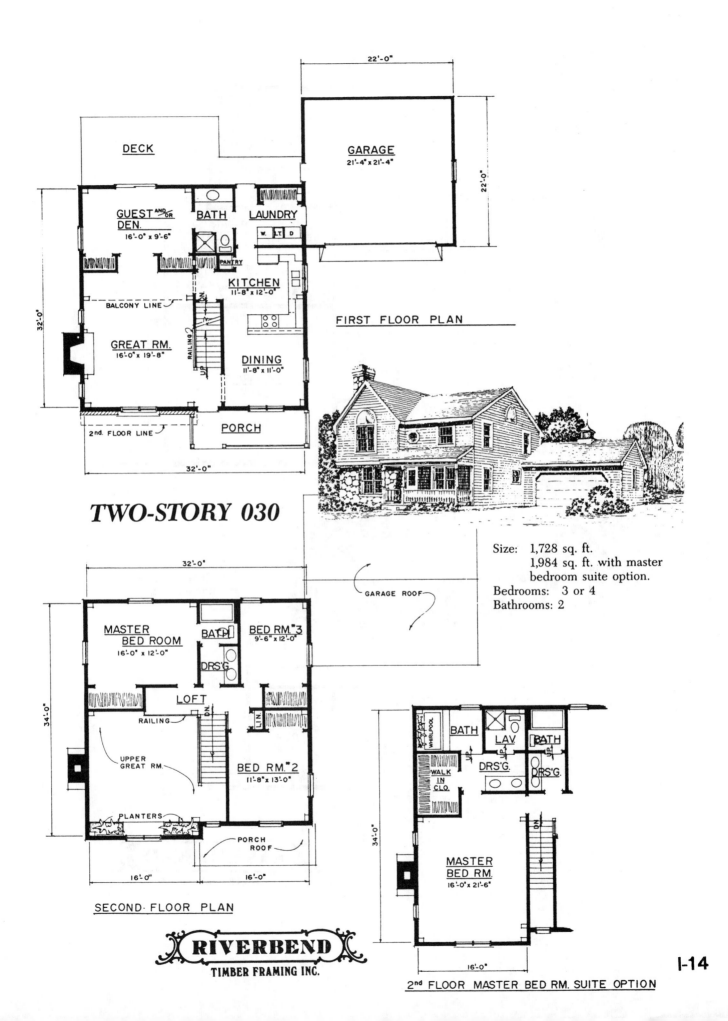

DECK

GARAGE
21'-4" x 21'-4"

22'-0"

22'-0"

GUEST ^AND^OR DEN.
16'-0" x 9'-6"

BATH

LAUNDRY

W. T D

PANTRY

KITCHEN
11'-8" x 12'-0"

BALCONY LINE

GREAT RM.
16'-0" x 19'-8"

RAILING

UP

DN

DINING
11'-8" x 11'-0"

32'-0"

2nd. FLOOR LINE

PORCH

32'-0"

FIRST FLOOR PLAN

TWO-STORY 030

Size: 1,728 sq. ft.
1,984 sq. ft. with master
bedroom suite option.
Bedrooms: 3 or 4
Bathrooms: 2

32'-0"

GARAGE ROOF

MASTER
BED ROOM
16'-0" x 12'-0"

BATH

BED RM.#3
9'-6" x 12'-0"

DRS'G

LOFT

RAILING

DN

LIN

UPPER
GREAT RM.

34'-0"

BED RM.#2
11'-8" x 13'-0"

PLANTERS

PORCH
ROOF

16'-0"

16'-0"

SECOND FLOOR PLAN

WHIRLPOOL

BATH

LAV

BATH

UP

UP

WALK
IN
CLO.

DRS'G

DRS'G

34'-0"

DN

MASTER
BED RM.
16'-0" x 21'-6"

16'-0"

2nd FLOOR MASTER BED RM. SUITE OPTION

RIVERBEND
TIMBER FRAMING INC.

I-14

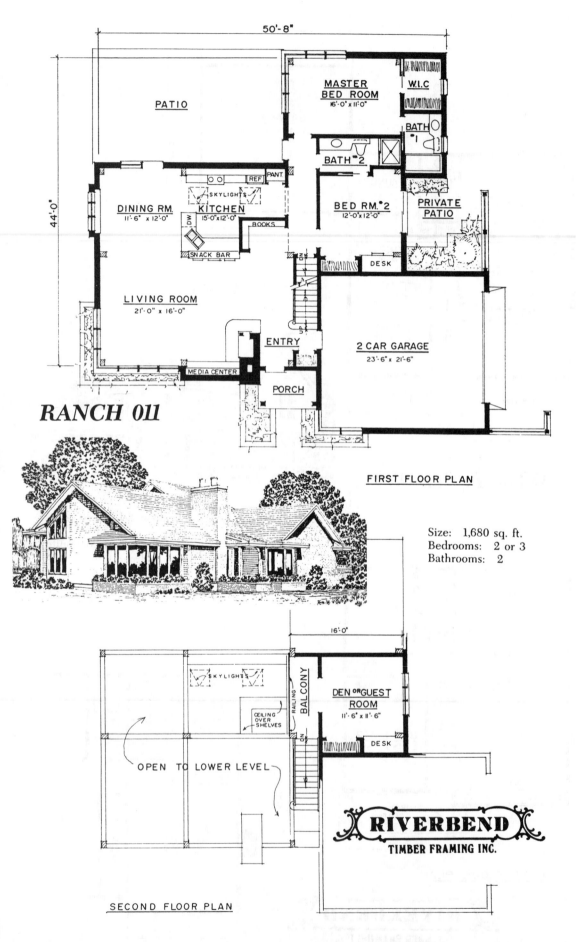

50'-8"

PATIO

MASTER
BED ROOM
16'-0" x 11'-0"

W.I.C

BATH
#1

BATH #2

44'-0"

DINING RM.
11'-6" x 12'-0"

KITCHEN
15'-0"x12'-0"

REF | PANT

SKYLIGHTS

BOOKS

BED RM. #2
12'-0"x12'-0"

PRIVATE
PATIO

DW

SNACK BAR

DESK

LIVING ROOM
21'-0" x 16'-0"

UP

2 CAR GARAGE
23'-6" x 21'-6"

MEDIA CENTER

ENTRY

PORCH

RANCH 011

FIRST FLOOR PLAN

Size: 1,680 sq. ft.
Bedrooms: 2 or 3
Bathrooms: 2

16'-0"

SKYLIGHTS

RAILING

BALCONY

DEN or GUEST
ROOM
11'-6" x 11'-6"

CEILING
OVER
SHELVES

DN

DESK

OPEN TO LOWER LEVEL

DN

RIVERBEND
TIMBER FRAMING INC.

SECOND FLOOR PLAN

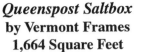

Queenspost Saltbox
by Vermont Frames
1,664 Square Feet

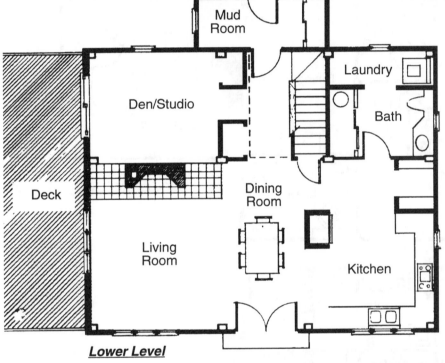

Mud
Room

Laundry

Den/Studio

Bath

Deck

Dining
Room

Living
Room

Kitchen

Lower Level

Upper Level

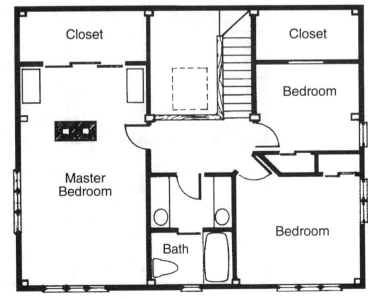

Closet

Closet

Bedroom

Master
Bedroom

Bath

Bedroom

The 26'×32' Queenspost Saltbox is the most popular of our frames and is designed to capture the most from a sunny location. The east facing living and dining areas provide a warm, naturally lit atmosphere for your daytime hours. A half bath, laundry room and north facing vestibule/mudroom make this a truly convenient home. Two or three bedrooms and full bath upstairs complete this traditional Saltbox home.

I-16

Arlington Heights
by Timbercraft Homes
3,526 Square Feet

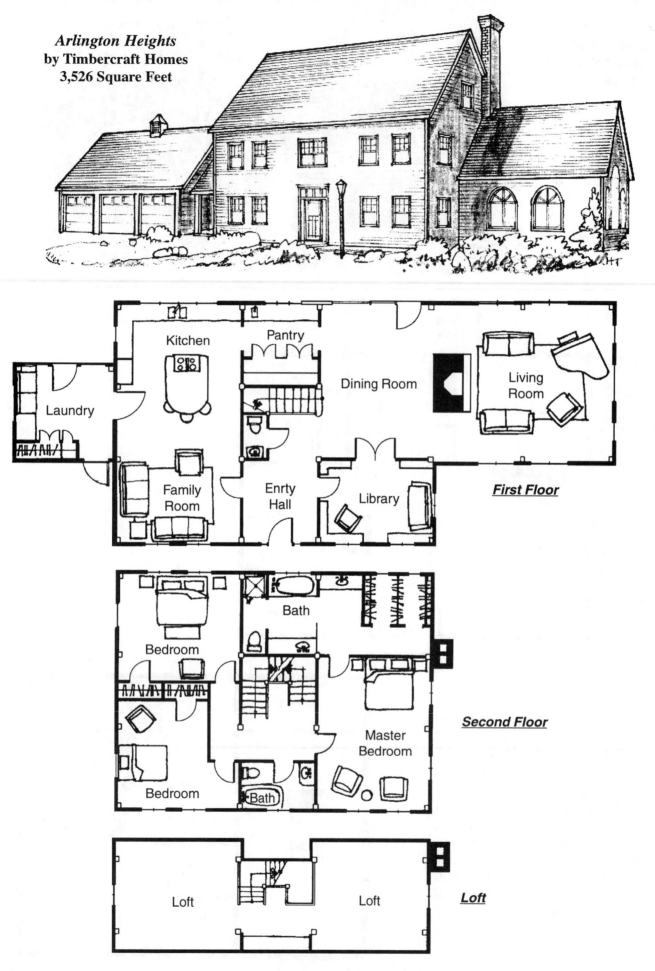

Kitchen

Pantry

Dining Room

Living Room

Laundry

Family Room

Enrty Hall

Library

First Floor

Bedroom

Bath

Master Bedroom

Bedroom

Bath

Second Floor

Loft

Loft

Loft

I-17

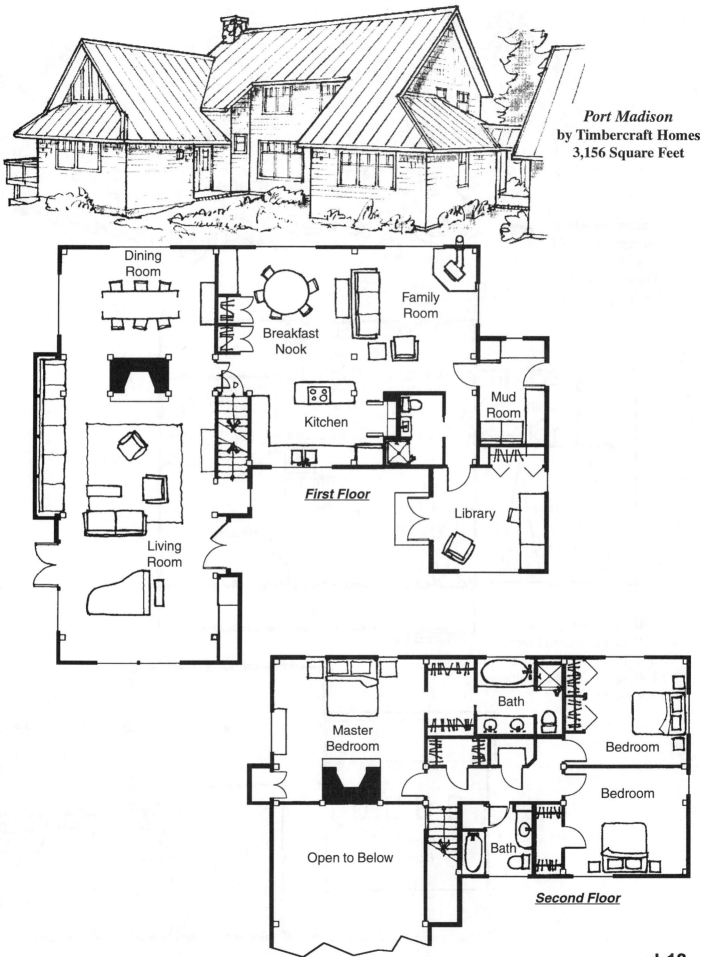

Port Madison
by Timbercraft Homes
3,156 Square Feet

Dining Room

Breakfast Nook

Family Room

Kitchen

Mud Room

First Floor

Library

Living Room

Master Bedroom

Bath

Bedroom

Bedroom

Bath

Open to Below

Second Floor

I-18

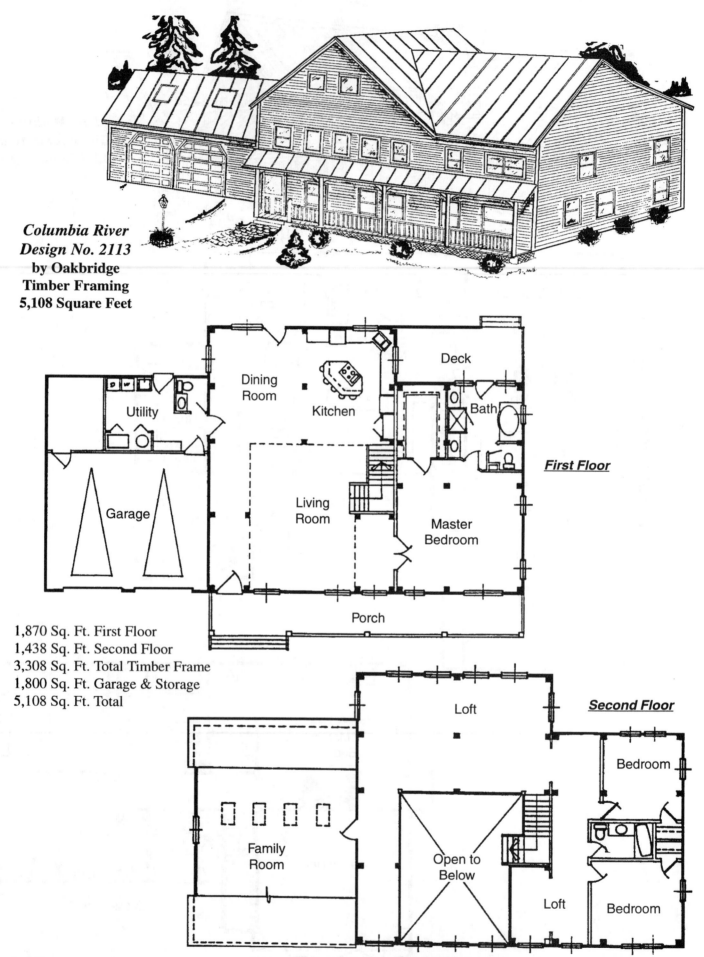

Columbia River
Design No. 2113
by Oakbridge
Timber Framing
5,108 Square Feet

Utility

Dining
Room

Kitchen

Deck

Bath

Garage

Living
Room

First Floor

Master
Bedroom

1,870 Sq. Ft. First Floor
1,438 Sq. Ft. Second Floor
3,308 Sq. Ft. Total Timber Frame
1,800 Sq. Ft. Garage & Storage
5,108 Sq. Ft. Total

Porch

Loft

Second Floor

Bedroom

Family
Room

Open to
Below

Loft

Bedroom

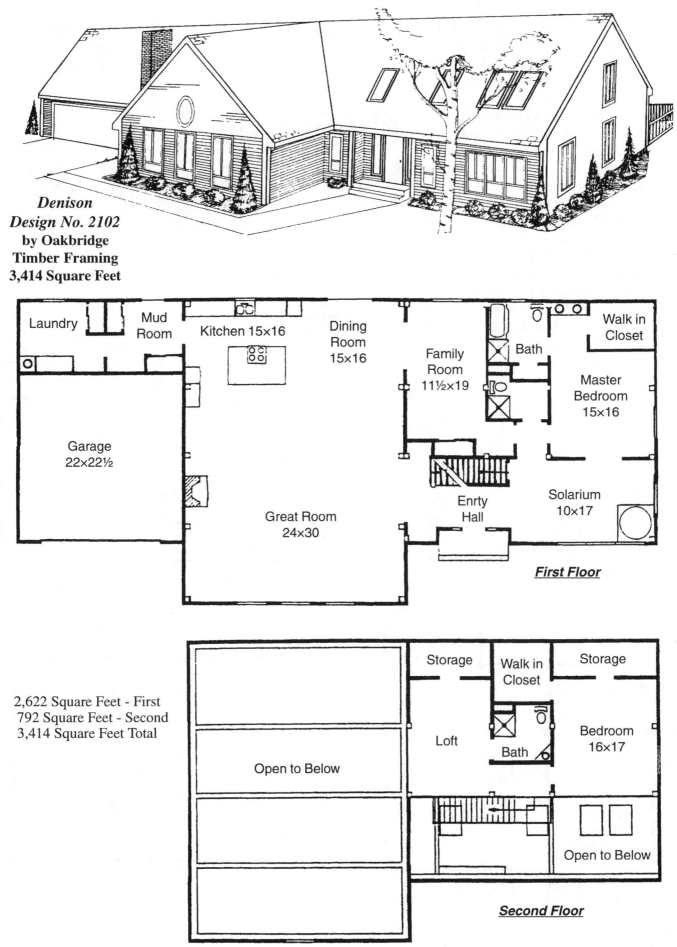

Denison
Design No. 2102
by Oakbridge
Timber Framing
3,414 Square Feet

Laundry

Mud Room

Kitchen 15×16

Dining Room 15×16

Family Room 11½×19

Bath

Walk in Closet

Master Bedroom 15×16

Garage 22×22½

Great Room 24×30

Enrty Hall

Solarium 10×17

First Floor

2,622 Square Feet - First
792 Square Feet - Second
3,414 Square Feet Total

Open to Below

Storage

Walk in Closet

Storage

Loft

Bath

Bedroom 16×17

Open to Below

Second Floor

I-20

A charming corner turret tops two complete floors of living space with a loft on the third level. The first floor features a front porch that leads to a closeted foyer, living room with fireplace, a study or library, dining room, family room and a kitchen with a large island. A half bath and laundry room is located to one side of the two car garage and also affords access to a rear deck. Another rear deck is just off the dining room. The second level features a large master bedroom with its own bathroom, whirlpool tub and a spacious walk-in closet. The other two bedrooms have a shared bathroom, and large closets. There are lots of windows throughout this lovely model with four arched windows in the master bedroom. The third level features a large loft area for a beautiful classic Victorian.

The Montpelier
by Classic Post & Beam
3,992 square feet

• 3 bedrooms
• 2 full baths
• 1 half bath
• First floor 1,732 square feet
• Second floor 1,480 square feet
• Third floor 780 square feet
• First floor 1,732 square feet
• Total living space 3,992 square feet

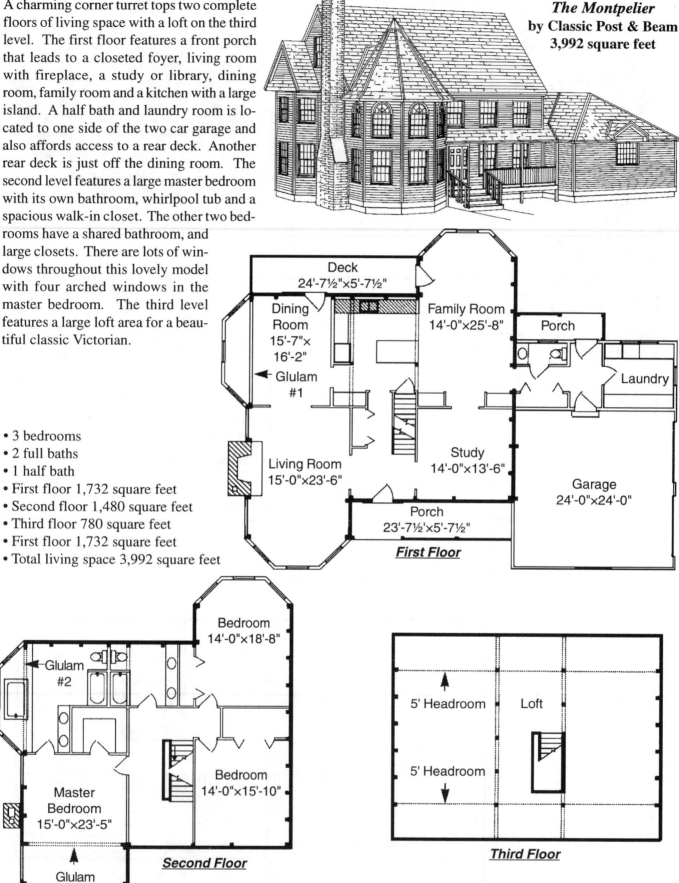

Deck
24'-7½"×5'-7½"

Dining Room
15'-7"×16'-2"

← Glulam #1

Family Room
14'-0"×25'-8"

Porch

Laundry

Living Room
15'-0"×23'-6"

Study
14'-0"×13'-6"

Garage
24'-0"×24'-0"

Porch
23'-7½"×5'-7½"

First Floor

← Glulam #2

Bedroom
14'-0"×18'-8"

Bedroom
14'-0"×15'-10"

Master Bedroom
15'-0"×23'-5"

↑ Glulam #3

Second Floor

5' Headroom   Loft

5' Headroom

Third Floor

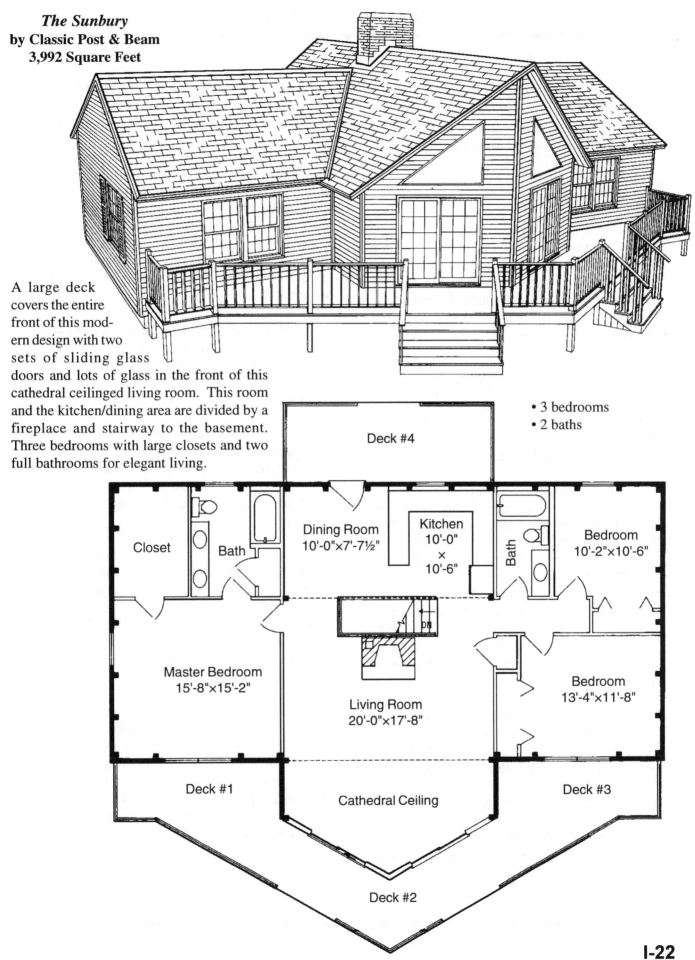

The Sunbury
by Classic Post & Beam
3,992 Square Feet

A large deck covers the entire front of this modern design with two sets of sliding glass doors and lots of glass in the front of this cathedral ceilinged living room. This room and the kitchen/dining area are divided by a fireplace and stairway to the basement. Three bedrooms with large closets and two full bathrooms for elegant living.

• 3 bedrooms
• 2 baths

Deck #4

Closet

Bath

Dining Room
10'-0"×7'-7½"

Kitchen
10'-0"
×
10'-6"

Bath

Bedroom
10'-2"×10'-6"

Master Bedroom
15'-8"×15'-2"

DN

Living Room
20'-0"×17'-8"

Bedroom
13'-4"×11'-8"

Deck #1

Cathedral Ceiling

Deck #3

Deck #2

I-22

A steel-framed house is very energy efficient, both for heating and cooling. Since all of the steel wall and roof framing is pre-drilled, you can bolt it together like a huge erector set. When the house is finished, you will not be able to tell if it has standard wood or steel framing. The steel components are galvanized so they will not corrode.

Three people often can complete the exterior shell of a steel-framed house in several days. Then you can complete the interior of the house as your time and budget allows. They are often less expensive to build than a standard site-built house.

Steel framing is actually lighter weight than wood framing. The high-strength-to-weight ratio of cold-formed light gauge steel components make them easy to work with. A steel roof truss weighs about 1/3 as much as a similar-sized wood truss.

The basic home package includes the following items - heavy gauge bolt-together steel columns and rafters, metal roof purlins, 8" steel stud system for exterior walls, metal framing components for all dormers, roof, and porch saddles, metal sub-fascia material for roof overhangs, metal studs and track for all interior walls, metal furring channels for all ceiling surfaces, metal second floor joists, all bolts and fasteners, and a complete set of working drawings including anchor bolt layout and erection instructions.

Steel-framed houses are ideal for utilizing passive solar energy. With the superior strength of steel framing, you have a clearspan interior with no interior load-bearing support walls.

This clearspan interior space allows freedom to locate interior walls for the optimum movement of the passive solar heat throughout the house. This is also a great benefit when using a wood-burning stove or space heaters. As the size and needs of your family change over time, you can easily remodel and change the room layout.

Using the strong steel framing, the wall studs are placed on 8-foot centers instead of 16-inch centers as with a standard wood studded wall. This reduces the thermal bridges (gaps) in the wall insulation. The deep steel framing also provides room for 9 inches of wall insulation yielding a total insulation value of about R-30.

Another energy advantage of steel framing is that steel settles very little over time. Therefore, the house should remain very airtight over its life and windows and doors should continue to fit and operate smoothly.

To build a steel-framed house, first pour the foundation. The anchor bolts are set in the wet concrete. Bolt each of the steel wall/roof framing assemblies together on the ground. Each assembly includes the side walls and the roof span.

Raise each assembly and bolt it to the foundation. Screw support purlins along the roof and wall framing members to hold the structure together. Attach standard sheathing to the outside of the steel framing. Then you can add any type of exterior finish - brick, siding, stucco, etc. as with any conventionally-built house.//

Steel-framed house manufacturers offer many styles of kits with standard floor plans from 700 to 7,000 square feet in size. The houses range from very traditional to contemporary solar designs. The steel framing is fire and termite-proof. This can often result in lower fire insurance premiums. They can also be designed to withstand 140 mph winds for hurricane regions of the country.

MANUFACTURERS OF STEEL-FRAMED HOUSES

ADVANCED FRAMING SYSTEMS, 215 W. Hickory St., Denton, TX 76201
(800) 252-0069   (817) 566-5656

ALL STEEL HOMES, 2626 Gribble St., N. Little Rock, AR 72114
(800) 278-0888   (501) 945-8092

CALIFORNIA BUILDING SYSTEMS, 4817 E. Sheila St., Los Angeles, CA 90040
(213) 260-5380

HEXA-PORT INTERNATIONAL, 178 Rt. 101, Bedford, NH 03110
(603) 472-8300

JEWELL BUILDING SYSTEMS, P.O. Box 397, Dallas, NC 28034
(704) 922-8652

SJV BUILDING SYSTEMS, 6645 N. Remmington Ave., Fresno, CA 93704
(209) 447-0340

STEEL TECHONOLGY BY MADRAY, P.O. Box 712, Okeechobee, FL 34973
(941) 763-8856

TRI-STEEL STRUCTURES, 5400 S. Stemmons, Denton, TX 76205
(817) 497-7070

WORLDWIDE BLDG. SALES, Rt. 1, Box 588, Peculiar, MO 64078
(816) 758-6762

The Lifetime Home Package

Shipping the home to the construction site in package form is just one of Tri-Steel's money-saving procedures. All structural members are prefabricated to strict tollerances to ensure quick, accurate assembly at the job site. Tri-Steel also utilizes the most modern computer scheduling and shipping programs to ensure that each package is complete and the shipment arrives at the job site precisely when needed.

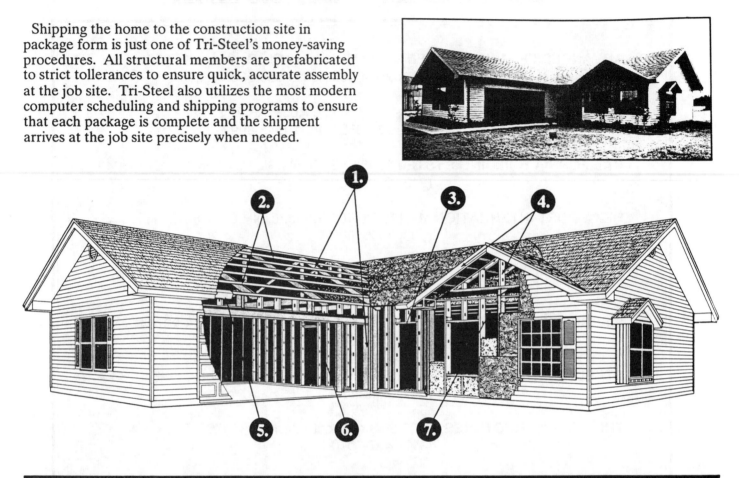

Basic Home Package Items

1. Heavy gauge bolt-together steel columns and rafters.

2. Metal roof purlins.

3. 8" steel stud system for exterior walls.

4. Metal framing components for all dormers, roof and porch saddles.

5. Metal sub-facia material for roof overhangs.

6. 3 5/8" metal studs and track for all interior walls.

7. Metal furring channels for all ceiling surfaces.

8. 8" metal second floor joists for all two story areas. *(Not Shown)*

9. All bolts and fasteners for:
   (1) Structural columns, rafters, joists and purlins.
   (2) Metal studs and furring.
   (3) Metal sub-facia framing.

10. Complete set of working drawings including anchor bolt layout and erection instructions.

Tri-Steel Structures

Options   Available from Tri-Steel.

1. Steel 1st floor system.

2. Chemical anchor bolts for pre-poured foundations.

3. Aluminum roof shakes in five colors.

4. Skylight framing kit.

5. Standard bay extensions and porch additions.

6. Longer columns for higher ceilings.

7. Decks, porches and detached garages.

SPECIAL NOTES

*Standard Package may be updated from time to time. *(See your TSS Distributor for current package contents.)*

*Sealed plans are available when required.

*Ultra high wind loads and snow loads are available for areas with extreme conditions.

Carmel

(AP7376SO1G)

FROM THE TRI-STEEL FAMILY OF FINE HOMES

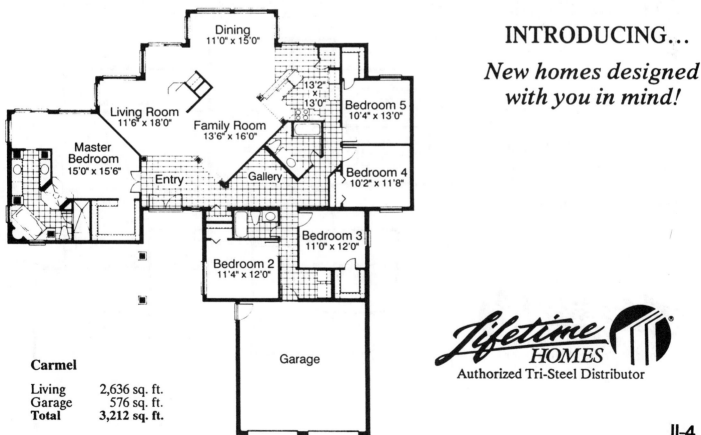

INTRODUCING...

New homes designed with you in mind!

Carmel

Living	2,636 sq. ft.
Garage	576 sq. ft.
Total	**3,212 sq. ft.**

Lifetime HOMES
Authorized Tri-Steel Distributor

II-4

Topaz

HC6781S01G

FROM THE TRI-STEEL FAMILY OF FINE HOMES

Changing The Way America Builds!

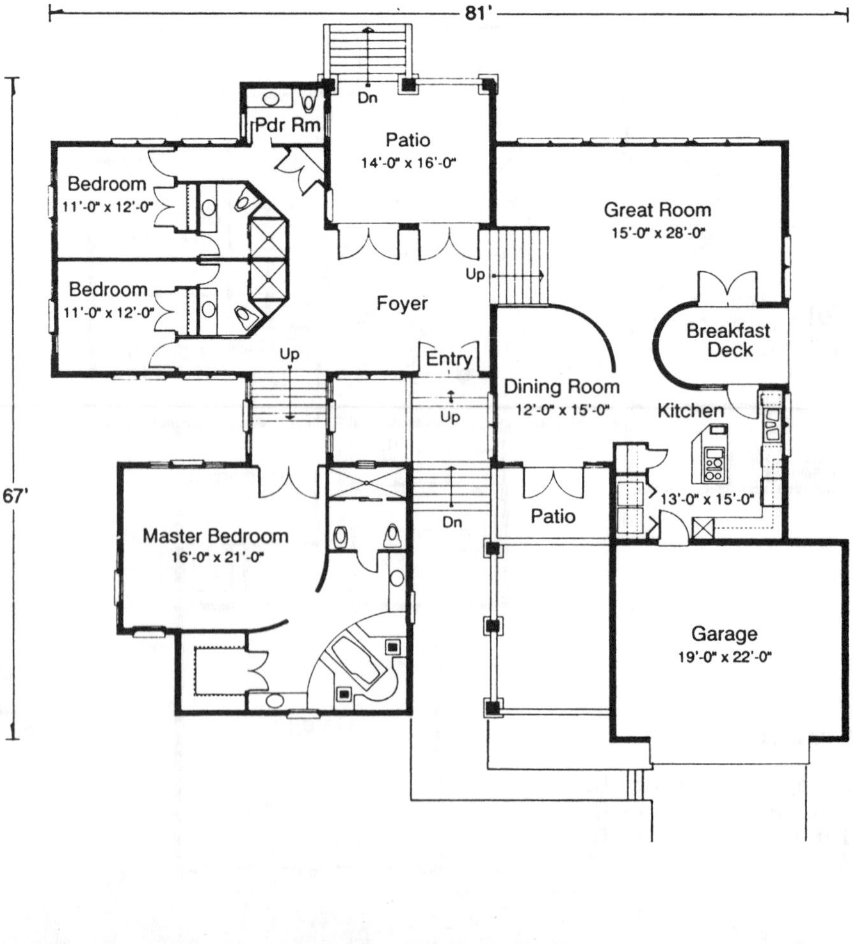

81'
67'
Dn
Pdr Rm
Patio
14'-0" x 16'-0"
Bedroom
11'-0" x 12'-0"
Bedroom
11'-0" x 12'-0"
Great Room
15'-0" x 28'-0"
Up
Foyer
Breakfast Deck
Up
Entry
Dining Room
12'-0" x 15'-0"
Up
Kitchen
13'-0" x 15'-0"
Master Bedroom
16'-0" x 21'-0"
Dn
Patio
Garage
19'-0" x 22'-0"

Living Area	2,912 sq.ft.
Porches/Deck	433 sq.ft.
Garage	480 sq.ft.
Total	**3,825 sq.ft.**

Lifetime HOMES®

Authorized Tri-Steel Distributor

Genesis

DS72124S01G

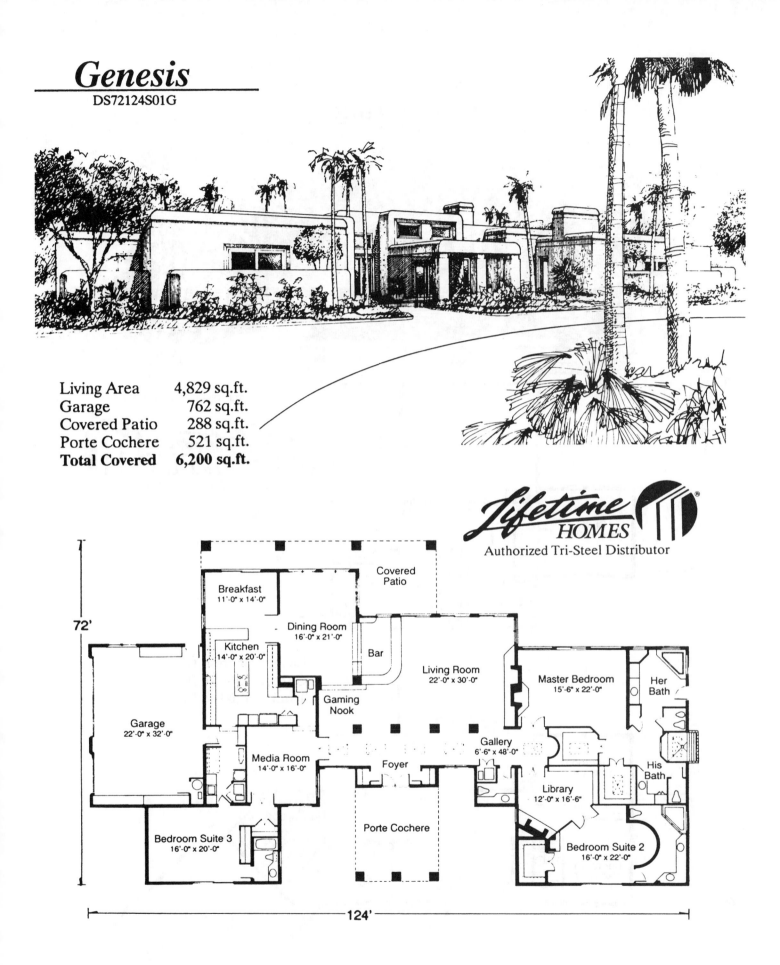

Living Area	4,829 sq.ft.
Garage	762 sq.ft.
Covered Patio	288 sq.ft.
Porte Cochere	521 sq.ft.
Total Covered	**6,200 sq.ft.**

Lifetime HOMES
Authorized Tri-Steel Distributor

72'

Breakfast
11'-0" x 14'-0"

Covered Patio

Dining Room
16'-0" x 21'-0"

Kitchen
14'-0" x 20'-0"

Bar

Living Room
22'-0" x 30'-0"

Master Bedroom
15'-6" x 22'-0"

Her Bath

Gaming Nook

Garage
22'-0" x 32'-0"

Gallery
6'-6" x 48'-0"

His Bath

Media Room
14'-0" x 16'-0"

Foyer

Library
12'-0" x 16'-6"

Bedroom Suite 3
16'-0" x 20'-0"

Porte Cochere

Bedroom Suite 2
16'-0" x 22'-0"

124'

II-6

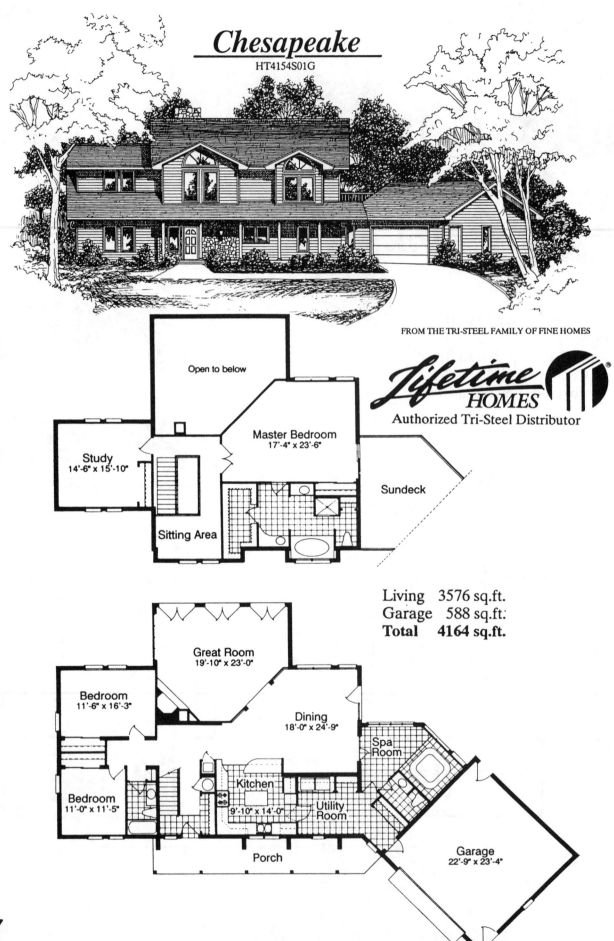

Chesapeake

HT4154S01G

FROM THE TRI-STEEL FAMILY OF FINE HOMES

Lifetime HOMES
Authorized Tri-Steel Distributor

Open to below

Study
14'-6" x 15'-10"

Master Bedroom
17'-4" x 23'-6"

Sundeck

Sitting Area

Living   3576 sq.ft.
Garage   588 sq.ft.
Total   4164 sq.ft.

Great Room
19'-10" x 23'-0"

Bedroom
11'-6" x 16'-3"

Dining
18'-0" x 24'-9"

Spa Room

Bedroom
11'-0" x 11'-5"

Kitchen
9'-10" x 14'-0"

Utility Room

Garage
22'-9" x 23'-4"

Porch

II-7

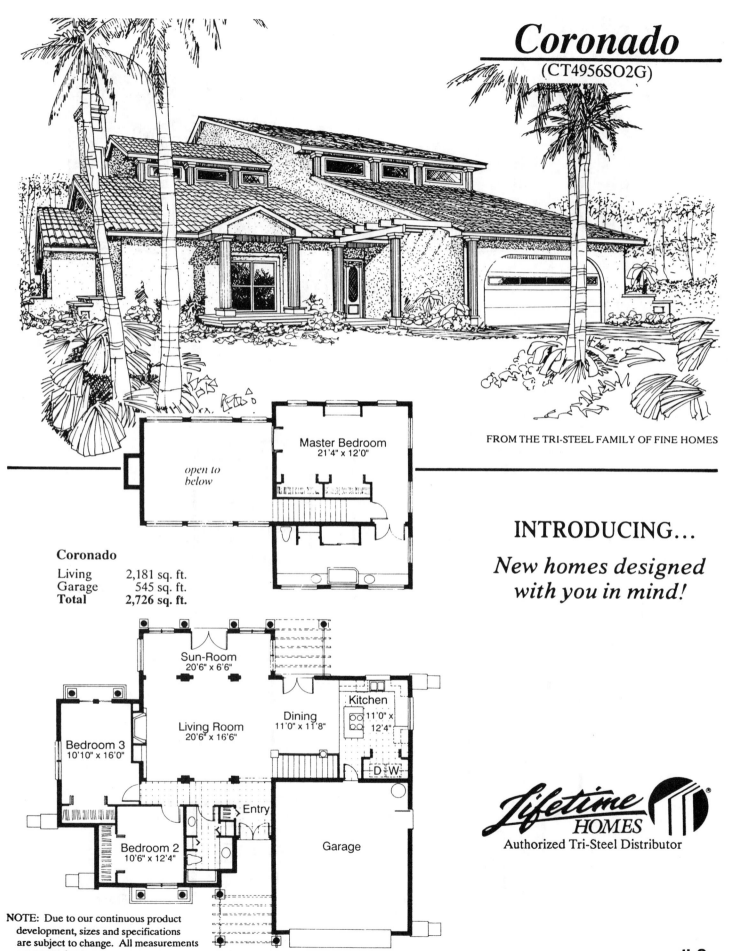

Coronado
(CT4956SO2G)

Master Bedroom
21'4" x 12'0"

open to
below

FROM THE TRI-STEEL FAMILY OF FINE HOMES

Coronado

Living   2,181 sq. ft.
Garage   545 sq. ft.
Total   **2,726 sq. ft.**

INTRODUCING...

*New homes designed
with you in mind!*

Sun-Room
20'6" x 6'6"

Kitchen
11'0" x
12'4"

Dining
11'0" x 11'8"

Living Room
20'6" x 16'6"

Bedroom 3
10'10" x 16'0"

D W

Entry

Bedroom 2
10'6" x 12'4"

Garage

Lifetime HOMES
Authorized Tri-Steel Distributor

NOTE: Due to our continuous product
development, sizes and specifications
are subject to change. All measurements
are approximate.

Montego

HTX7096S01G

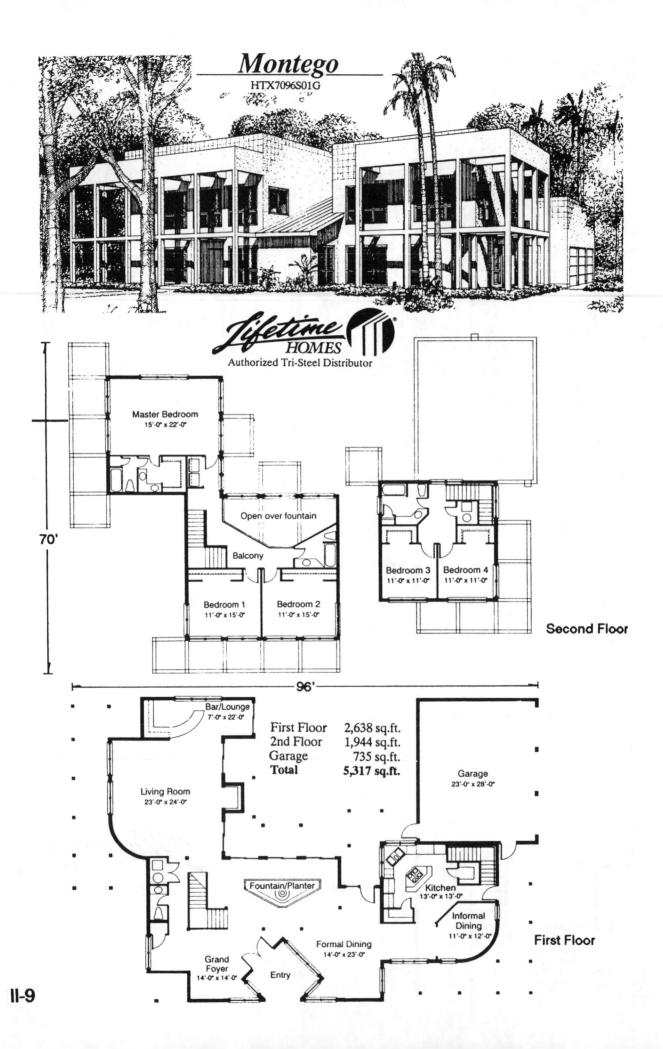

Lifetime HOMES
Authorized Tri-Steel Distributor

Second Floor

Master Bedroom
15'-0" x 22'-0"

Open over fountain

Balcony

Bedroom 1
11'-0" x 15'-0"

Bedroom 2
11'-0" x 15'-0"

Bedroom 3
11'-0" x 11'-0"

Bedroom 4
11'-0" x 11'-0"

70'

96'

Bar/Lounge
7'-0" x 22'-0"

First Floor	2,638 sq.ft.
2nd Floor	1,944 sq.ft.
Garage	735 sq.ft.
Total	**5,317 sq.ft.**

Living Room
23'-0" x 24'-0"

Garage
23'-0" x 28'-0"

Fountain/Planter

Kitchen
13'-0" x 13'-0"

Informal Dining
11'-0" x 12'-0"

First Floor

Grand Foyer
14'-0" x 14'-0"

Entry

Formal Dining
14'-0" x 23'-0"

II-9

Contempo

(CT4861SO1G)

FROM THE TRI-STEEL FAMILY OF FINE HOMES

Changing The Way America Builds!

CONTEMPO

Living	2395 sq. ft.
Porch	144 sq. ft.
Garage	534 sq. ft.
Total	**3073 sq. ft.**

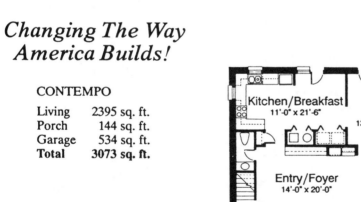

Lifetime HOMES

Bedroom 10'-3" x 12'-3"

Bedroom 10'-3" x 12'-0"

Bedroom 12'-0" x 14'-3"

Master Bedroom 14'-3" x 16'-3"

Kitchen/Breakfast 11'-0" x 21'-6"

Dining 13'-3" x 14'-0"

Entry/Foyer 14'-0" x 20'-0"

Living 11'-0" x 25'-0"

Garage 20'-6" x 23'-0"

Salsbury

WB3673SR1G

FROM THE TRI-STEEL FAMILY OF FINE HOMES

Changing The Way America Builds!

Living 2846 sq.ft.
Garage 622 sq.ft.
Total 3468 sq.ft.

Second Floor

Bedroom
10'-5" x 13'-0"

OPEN TO BELOW

Bedroom
10'-10" x 12'-10"

Master Bedroom
13'-10" x 15'-9"

OPEN TO BELOW

Bedroom
11'-9" x 15'-5"

First Floor

WORK BENCH

Utility

Kitchen
13'-10" x 15'-5"

Break fast Room
7'-0" x 13'-10"

Family Room
13'-10" x 23'-1"

Garage
22'-4" x 24'-1"

Dining
13'-10" x 19'-9"

Entry

Living
13'-10" x 15'-1"

Lifetime HOMES
Authorized Tri-Steel Distributor

II-11

Columbia Duplex

(CD4264SO1G)

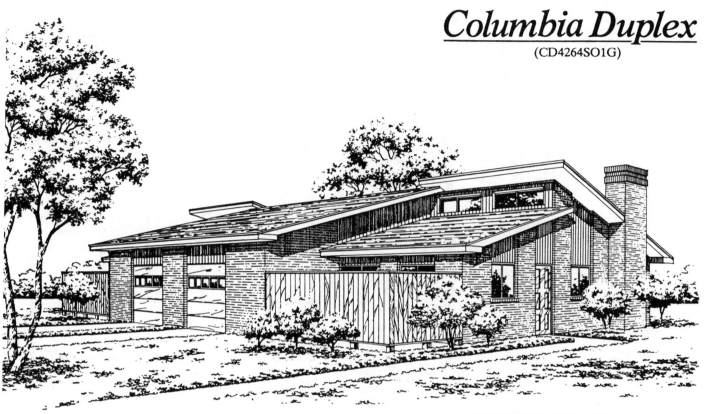

FROM THE TRI-STEEL FAMILY OF FINE HOMES

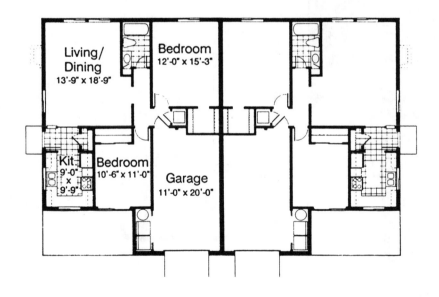

Changing The Way America Builds!

COLUMBIA DUPLEX

Living Per Unit   921 sq. ft.
Garage Per Unit   302 sq. ft.
Total Per Unit   **1223 sq. ft.**
Total Building   **2446 sq. ft.**

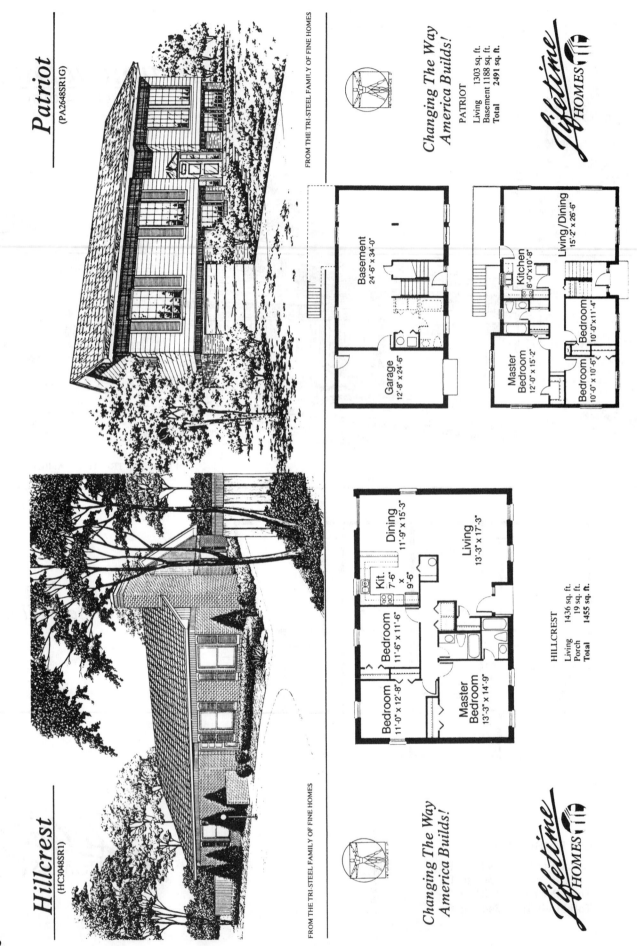

Patriot
(PA2648SR1G)

FROM THE TRI-STEEL FAMILY OF FINE HOMES

Changing The Way America Builds!

PATRIOT
Living 1303 sq. ft.
Basement 1188 sq. ft.
Total 2491 sq. ft.

Lifetime HOMES

Basement 24'-6" x 34'-0"

Garage 12'-8" x 24'-6"

Master Bedroom 12'-0" x 15'-2"

Kitchen 8'-0" x 10'-8"

Living/Dining 15'-2" x 26'-6"

Bedroom 10'-0" x 11'-4"

Bedroom 10'-0" x 10'-6"

Hillcrest
(HC3048SR1)

FROM THE TRI-STEEL FAMILY OF FINE HOMES

Changing The Way America Builds!

HILLCREST
Living 1436 sq. ft.
Porch 19 sq. ft.
Total 1455 sq. ft.

Lifetime HOMES

Dining 11'-9" x 15'-3"

Kit. 7'-6" x 9'-6"

Living 13'-3" x 17'-3"

Bedroom 11'-6" x 11'-6"

Bedroom 11'-0" x 12'-8"

Master Bedroom 13'-3" x 14'-9"

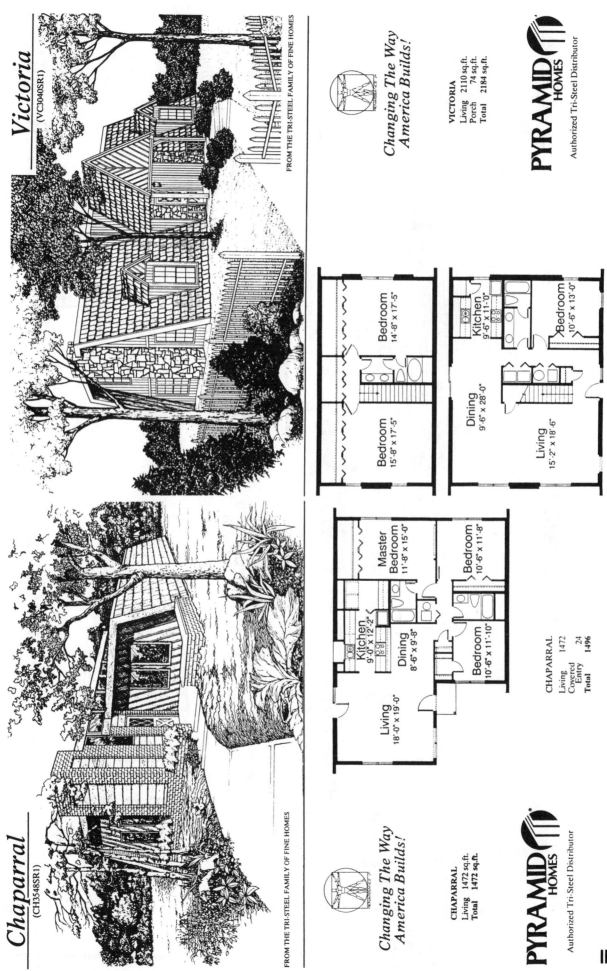

Victoria
(VC3040SR1)

FROM THE TRI-STEEL FAMILY OF FINE HOMES

Bedroom 14'-8" x 17'-5"

Bedroom 15'-8" x 17'-5"

Kitchen 9'-6" x 11'-0"

Bedroom 10'-6" x 13'-0"

Dining 9'-6" x 28'-0"

Living 15'-2" x 18'-6"

Changing The Way America Builds!

VICTORIA
Living 2110 sq.ft.
Porch 74 sq.ft.
Total 2184 sq.ft.

PYRAMID HOMES
Authorized Tri-Steel Distributor

Chaparral
(CH3548SR1)

FROM THE TRI-STEEL FAMILY OF FINE HOMES

Master Bedroom 11'-8" x 15'-0"

Kitchen 9'-0" x 12'-2"

Dining 8'-6" x 9'-8"

Bedroom 10'-6" x 11'-8"

Living 18'-0" x 19'-0"

Bedroom 10'-6" x 11'-10"

Changing The Way America Builds!

CHAPARRAL
Living 1472 sq.ft.
Total 1472 sq.ft.

CHAPARRAL
Living 1472
Covered
Entry 24
Total 1496

PYRAMID HOMES
Authorized Tri-Steel Distributor

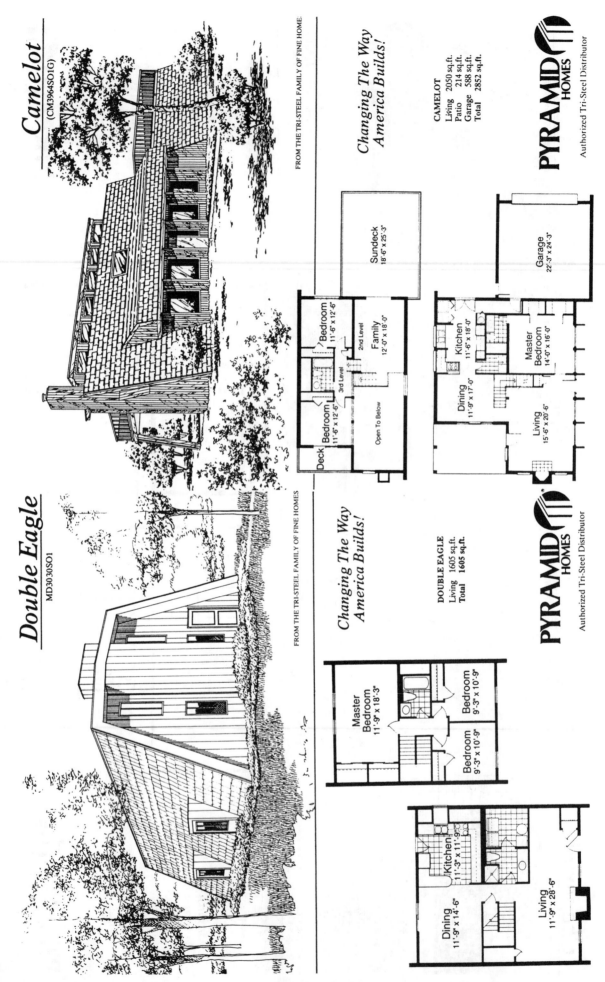

Camelot
(CM3964SO1G)

FROM THE TRI-STEEL FAMILY OF FINE HOMES

Changing The Way America Builds!

CAMELOT

Living	2050 sq.ft.
Patio	214 sq.ft.
Garage	588 sq.ft.
Total	2852 sq.ft.

PYRAMID HOMES
Authorized Tri-Steel Distributor

Bedroom 11'-6" x 12'-6"

Deck

Bedroom 11'-6" x 12'-6"

3rd Level

2nd Level

Family 12'-0" x 18'-0"

Open To Below

Sundeck 18'-6" x 25'-3"

Kitchen 11'-6" x 18'-0"

Dining 11'-9" x 17'-0"

Master Bedroom 14'-0" x 16'-0"

Living 15'-6" x 20'-6"

Garage 22'-3" x 24'-3"

Double Eagle
MD3030SO1

FROM THE TRI-STEEL FAMILY OF FINE HOMES

Changing The Way America Builds!

DOUBLE EAGLE

Living	1605 sq.ft.
Total	**1605 sq.ft.**

PYRAMID HOMES
Authorized Tri-Steel Distributor

Master Bedroom 11'-9" x 18'-3"

Bedroom 9'-3" x 10'-9"

Bedroom 9'-3" x 10'-9"

Dining 11'-9" x 14'-6"

Kitchen 11'-3" x 11'-9"

Living 11'-9" x 28'-6"

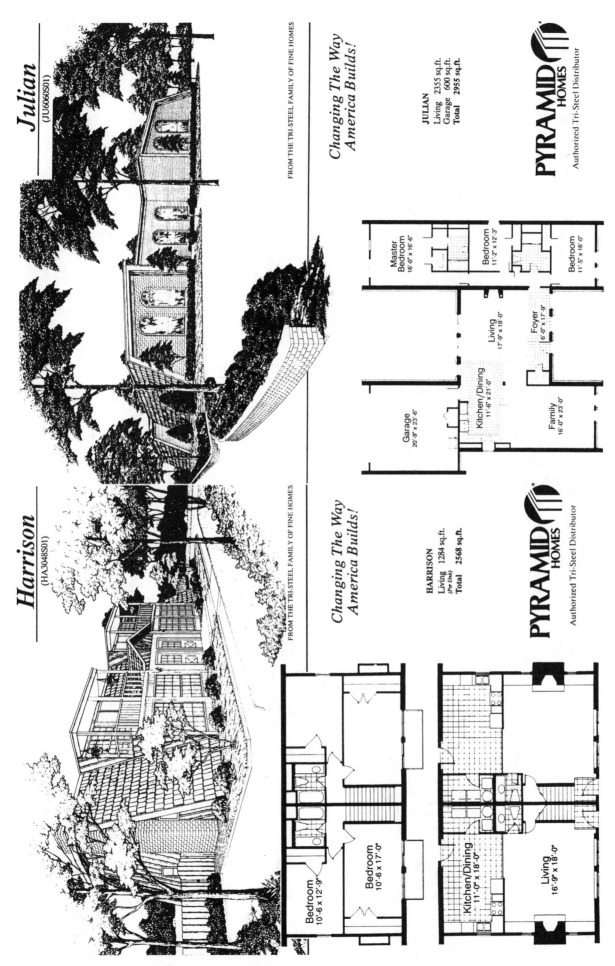

Julian
(JU6060S01)

Harrison
(HA3048S01)

FROM THE TRI-STEEL FAMILY OF FINE HOMES

FROM THE TRI-STEEL FAMILY OF FINE HOMES

*Changing The Way
America Builds!*

*Changing The Way
America Builds!*

JULIAN
Living   2355 sq.ft.
Garage   600 sq.ft.
Total   2955 sq.ft.

HARRISON
Living   1284 sq.ft.
(Per Unit)
Total   2568 sq.ft.

PYRAMID HOMES
Authorized Tri-Steel Distributor

PYRAMID HOMES
Authorized Tri-Steel Distributor

Master
Bedroom
16'-0" x 16'-6"

Bedroom
11'-2" x 12'-3"

Bedroom
11'-5" x 16'-0"

Garage
20'-9" x 23'-6"

Kitchen/Dining
11'-6" x 21'-0"

Living
17'-9" x 18'-0"

Foyer
6'-0" x 17'-9"

Family
16'-0" x 23'-0"

Bedroom
10'-6 x 12'-9"

Bedroom
10'-6 x 17'-0"

Kitchen/Dining
11'-0" x 18'-0"

Living
16'-9 x 18'-0"

II-16

Estate II
(ES4256SR1G)

Excalibur
(EX4672SR1G)

FROM THE TRI-STEEL FAMILY OF FINE HOMES

Changing The Way America Builds!

EXCALIBUR
Living 3134 sq. ft.
Patio 348 sq. ft.
Garage 622 sq. ft.
Total 4104 sq. ft.

PYRAMID HOMES
Authorized Tri-Steel Distributor

Bedroom
16'-3" x 16'-6"

Sundeck
22'-6" x 25'-6"

Bedroom
15'-6" x 16'-3"

3rd Level

Gameroom
15'-5" x 15'-6"

2nd Level

Sundeck
15'-6" x 16'-6"

Open To Below

Kitchen
15'-6" x 21'-0"

Garage
20'-6" x 28'-4"

Dining
18'-8" x 20'-6"

Master Bedroom
16'-0" x 16'-0"

Patio
16'-0" x 21'-4"

Living
19'-2" x 23'-6"

FROM THE TRI-STEEL FAMILY OF FINE HOMES

Changing The Way America Builds!

ESTATE II
Living 2460 sq.ft.
Garage 724 sq.ft.
Total 3184 sq.ft.

PYRAMID HOMES
Authorized Tri-Steel Distributor

Master Bedroom
15'-4" x 15'-5"

Sundeck
22'-0" x 25'-0"

3rd Level

Bedroom
12'-1" x 13'-7"

2nd Level

Bedroom
11'-1" x 13'-7"

Living/Dining
20'-4" x 31'-0"

Garage
23'-4" x 28'-4"

Kitchen
15'-6" x 19'-0"

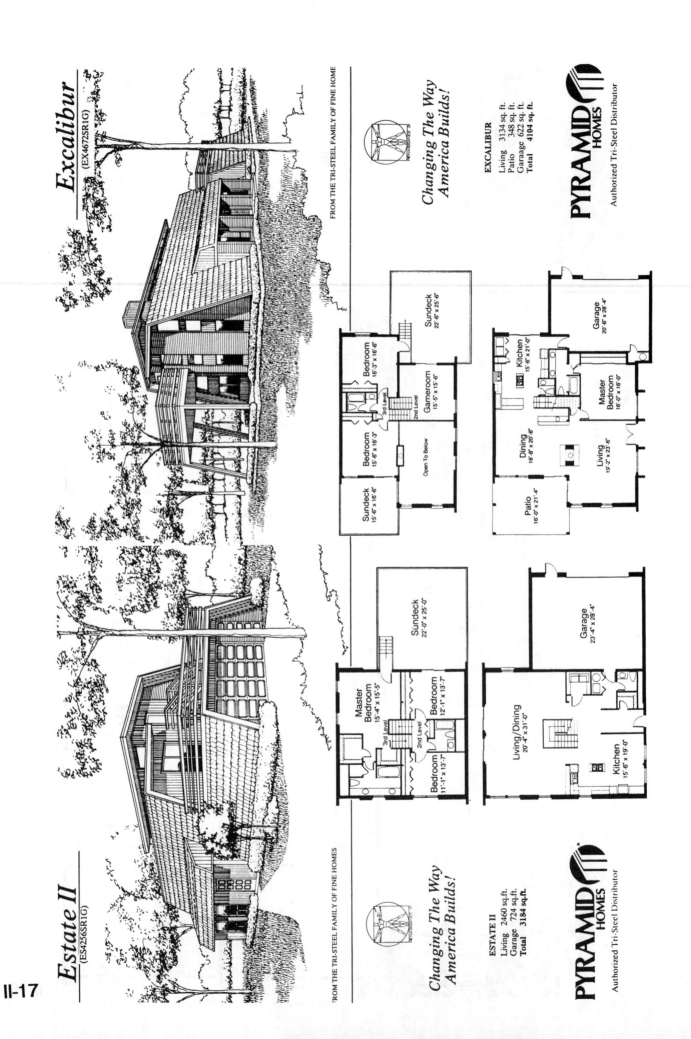

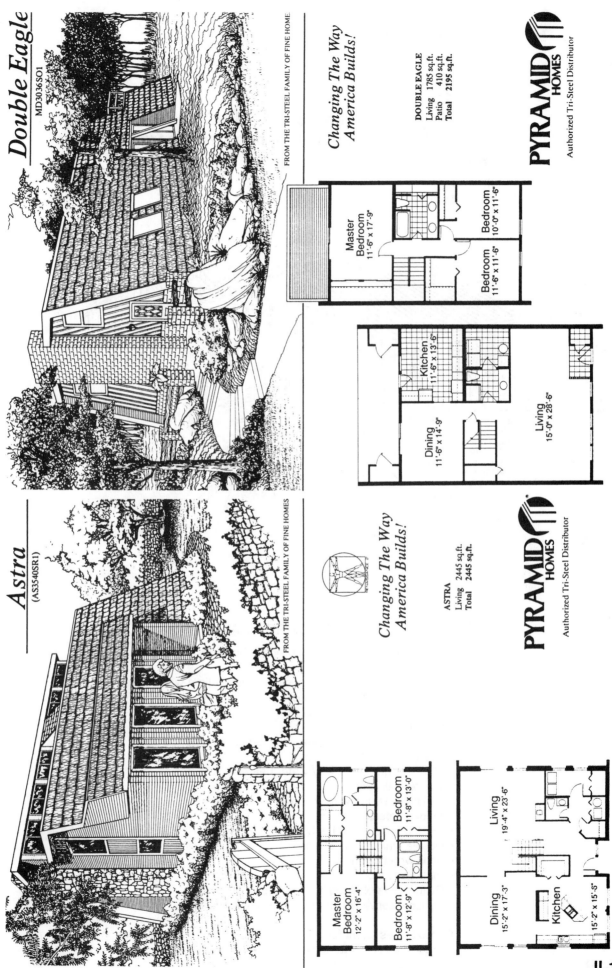

Double Eagle

MD3036SO1

FROM THE TRI-STEEL FAMILY OF FINE HOMES

Changing The Way America Builds!

DOUBLE EAGLE
Living 1785 sq.ft.
Patio 410 sq.ft.
Total 2195 sq.ft.

PYRAMID HOMES
Authorized Tri-Steel Distributor

Master Bedroom
11'-6" x 17'-9"

Bedroom
11'-6" x 11'-6"

Bedroom
10'-0" x 11'-6"

Kitchen
11'-6" x 13'-6"

Dining
11'-6" x 14'-9"

Living
15'-0" x 28'-6"

Astra

(AS3540SR1)

FROM THE TRI-STEEL FAMILY OF FINE HOMES

Changing The Way America Builds!

ASTRA
Living 2445 sq.ft.
Total 2445 sq.ft.

PYRAMID HOMES
Authorized Tri-Steel Distributor

Master Bedroom
12'-2" x 16'-4"

Bedroom
11'-8" x 12'-9"

Bedroom
11'-8" x 13'-0"

Dining
15'-2" x 17'-3"

Living
19'-4" x 23'-6"

Kitchen
15'-2" x 15'-5"

What makes 1st CHOICE HOMES stronger, safer, maintenance free, energy efficient?

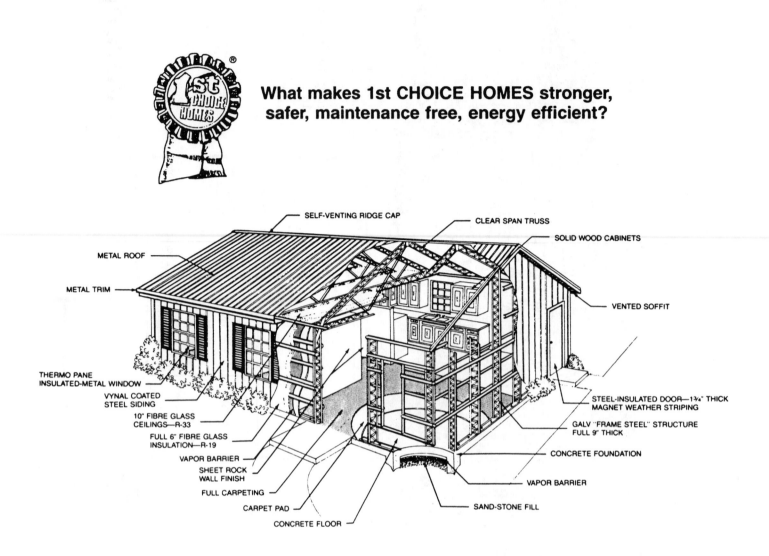

SELF-VENTING RIDGE CAP
CLEAR SPAN TRUSS
SOLID WOOD CABINETS
METAL ROOF
METAL TRIM
VENTED SOFFIT
THERMO PANE INSULATED-METAL WINDOW
VYNAL COATED STEEL SIDING
10" FIBRE GLASS CEILINGS—R-33
FULL 6" FIBRE GLASS INSULATION—R-19
VAPOR BARRIER
SHEET ROCK WALL FINISH
FULL CARPETING
CARPET PAD
CONCRETE FLOOR
STEEL-INSULATED DOOR—1¾" THICK MAGNET WEATHER STRIPING
GALV "FRAME STEEL" STRUCTURE FULL 9" THICK
CONCRETE FOUNDATION
VAPOR BARRIER
SAND-STONE FILL

STANDARD FEATURES

- Strong steel framing that will withstand winds up to 150 mph and not burn down.
- Maintenance free vynasteel siding with lifetime warranty.
- 6 in. R-19 insulation in walls.
- 10 in. R-30 insulation in ceiling.
- Insulated windows.
- Foam insulated steel doors w/magnetic weather stripping.
- Energy efficient appliances.
- 40-gallon quick recovery water heater.
- Wall to wall carpet.
- Window seat in every window.
- Smoke detector.
- Electric base board heat.
- Double stainless steel sink.
- Solid wood cabinets.
- Fiberglass tub.
- Cultured marbled top bath vanities.
- Optional conventional roof and sidings available.

Consult sales agent for information on optional storage areas, heat pumps, fireplaces, garages, porches, and foundations.

JEWELL
BUILDING SYSTEMS, INC.

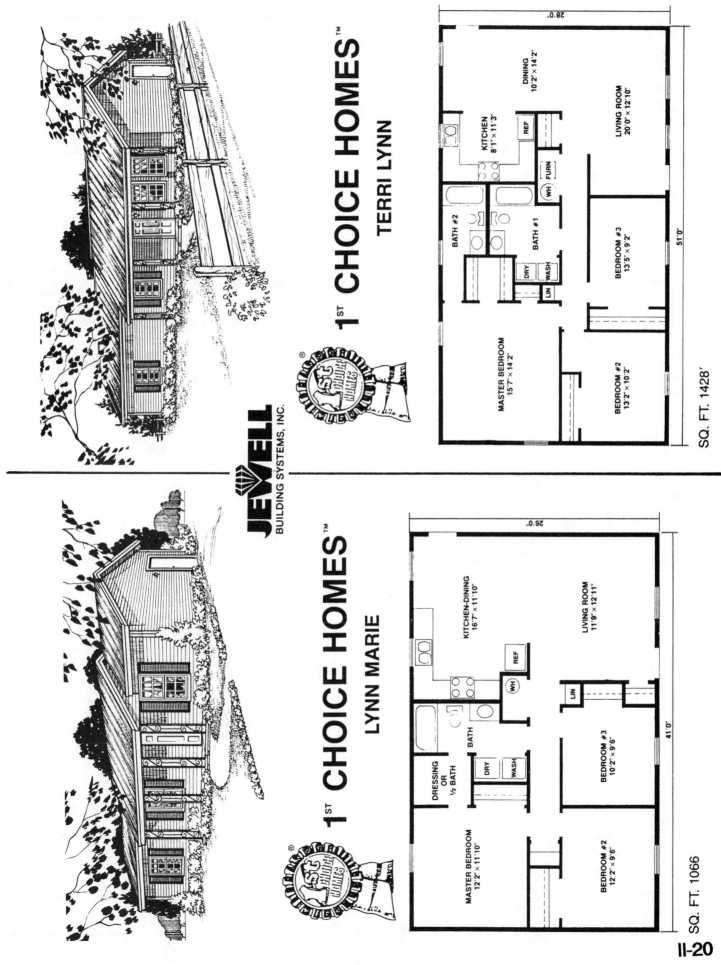

1ST CHOICE HOMES™

TERRI LYNN

JEWELL
BUILDING SYSTEMS, INC.

28'0"

KITCHEN
8'1" × 11'3"

DINING
10'2" × 14'2"

REF

FURN

WH

BATH #2

BATH #1

DRY   WASH

LIN

LIVING ROOM
20'0" × 12'10"

BEDROOM #3
13'5" × 9'2"

MASTER BEDROOM
15'7" × 14'2"

BEDROOM #2
13'2" × 10'2"

51'0"

SQ. FT. 1428'

1ST CHOICE HOMES™

LYNN MARIE

26'0"

KITCHEN-DINING
16'7" × 11'10"

REF

WH

DRESSING
OR
½ BATH

BATH

DRY   WASH

LIN

LIVING ROOM
11'9" × 12'11"

MASTER BEDROOM
12'2" × 11'10"

BEDROOM #3
10'2" × 9'6"

BEDROOM #2
12'2" × 9'6"

41'0"

SQ. FT. 1066

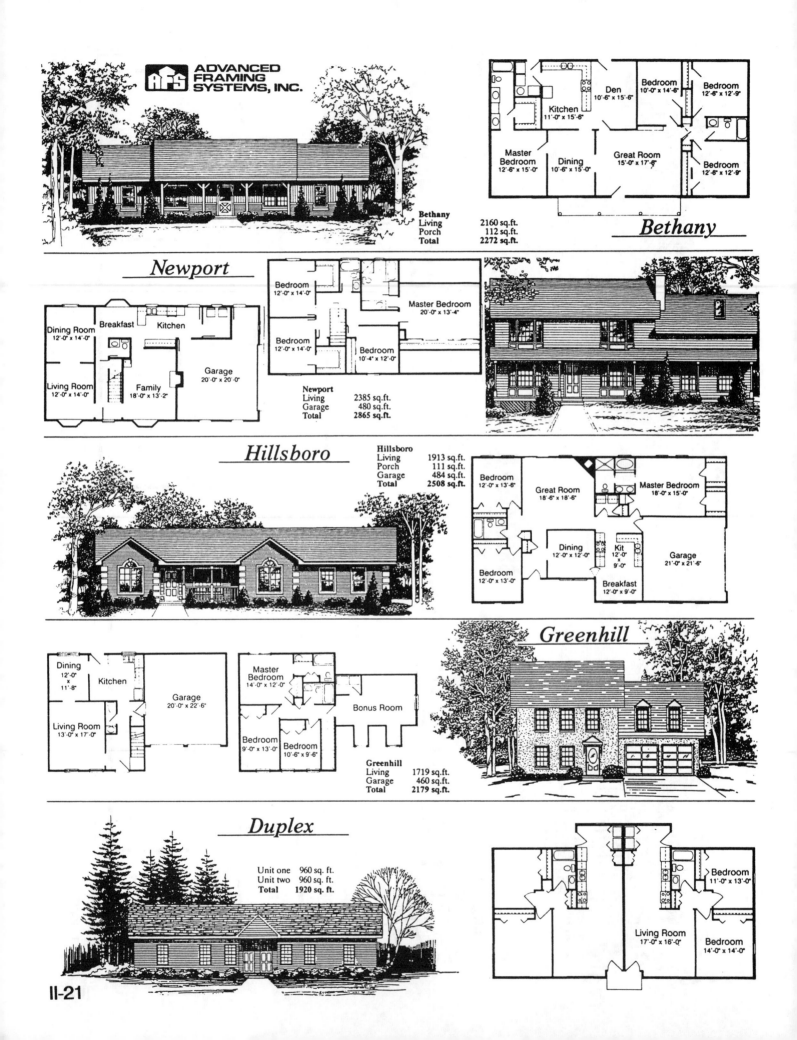

ADVANCED FRAMING SYSTEMS, INC.

Bethany
Living	2160 sq. ft.
Porch	112 sq. ft.
Total	2272 sq. ft.

Kitchen 11'-0" x 15'-6"

Den 10'-6" x 15'-6"

Bedroom 10'-0" x 14'-6"

Bedroom 12'-6" x 12'-9"

Master Bedroom 12'-6" x 15'-0"

Dining 10'-6" x 15'-0"

Great Room 15'-0" x 17'-6"

Bedroom 12'-6" x 12'-9"

Bethany

Newport

Dining Room 12'-0" x 14'-0"

Breakfast

Kitchen

Living Room 12'-0" x 14'-0"

Family 18'-0" x 13'-2"

Garage 20'-0" x 20'-0"

Bedroom 12'-0" x 14'-0"

Bedroom 12'-0" x 14'-0"

Bedroom 10'-4" x 12'-0"

Master Bedroom 20'-0" x 13'-4"

Newport
Living	2385 sq. ft.
Garage	480 sq. ft.
Total	2865 sq. ft.

Hillsboro

Hillsboro
Living	1913 sq. ft.
Porch	111 sq. ft.
Garage	484 sq. ft.
Total	2508 sq. ft.

Bedroom 12'-0" x 13'-6"

Great Room 18'-6" x 18'-6"

Master Bedroom 18'-0" x 15'-0"

Bedroom 12'-0" x 13'-0"

Dining 12'-0" x 12'-0"

Kit 12'-0" x 9'-0"

Garage 21'-0" x 21'-6"

Breakfast 12'-0" x 9'-0"

Greenhill

Dining 12'-0" x 11'-8"

Kitchen

Garage 20'-0" x 22'-6"

Living Room 13'-0" x 17'-0"

Master Bedroom 14'-0" x 12'-0"

Bonus Room

Bedroom 9'-0" x 13'-0"

Bedroom 10'-6" x 9'-6"

Greenhill
Living	1719 sq. ft.
Garage	460 sq. ft.
Total	2179 sq. ft.

Duplex

Duplex
Unit one	960 sq. ft.
Unit two	960 sq. ft.
Total	1920 sq. ft.

Bedroom 11'-0" x 13'-0"

Living Room 17'-0" x 16'-0"

Bedroom 14'-0" x 14'-0"

II-21

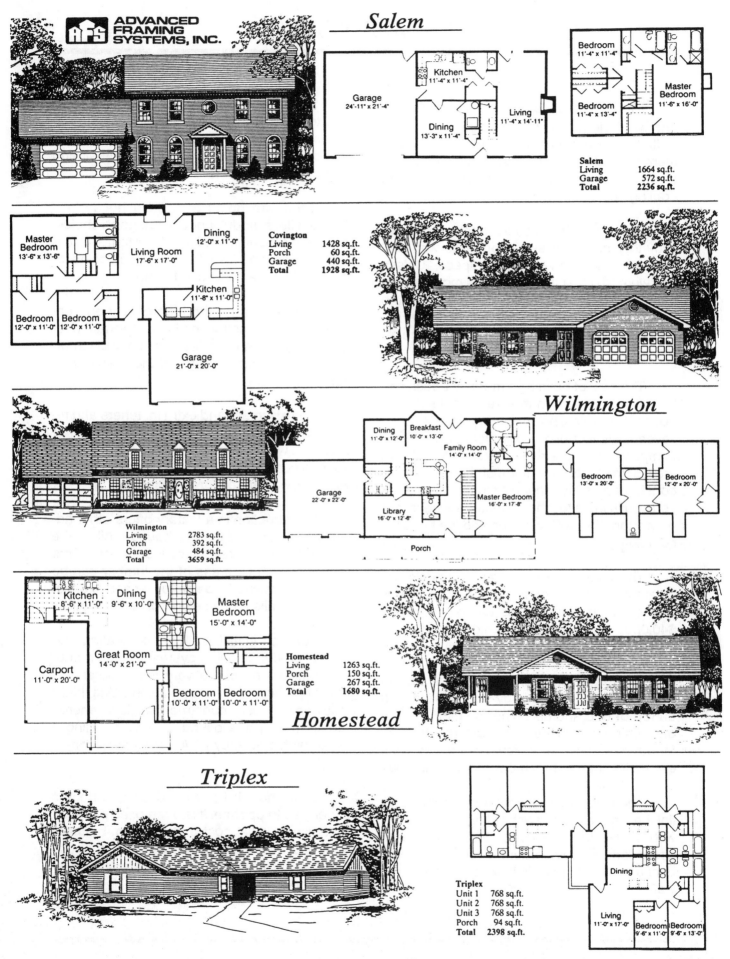

Salem

ADVANCED FRAMING SYSTEMS, INC.

Garage 24'-11" x 21'-4"

Kitchen 11'-4" x 11'-4"

Dining 13'-3" x 11'-4"

Living 11'-4" x 14'-11"

Bedroom 11'-4" x 11'-4"

Bedroom 11'-4" x 13'-4"

Master Bedroom 11'-6" x 16'-0"

Salem
Living 1664 sq.ft.
Garage 572 sq.ft.
Total 2236 sq.ft.

Master Bedroom 13'-6" x 13'-6"

Dining 12'-0" x 11'-0"

Living Room 17'-6" x 17'-0"

Kitchen 11'-8" x 11'-0"

Bedroom 12'-0" x 11'-0"

Bedroom 12'-0" x 11'-0"

Garage 21'-0" x 20'-0"

Covington
Living 1428 sq.ft.
Porch 60 sq.ft.
Garage 440 sq.ft.
Total 1928 sq.ft.

Wilmington

Dining 11'-0" x 12'-0"

Breakfast 10'-0" x 13'-0"

Family Room 14'-0" x 14'-0"

Garage 22'-0" x 22'-0"

Library 16'-0" x 12'-6"

Master Bedroom 16'-0" x 17'-8"

Porch

Bedroom 13'-0" x 20'-0"

Bedroom 12'-0" x 20'-0"

Wilmington
Living 2783 sq.ft.
Porch 392 sq.ft.
Garage 484 sq.ft.
Total 3659 sq.ft.

Kitchen 8'-6" x 11'-0"

Dining 9'-6" x 10'-0"

Master Bedroom 15'-0" x 14'-0"

Carport 11'-0" x 20'-0"

Great Room 14'-0" x 21'-0"

Bedroom 10'-0" x 11'-0"

Bedroom 10'-0" x 11'-0"

Homestead
Living 1263 sq.ft.
Porch 150 sq.ft.
Garage 267 sq.ft.
Total 1680 sq.ft.

Homestead

Triplex

Dining

Living 11'-0" x 17'-0"

Bedroom 9'-6" x 11'-0"

Bedroom 9'-6" x 13'-0"

Triplex
Unit 1 768 sq.ft.
Unit 2 768 sq.ft.
Unit 3 768 sq.ft.
Porch 94 sq.ft.
Total 2398 sq.ft.

Modular houses are very well built and energy efficient. They are constructed just like a site-built house, but in the controlled environment of a factory. With the strict quality control, these houses can be built for low heating and cooling costs.

They range from small ranches to large, two-story colonials and cape cods with well over 3,000 square feet of floor space. Unless you were told that the house was modular and built in a factory, you would not know it from the interior or exterior. Since they are built like site-built houses, they meet building code requirements.

The cost of building a modular house can be equal to or less than a traditional site-built house. In a typical house factory, it takes about seven days to build a complete house (95% complete when it arrives at your site.) There are as many as 15 modular houses under construction simultaneously in the factory. At your building site, the modular sections are pulled together with winches and the house is complete.

The smaller modular ranch models are ideal for first-time house buyers. The overall finished price of the house can be as low as $40,000. These houses use high-quality components.

The larger two-story houses use several modules connected side-by-side and stacked on top of one another. The top modules are often shipped with the roof structure attached. Modular houses are typically somewhat less expensive than comparable site-built houses.

The exteriors of modular houses can be finished in the factory with siding, or at the site with brick, stucco, siding, etc.. Stucco is a particularly energy-efficient exterior wall finish because it reduces air leakage through the walls.

Some manufacturers and builders allow you to order a modular house to varying degrees of finish. If you are handy with tools, you can do some of the finish work yourself and reduce the total costs.

If you are going to build a house in a remote site, a modular house is a good choice. It is often difficult to find a builder to travel to a remote location. Also, transportation costs for the building materials can be high.

One reason for the high-quality and energy-efficient construction is transportation requirements. The modules must be built strong enough to withstand long-distance transportation on trucks.

Heavy lumber and extra fasteners and reinforcing straps are used for strength. For example, wall construction using 2x6 studs on 16-inch centers is common. The six-inch thick walls provide space for extra insulation.

Construction in a factory offers other advantages over a site-built house. All of the building materials are stored indoors out of the weather. Certain areas of the lumber can be nailed and fastened together better and stronger when the walls aren't setting on a foundation.

You can install any type of heating and central air-conditioning system. Since modular houses are built to very tight tolerances, they are inherently energy efficient. With high-efficiency house construction (low energy requirements), the payback from installing a super-high-efficiency HVAC system becomes longer.

Even though baseboard electric heat is expensive to operate, it is often used because of its lower initial cost and its room-by-room control of the heat. With a very efficient house and the ability to zone heat it, electric baseboard heat is a viable option.

ACTIVE HOMES CORP., 7938 S. Van Dyke, Marlette, MI 48453
(517) 635-3532

ALL AMERICAN HOMES, P.O. Box 3300, Elkhart, IN 46515
(219) 262-0123

ALOUETTE HOMES, P.O. Box 187, Newport, VT 05855
(514) 539-3100

AVIS AMERICA, P.O. Box 420, Avis, PA 17721
(800) 233-3052 (717) 753-3700

BROWNSTONE CORP., 1350 Thornton Ave SW, Pacific, WA 98047
(206) 833-3113

CARDINAL HOMES, P.O. Box 10, Wylliesburg, VA 23976
(804) 735-8111

CHELSEA MODULAR HOMES INC., P.O. Box 1108, Marlboro, NY 12542
(914) 236-3311

CONTEMPRI HOMES, P.O. Box 69, Pickneyville, IL 62274
(608) 357-3312

CREST HOMES, 30 N. Industrial Park Rd., Milton, PA 17847
(800) 927-4567 (717) 742-8521

CUSTOMIZED STRUCTURES, P.O. Box 884, Claremont, NH 03743
(800) 523-2033 (603) 543-1236

DELUXE HOMES OF PA, P.O. Box 323, Berwick, PA 18603
(717) 752-5914

DESIGNER HOMES, P.O. Box 70, Mifflinburg, PA 17844
(717) 966-1053

DESIGNER HOMES, P.O. Box 411, Mifflinville, PA 18631
(800) 242-5379 (717) 752-1001

DYNAMIC HOMES, 525 Roosevelt Ave., Detroit Lakes, MN 56501
(800) 492-4833 (218) 847-2611

EPOCH CORP., P.O. Box 235, Pembroke, NH 03275
(603) 225-3907

FUTURE HOME TECH., INC., P.O. Box 4255, Port Jervis, NY 12771
(800) 342-8650 (914) 856-9033

GENERAL HOUSING CORP., 900 Andre St., Bay City MI 48706
(517) 684-8078

GUERDON HOMES, 5285 S.W. Meadows, #131, Lake Oswego, OR 97035
(503) 624-6400

HAVEN HOMES, P.O. Box 178, Beech Creek, PA 16822
(800) 543-7852 (717) 962-2111

HECKAMAN HOMES, P.O. Box 229, Nappanee, IN 46550
(219) 773-4167

HELP•U•BUILD, P.O. Box 151, Brick, NJ 08723
(800) 992-0386

HOMERA HOMES OF MINNESOTA, 900 E. Fourth St., Tracy, MN 56175
(507) 629-3493

HUNTINGTON HOMES, P.O. Box 99, E. Montpelier, VT 05651
(802) 479-3625

KAN-BUILD OF COLORADO, INC., 999 N. Van Buren, Loveland, CO 80538
(303) 667-2676

KEISER INDUSTRIES, INC., P.O. Box 9000, Oxford, ME 04270
(207) 539-8883

MOD-U-KRAF HOMES, P.O. Box 573, Rocky Mount, VA 24151
(540) 483-0291

MUNCY HOMES, P.O. Box 246, Muncy, PA 17756
(717) 546-5444
NANTICOKE HOMES, P.O. Box F, Greenwood, DE 19950
(302) 349-4561
NATIONWIDE HOMES, P.O. Box 5511, Martinsville, VA 24115
(540) 632-7101
NEW CENTURY HOMES, P.O. Box 9, Topeka, IN 46471
(800) 777-6637 (219) 593-2962
NEW ENGLAND HOMES, 270 Ocean Rd., Greenland, NH 03840
(603) 436-8830
NORTH AMERICAN HOUSING, P.O.Box 145, Point of Rocks, MD 21777
(301) 694-9100
NORTHOMES, INC., 4503 20th St. East, Tacoma, WA 98424
(206) 922-2791
PENN LYON HOmes, RR 1, Box 131K, Selinsgrove, PA 17870
(717) 374-4004
PRE BUILT STRUCTURES, N. 5315 Corrigan Rd., Otis Orchards, WA 99027
(509) 928-1442
PRINCETON HOMES CORP., P.O. Box 2086, Danville, VA 24541
(804) 797-3144
RANDAL HOMES CORP., P.O. Box 337, Piketon, OH 45661
(614) 947-1527
RICHARD HOMES, INC., 851 Cedar St., Carrollton, GA 30117
(770) 832-6376
SCHULT HOMES CORP., P.O. Box 219, Elkton, MD 21922
(410) 398-2100
SHOWCASE HOMES, P.O. Box 489, Nappanee, IN 46550
(800) 777-0745
SIGNATURE BUILDING SYSTEMS, P.O. Box 482, Clarks Summit, PA 18441
(717) 586-0169
STRATFORD HOMES, P.O. Box 37, Stratford, WI 54484
(715) 687-3133
TAYLOR HOMES, P.O. Box 438, Anderson, MO 64831
(417) 845-3311
TEAM, 302760 Rancho Viejo Rd., Ste. E, San Juan Capistrano, CA 92675
(714) 443-3525
TERRA QUEST HOMES INC., 36696 Sugar Ridge Rd., N. Ridgeville, OH 44039
(216) 327-6969
TERRACE HOMES, P.O. Box 680, Friendship, WI 53934
(608) 339-7888
TIMBERLAND HOMES, INC., 1201 37th N.W., Auburn, WA 98001
(206) 735-3435
U.S. HOUSING COMPONENTS, 5890 Sawmill Rd., Dublin, OH 43017
(614) 766-5501
UNIBILT INDUSTRIES, P.O. Box 373, Vandalia, OH 45377
(513) 890-7570
WAUSAU HOMES, P.O. Box 8005, Wausau, WI 54402
(715) 359-7272
WESTCHESTER MODULAR HOMES, Reagans Mill Rd., Wingdale, NY 12594
(914) 832-9400

HECKAMAN HOMES

Value Features

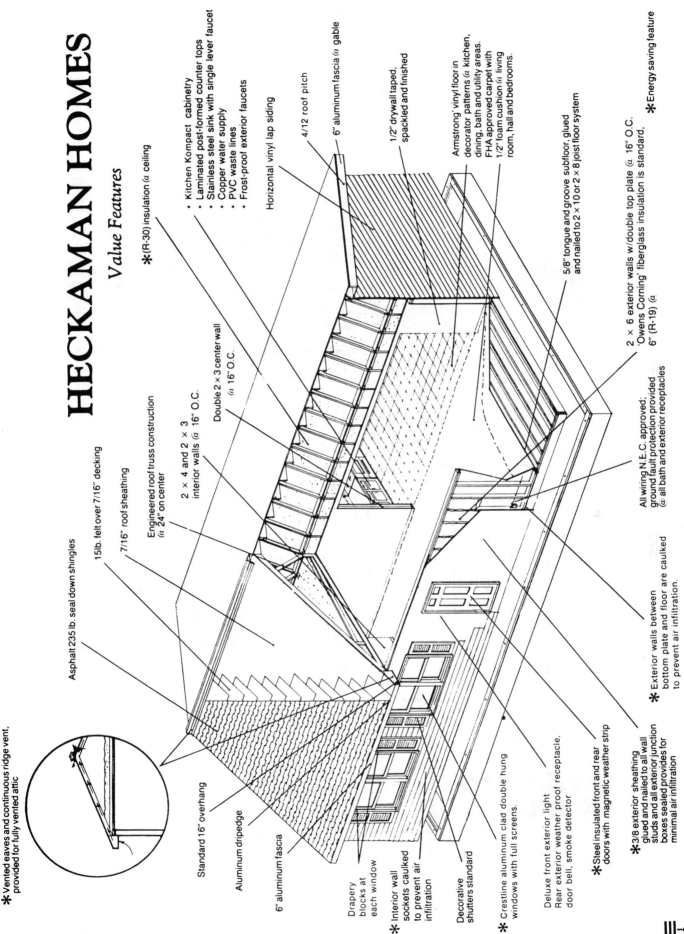

* (R-30) insulation @ ceiling

- Kitchen Kompact cabinetry
- Laminated post-formed counter tops
- Stainless steel sink with single lever faucet
- Copper water supply
- PVC waste lines
- Frost-proof exterior faucets

Horizontal vinyl lap siding

4/12 roof pitch

6" aluminum fascia @ gable

1/2" drywall taped, spackled and finished

Armstrong' vinyl floor in decorator patterns @ kitchen, dining, bath and utility areas. FHA approved carpet with 1/2" foam cushion @ living room, hall and bedrooms.

5/8" tongue and groove subfloor, glued and nailed to 2 × 10 or 2 × 8 joist floor system

2 × 6 exterior walls w/double top plate @ 16" O.C. 'Owens Corning' fiberglass insulation is standard, 6" (R-19) @

* Energy saving feature

Double 2 × 3 center wall @ 16" O.C.

2 × 4 and 2 × 3 interior walls @ 16" O.C.

Engineered roof truss construction @ 24" on center

7/16" roof sheathing

15lb. felt over 7/16" decking

Asphalt 235 lb. seal down shingles

All wiring N.E.C. approved; ground fault protection provided @ all bath and exterior receptacles

* Exterior walls between bottom plate and floor are caulked to prevent air infiltration.

* Vented eaves and continuous ridge vent, provided for fully vented attic

Standard 16" overhang

Aluminum dripedge

6" aluminum fascia

Drapery blocks at each window

* Interior wall sockets caulked to prevent air infiltration

Decorative shutters standard

Crestline aluminum clad double hung windows with full screens.

Deluxe front exterior light
Rear exterior weather proof receptacle, door bell, smoke detector

* Steel insulated front and rear doors with magnetic weather strip

* 3/8 exterior sheathing glued and nailed to all wall studs and all exterior junction boxes sealed provides for minimal air infiltration

III-4

Roosevelt

ELEVATION SHOWS OPTIONAL WINDOW GRIDS, TWO COACH LIGHTS, TWO SIDE LIGHTS, GABLE GARAGE ROOF. BRICK: BY BUILDER.

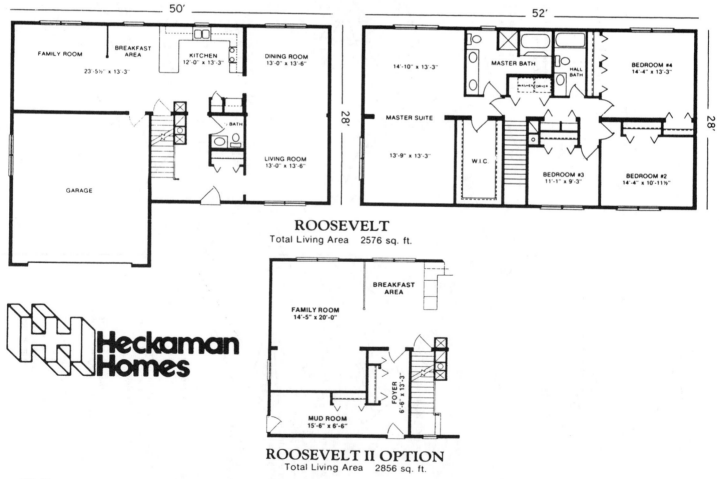

ROOSEVELT
Total Living Area 2576 sq. ft.

ROOSEVELT II OPTION
Total Living Area 2856 sq. ft.

Heckaman Homes

Hermitage

ELEVATION SHOWS OPTIONAL DOUBLE SIDELIGHTS, DOUBLE COACH LIGHTS, WINDOW GRIDS, SIDE ENTRY GARAGE W/SINGLE DOORS.
GARAGE, SHUTTERS ON GARAGE WINDOWS, BRICK BY BUILDER.

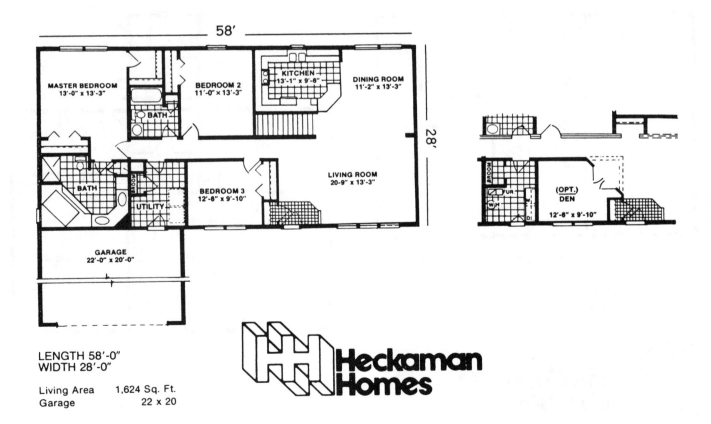

LENGTH 58'-0"
WIDTH 28'-0"

Living Area   1,624 Sq. Ft.
Garage   22 x 20

Heckaman Homes

Jefferson

ELEVATION SHOWS OPTIONAL ACORN PEDIMENT WITH PILLASTERS, SIDE
LIGHT, COACH LIGHT. BY BUILDER: BRICK ON FRONT AND TWO CAR GARAGE.

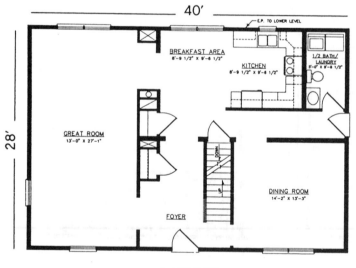

1st FLOOR

Length 40'-0"   Depth 28'-0"
Living Area   2240 sq. ft.

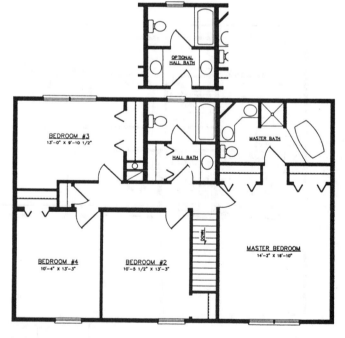

2nd FLOOR

Heckaman Homes

III-7

Carolina

ELEVATION SHOWS OPTIONAL WINDOW GRIDS, FRONT DOOR SIDELIGHT, GARAGE COACH LIGHTS, SINGLE GARAGE DOORS.
BY BUILDER: WINDOWS IN LOWER LEVEL AND STONE.

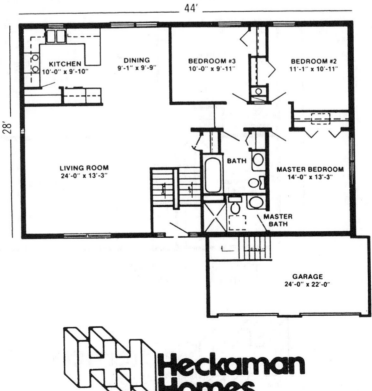

Heckaman Homes

Upper Floor

Living Area	1,236 Sq. Ft.
Garage	528 Sq. Ft.
Total Area	1,854 Sq. Ft.

Lower Level By Builder

III-8

Willowbrook

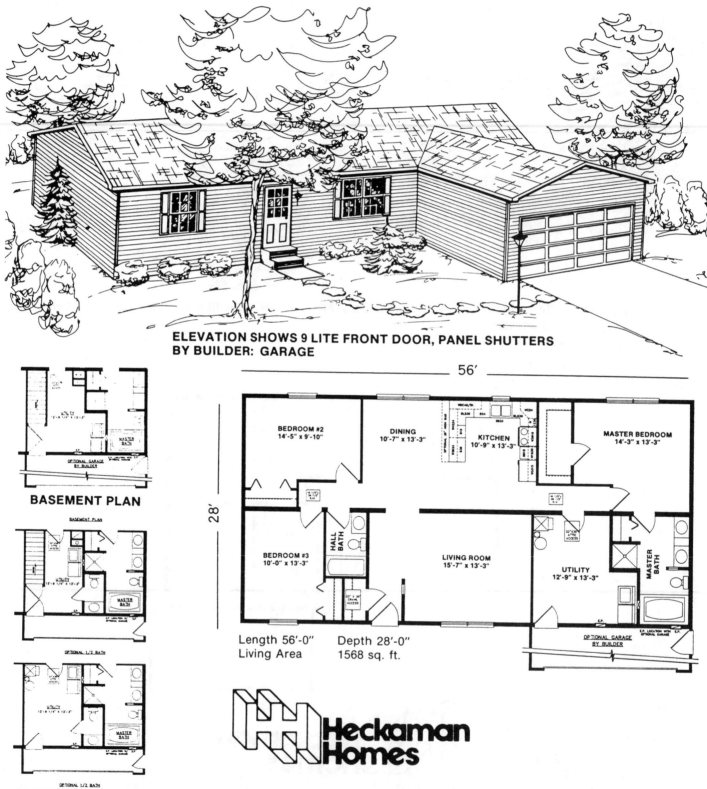

ELEVATION SHOWS 9 LITE FRONT DOOR, PANEL SHUTTERS BY BUILDER: GARAGE

BASEMENT PLAN

CRAWLSPACE PLAN

56'

28'

BEDROOM #2
14'-5" x 9'-10"

DINING
10'-7" x 13'-3"

KITCHEN
10'-9" x 13'-3"

MASTER BEDROOM
14'-3" x 13'-3"

BEDROOM #3
10'-0" x 13'-3"

HALL BATH

LIVING ROOM
15'-7" x 13'-3"

UTILITY
12'-9" x 13'-3"

MASTER BATH

OPTIONAL GARAGE BY BUILDER

Length 56'-0"
Living Area

Depth 28'-0"
1568 sq. ft.

Heckaman Homes

Countryside

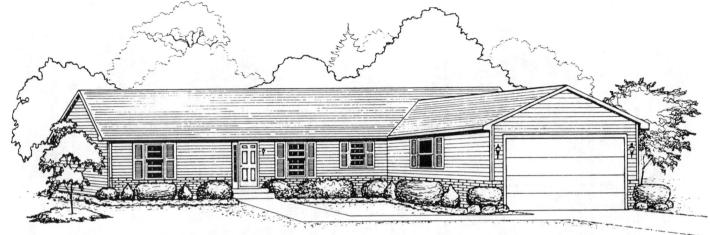

**ELEVATION SHOWS OPTIONAL
GARAGE WITH COACH LIGHTS,
WINDOW GRIDS,
FRONT DOOR SIDE LIGHT
BRICK BY BUILDER.**

MASTER BEDROOM
14'-3" x 13'-3"

OPTIONAL BASEMENT PLAN

DINING ROOM
8'-9" x 13'-3"

KITCHEN
10'-0" x 13'-3"

OPTIONAL KITCHEN PLAN A

BEDROOM #2
15'-3½" x 9'-10½"

LIVING ROOM
24'-6" x 13'-3"

MASTER BEDROOM
14'-3" x 13'-3"

BATH

BEDROOM #3
10'-0" x 13'-3"

FOYER
5'-9" x 13'-3"

KITCHEN
10'-0" x 13'-3"

DINING ROOM
8'-9" x 13'-3"

UTILITY
5'-9" x 13'-3"

MASTER
BATH

Length 60' - 0"   Depth 28' - 0"
Living Area   1680 sq. ft.

Heckaman Homes

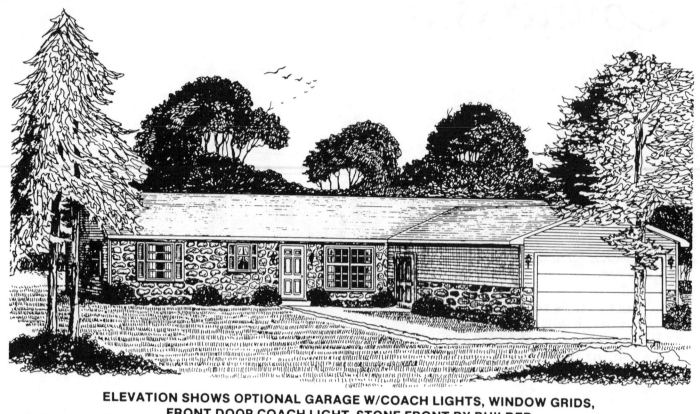

ELEVATION SHOWS OPTIONAL GARAGE W/COACH LIGHTS, WINDOW GRIDS, FRONT DOOR COACH LIGHT, STONE FRONT BY BUILDER

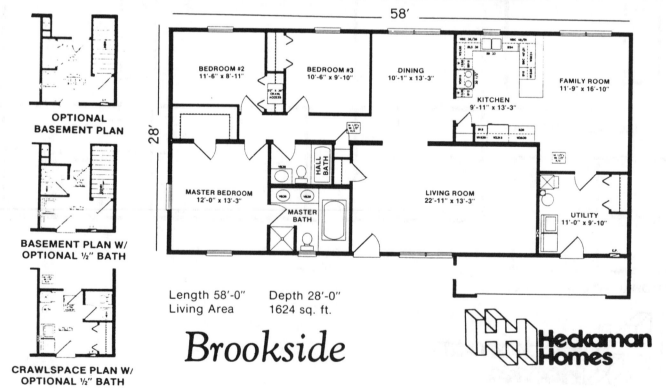

OPTIONAL BASEMENT PLAN

BASEMENT PLAN W/ OPTIONAL ½" BATH

CRAWLSPACE PLAN W/ OPTIONAL ½" BATH

58'

28'

BEDROOM #2
11'-6" x 8'-11"

BEDROOM #3
10'-6" x 9'-10"

DINING
10'-1" x 13'-3"

FAMILY ROOM
11'-9" x 16'-10"

KITCHEN
9'-11" x 13'-3"

MASTER BEDROOM
12'-0" x 13'-3"

HALL BATH

MASTER BATH

LIVING ROOM
22'-11" x 13'-3"

UTILITY
11'-0" x 9'-10"

Length 58'-0"
Living Area

Depth 28'-0"
1624 sq. ft.

Brookside

Heckaman Homes

Cambridge

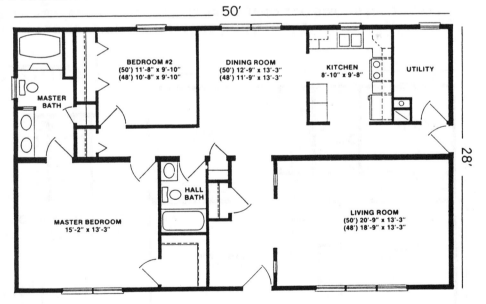

ELEVATION SHOWS OPTIONAL DOUBLE SIDE LIGHT, COACH LIGHT, SHUTTER
ON END WINDOW. BY BUILDER: BRICK ON FRONT AND GARAGE.

50'

BEDROOM #2
(50') 11'-8" x 9'-10"
(48') 10'-8" x 9'-10"

DINING ROOM
(50') 12'-9" x 13'-3"
(48') 11'-9" x 13'-3"

KITCHEN
8'-10" x 9'-8"

UTILITY

MASTER
BATH

28'

HALL
BATH

MASTER BEDROOM
15'-2" x 13'-3"

LIVING ROOM
(50') 20'-9" x 13'-3"
(48') 18'-9" x 13'-3"

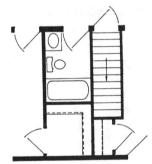

**FLOOR PLAN MODIFICATION
WITH BASEMENT OPTION**

LENGTH 50'   DEPTH 28'
Living Area   1,400 Sq. Ft.

LENGTH 48'   DEPTH 28'
Living Area   1,344 Sq. Ft.

Heckaman
Homes

ELEVATION SHOWS OPTIONAL DORMERS, WINDOW GRIDS, 3056 WINDOWS IN LIVING ROOM, FRONT DOOR COACH LIGHT, GARAGE BY BUILDER

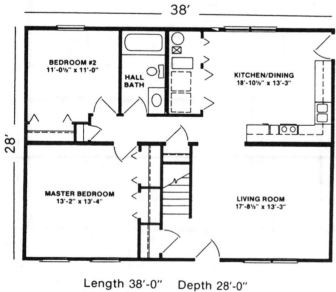

Pembrooke

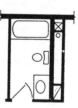

NO UTILITY ROOM
w/BASEMENT OPTION

OPTIONAL BASEMENT

Heckaman Homes

Length 38'-0"   Depth 28'-0"
Living Area   1064 sq. ft.

Upper Level   15' x 38'

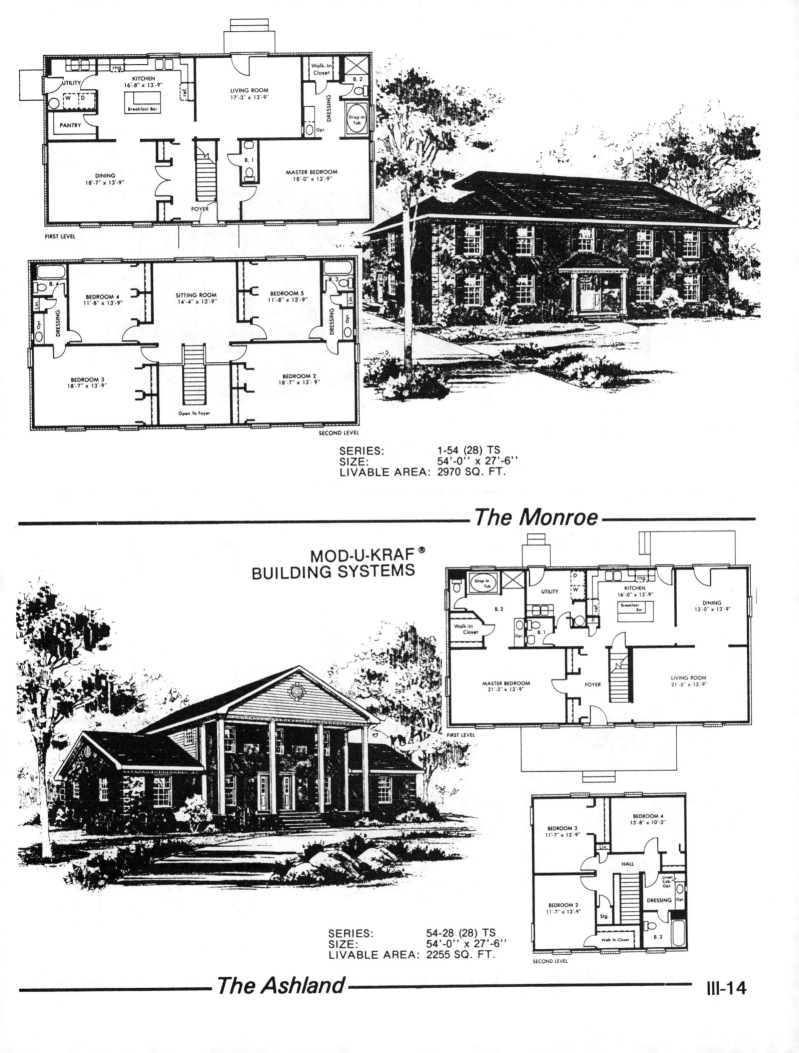

FIRST LEVEL

UTILITY

KITCHEN
16'-8" x 13'-9"

rng.

Breakfast Bar

ref.

W D

PANTRY

DINING
18'-7" x 13'-9"

FOYER

B. 1

LIVING ROOM
17'-3" x 13'-9"

DRESSING

Walk-In Closet

B. 2

Drop-In Tub

Opt.

MASTER BEDROOM
18'-0" x 13'-9"

SECOND LEVEL

B. 4

Opt.

DRESSING

BEDROOM 4
11'-8" x 13'-9"

SITTING ROOM
14'-4" x 13'-9"

BEDROOM 5
11'-8" x 13'-9"

B. 3

DRESSING

Opt.

BEDROOM 3
18'-7" x 13'-9"

Open To Foyer

BEDROOM 2
18'-7" x 13'-9"

SERIES: 1-54 (28) TS
SIZE: 54'-0'' x 27'-6''
LIVABLE AREA: 2970 SQ. FT.

The Monroe

MOD-U-KRAF®
BUILDING SYSTEMS

FIRST LEVEL

Drop-In Tub

B. 2

UTILITY

D

W

KITCHEN
16'-0" x 13'-9"

rng.

Breakfast Bar

DINING
13'-0" x 13'-9"

Walk-In Closet

Opt.

B. 1

MASTER BEDROOM
21'-3" x 13'-9"

FOYER

LIVING ROOM
21'-0" x 13'-9"

SECOND LEVEL

BEDROOM 3
11'-7" x 13'-9"

BEDROOM 4
13'-8" x 10'-3"

HALL

Linen Cab. Opt.

BEDROOM 2
11'-7" x 13'-9"

Stg.

DRESSING

Opt.

Walk-In Closet

B. 3

SERIES: 54-28 (28) TS
SIZE: 54'-0'' x 27'-6''
LIVABLE AREA: 2255 SQ. FT.

The Ashland

III-14

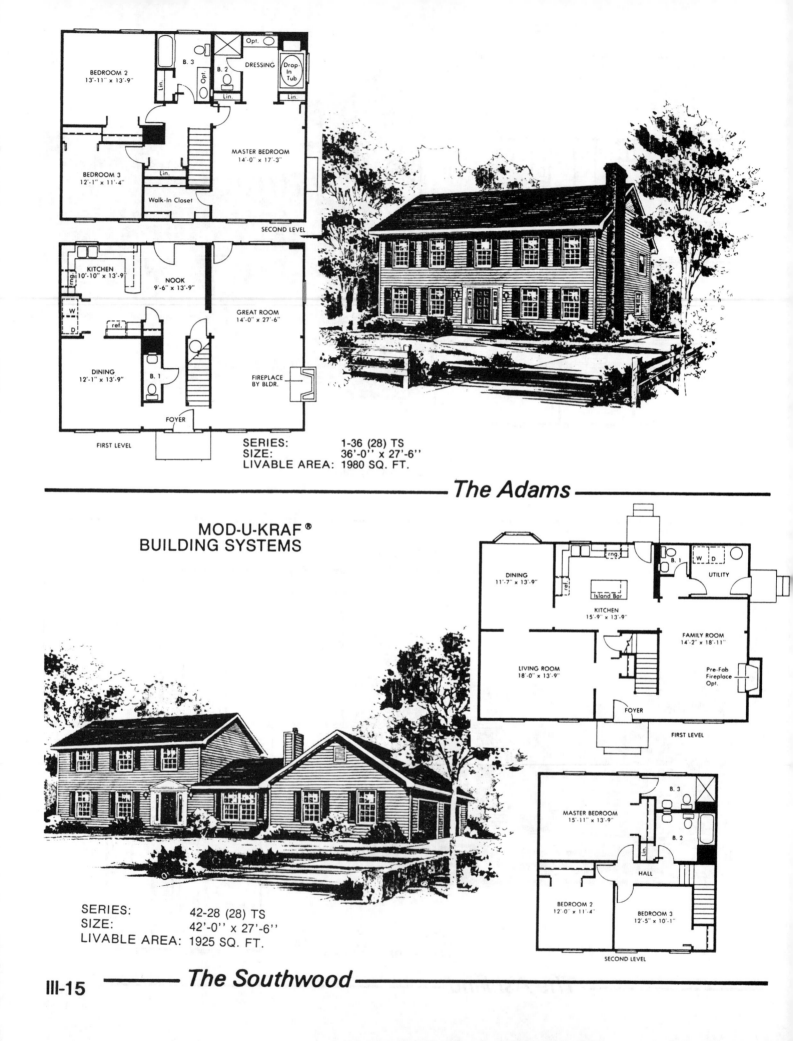

The Adams

BEDROOM 2
13'-11" x 13'-9"

B. 3

B. 2

Opt.

DRESSING

Drop-In Tub

Lin.

Lin.

Lin.

BEDROOM 3
12'-1" x 11'-4"

MASTER BEDROOM
14'-0" x 17'-3"

Lin.

Walk-In Closet

SECOND LEVEL

KITCHEN
10'-10" x 13'-9"

rng.

NOOK
9'-6" x 13'-9"

W

D

ref.

GREAT ROOM
14'-0" x 27'-6"

DINING
12'-1" x 13'-9"

B. 1

FIREPLACE
BY BLDR.

FOYER

FIRST LEVEL

SERIES: 1-36 (28) TS
SIZE: 36'-0'' x 27'-6''
LIVABLE AREA: 1980 SQ. FT.

MOD-U-KRAF®
BUILDING SYSTEMS

DINING
11'-7" x 13'-9"

rng.

B. 1

W   D

UTILITY

ref.

Island Bar

KITCHEN
15'-9" x 13'-9"

FAMILY ROOM
14'-2" x 18'-11"

LIVING ROOM
18'-0" x 13'-9"

Pre-Fab
Fireplace
Opt.

FOYER

FIRST LEVEL

MASTER BEDROOM
15'-11" x 13'-9"

B. 3

B. 2

Lin.

HALL

BEDROOM 2
12'-0" x 11'-4"

BEDROOM 3
12'-5" x 10'-1"

SECOND LEVEL

SERIES: 42-28 (28) TS
SIZE: 42'-0'' x 27'-6''
LIVABLE AREA: 1925 SQ. FT.

The Southwood

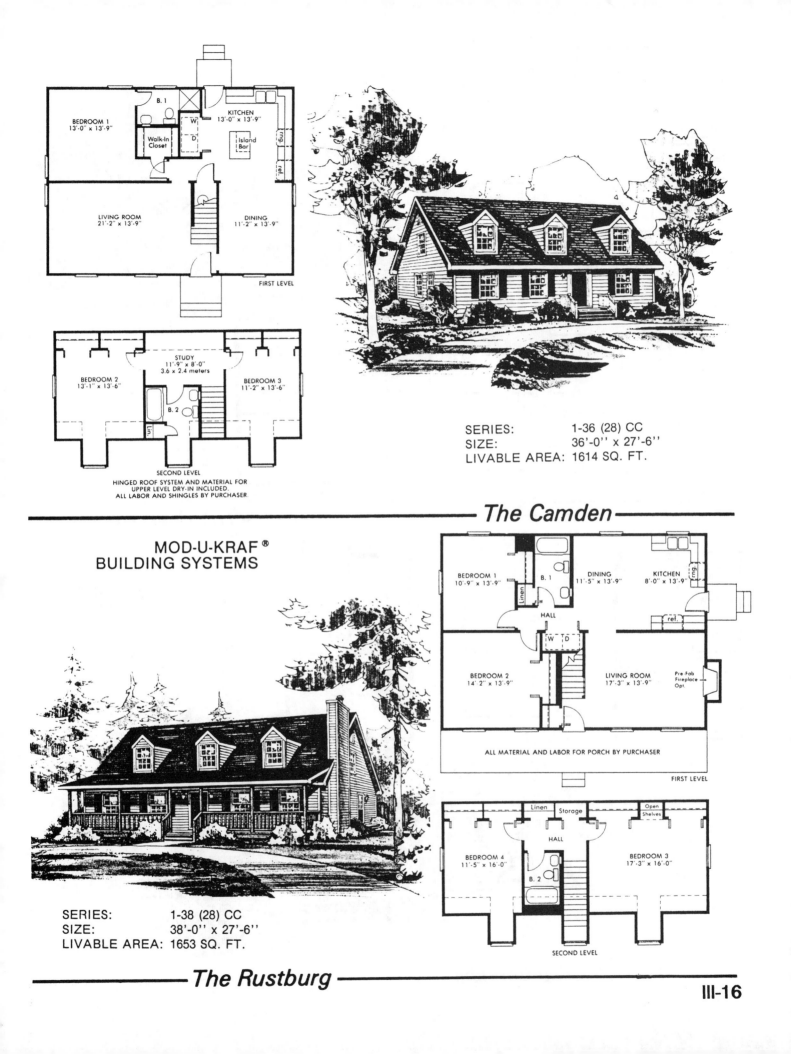

BEDROOM 1
13'-0'' x 13'-9''

B. 1

KITCHEN
13'-0'' x 13'-9''

W
D

Walk-In
Closet

Island
Bar

LIVING ROOM
21'-2'' x 13'-9''

DINING
11'-2'' x 13'-9''

FIRST LEVEL

BEDROOM 2
13'-1'' x 13'-6''

STUDY
11'-9'' x 8'-0''
3.6 x 2.4 meters

B. 2

BEDROOM 3
11'-2'' x 13'-6''

Lin'

SECOND LEVEL

HINGED ROOF SYSTEM AND MATERIAL FOR
UPPER LEVEL DRY-IN INCLUDED.
ALL LABOR AND SHINGLES BY PURCHASER.

SERIES: 1-36 (28) CC
SIZE: 36'-0'' x 27'-6''
LIVABLE AREA: 1614 SQ. FT.

The Camden

MOD-U-KRAF®
BUILDING SYSTEMS

BEDROOM 1
10'-9'' x 13'-9''

B. 1

DINING
11'-5'' x 13'-9''

KITCHEN
8'-0'' x 13'-9''

Linen

HALL

ref.

W D

BEDROOM 2
14'-2'' x 13'-9''

LIVING ROOM
17'-3'' x 13'-9''

Pre-Fab
Fireplace
Opt.

ALL MATERIAL AND LABOR FOR PORCH BY PURCHASER

FIRST LEVEL

Linen   Storage

Open
Shelves

HALL

BEDROOM 4
11'-5'' x 16'-0''

B. 2

BEDROOM 3
17'-3'' x 16'-0''

SECOND LEVEL

SERIES: 1-38 (28) CC
SIZE: 38'-0'' x 27'-6''
LIVABLE AREA: 1653 SQ. FT.

The Rustburg

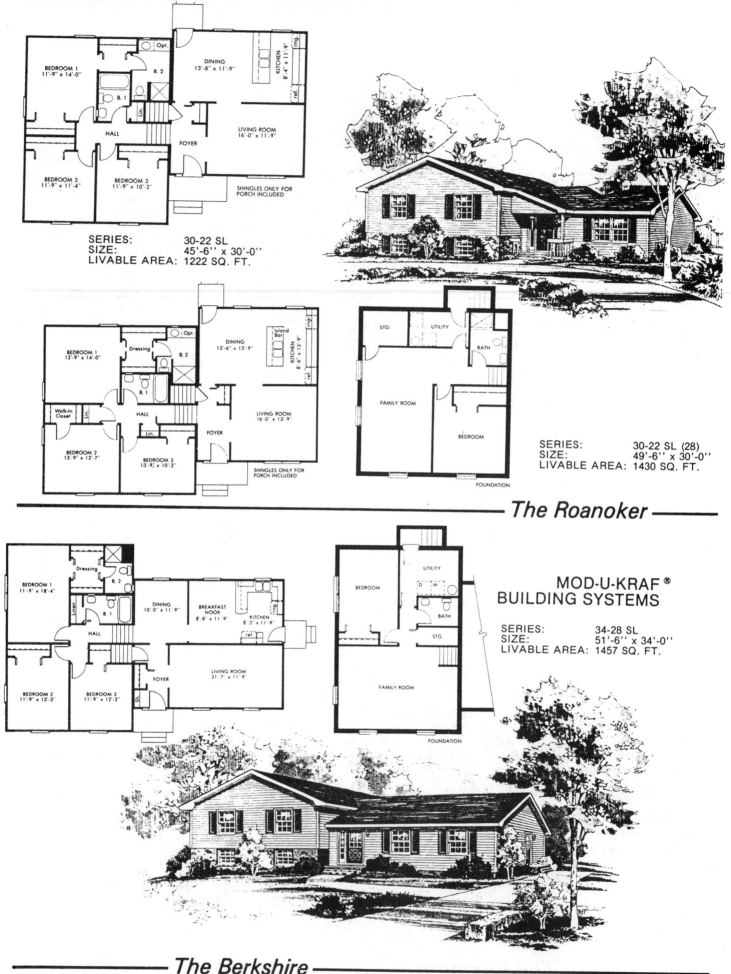

BEDROOM 1
11'-9" x 14'-0"

B. 2

Opt.

DINING
13'-8" x 11'-9"

KITCHEN
8'-4" x 11'-9"

rng.

ref.

B. 1

Lin.

HALL

LIVING ROOM
16'-0" x 11'-9"

FOYER

BEDROOM 2
11'-9" x 11'-4"

BEDROOM 3
11'-9" x 10'-2"

SHINGLES ONLY FOR
PORCH INCLUDED

SERIES: 30-22 SL
SIZE: 45'-6'' x 30'-0''
LIVABLE AREA: 1222 SQ. FT.

BEDROOM 1
13'-9" x 14'-0"

Dressing

B. 2

Opt.

DINING
13'-6" x 13'-9"

Island
Bar

KITCHEN
8'-6" x 13'-9"

rng.

ref.

Walk-In
Closet

Lin.

B. 1

HALL

Lin.

LIVING ROOM
16'-0" x 13'-9"

FOYER

BEDROOM 2
13'-9" x 12'-7"

BEDROOM 3
13'-9" x 10'-2"

SHINGLES ONLY FOR
PORCH INCLUDED

STG.

UTILITY

BATH

FAMILY ROOM

BEDROOM

FOUNDATION

SERIES: 30-22 SL (28)
SIZE: 49'-6'' x 30'-0''
LIVABLE AREA: 1430 SQ. FT.

The Roanoker

BEDROOM 1
11'-9" x 18'-4"

Dressing

B. 2

Linen

DINING
10'-0" x 11'-9"

BREAKFAST
NOOK
8'-8" x 11'-9"

KITCHEN
8'-3" x 11'-9"

rng.

ref.

B. 1

HALL

LIVING ROOM
21'-7" x 11'-9"

FOYER

Sh.

BEDROOM 2
11'-9" x 13'-3"

BEDROOM 3
11'-9" x 12'-2"

BEDROOM

UTILITY

D   W

BATH

STG.

FAMILY ROOM

FOUNDATION

MOD-U-KRAF ®
BUILDING SYSTEMS

SERIES: 34-28 SL
SIZE: 51'-6'' x 34'-0''
LIVABLE AREA: 1457 SQ. FT.

The Berkshire

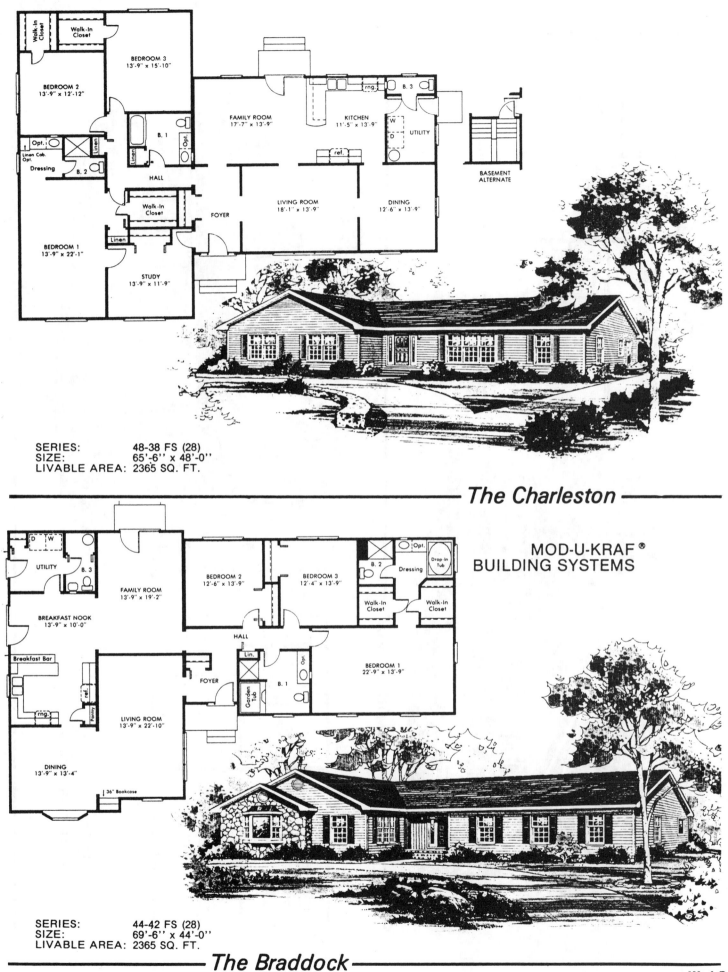

SERIES: 48-38 FS (28)
SIZE: 65'-6'' x 48'-0''
LIVABLE AREA: 2365 SQ. FT.

The Charleston

MOD-U-KRAF ®
BUILDING SYSTEMS

SERIES: 44-42 FS (28)
SIZE: 69'-6'' x 44'-0''
LIVABLE AREA: 2365 SQ. FT.

The Braddock

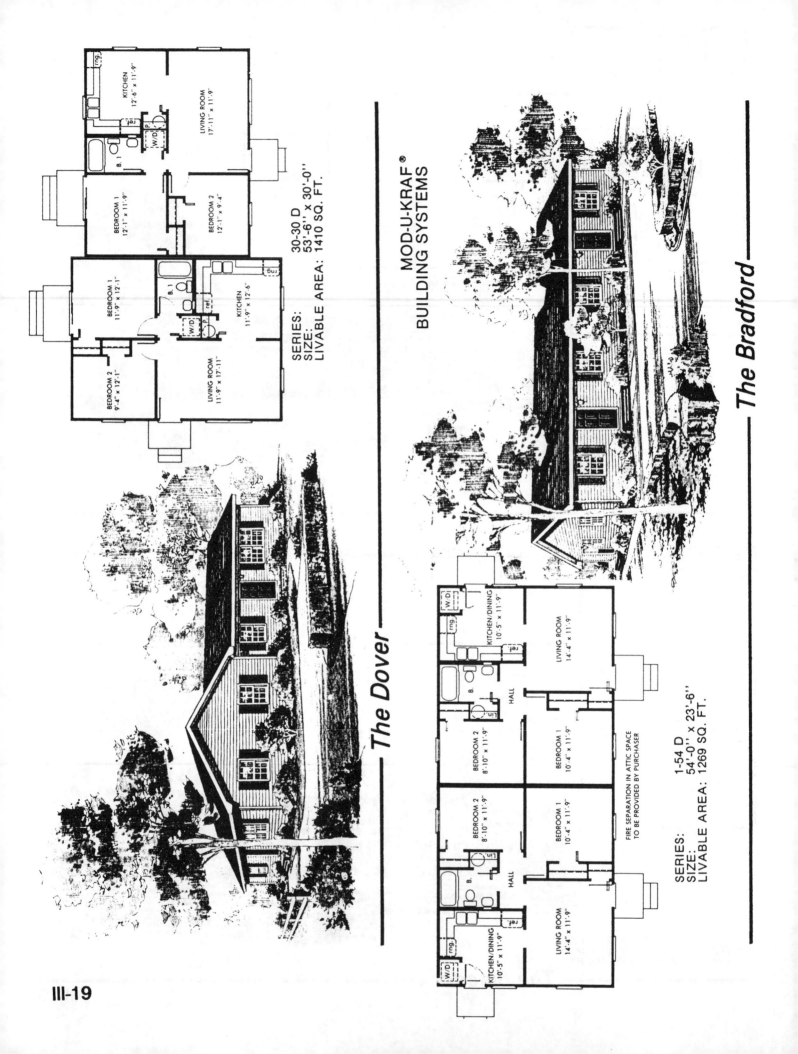

The Dover

KITCHEN
12'-6" x 11'-9"

LIVING ROOM
17'-11" x 11'-9"

BEDROOM 1
12'-1" x 11'-9"

BEDROOM 2
12'-1" x 9'-4"

B.

W/D

ref.

BEDROOM 1
11'-9" x 12'-1"

BEDROOM 2
9'-4" x 12'-1"

LIVING ROOM
11'-9" x 17'-11"

KITCHEN
11'-9" x 12'-6"

B.

W/D

ref.

SERIES: 30-30 D
SIZE: 53'-6" x 30'-0"
LIVABLE AREA: 1410 SQ. FT.

MOD-U-KRAF®
BUILDING SYSTEMS

The Bradford

W/D

rng.

KITCHEN/DINING
10'-5" x 11'-9"

ref.

B.

HALL

BEDROOM 2
8'-10" x 11'-9"

BEDROOM 1
10'-4" x 11'-9"

LIVING ROOM
14'-4" x 11'-9"

FIRE SEPARATION IN ATTIC SPACE
TO BE PROVIDED BY PURCHASER

BEDROOM 2
8'-10" x 11'-9"

BEDROOM 1
10'-4" x 11'-9"

LIVING ROOM
14'-4" x 11'-9"

HALL

B.

ref.

KITCHEN/DINING
10'-5" x 11'-9"

W/D

rng.

SERIES: 1-54 D
SIZE: 54'-0" x 23'-6"
LIVABLE AREA: 1269 SQ. FT.

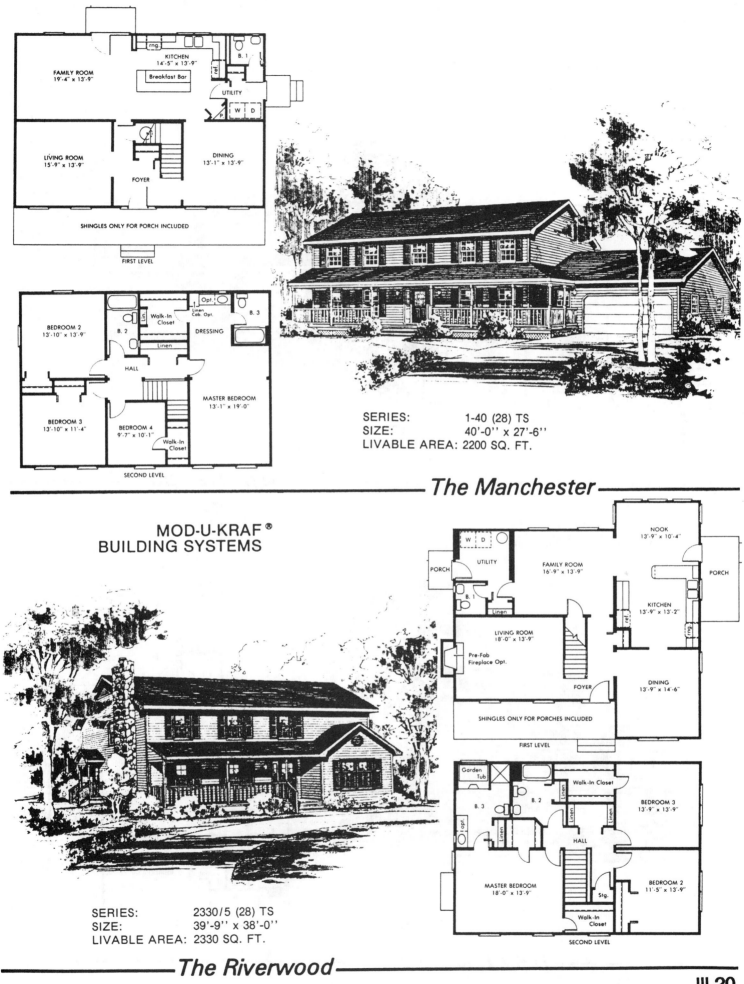

FAMILY ROOM
19'-4" x 13'-9"

KITCHEN
14'-5" x 13'-9"

Breakfast Bar

rng.

B. 1

ref.

UTILITY

W D

LIVING ROOM
15'-9" x 13'-9"

DINING
13'-1" x 13'-9"

FOYER

SHINGLES ONLY FOR PORCH INCLUDED

FIRST LEVEL

BEDROOM 2
13'-10" x 13'-9"

Opt.

Linen Cab. Opt.

B. 3

Walk-In Closet

DRESSING

B. 2

Linen

HALL

BEDROOM 3
13'-10" x 11'-4"

BEDROOM 4
9'-7" x 10'-1"

Walk-In Closet

MASTER BEDROOM
13'-1" x 19'-0"

SECOND LEVEL

SERIES: 1-40 (28) TS
SIZE: 40'-0'' x 27'-6''
LIVABLE AREA: 2200 SQ. FT.

The Manchester

MOD-U-KRAF ®
BUILDING SYSTEMS

W D

UTILITY

PORCH

B. 1

Linen

FAMILY ROOM
16'-9" x 13'-9"

NOOK
13'-9" x 10'-4"

ref.

KITCHEN
13'-9" x 13'-2"

rng.

PORCH

LIVING ROOM
18'-0" x 13'-9"

Pre-Fab
Fireplace Opt.

FOYER

DINING
13'-9" x 14'-6"

SHINGLES ONLY FOR PORCHES INCLUDED

FIRST LEVEL

Garden Tub

Walk-In Closet

B. 3

B. 2

Linen

Linen

BEDROOM 3
13'-9" x 13'-9"

opt.

Linen

HALL

MASTER BEDROOM
18'-0" x 13'-9"

Stg.

BEDROOM 2
11'-5" x 13'-9"

Walk-In Closet

SECOND LEVEL

SERIES: 2330/5 (28) TS
SIZE: 39'-9'' x 38'-0''
LIVABLE AREA: 2330 SQ. FT.

The Riverwood

III-20

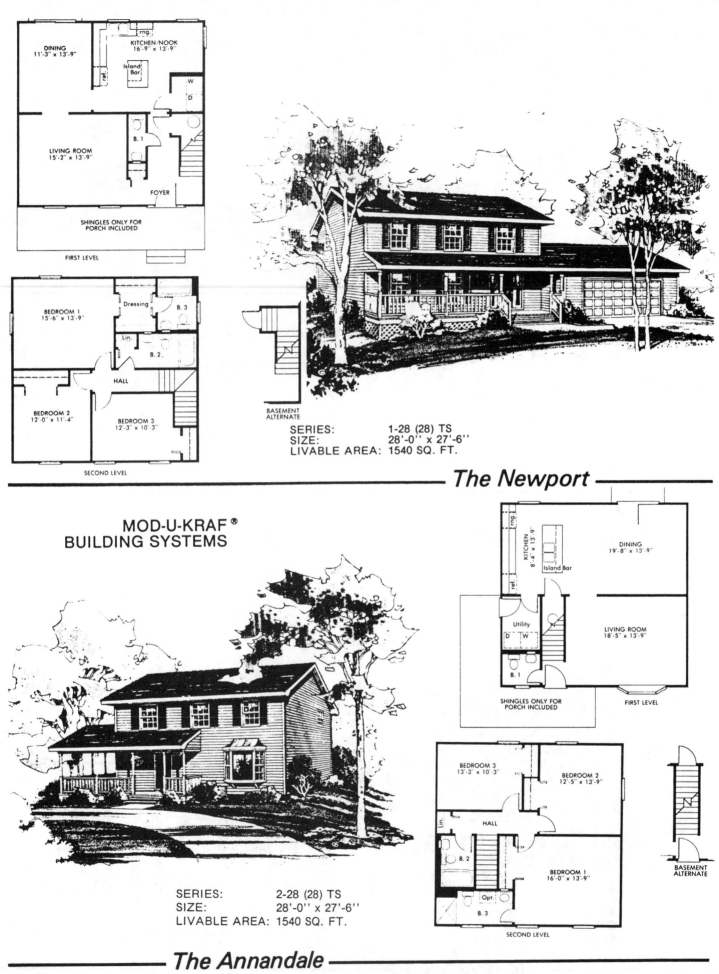

DINING
11'-3" x 13'-9"

KITCHEN/NOOK
16'-9" x 13'-9"

rng.

Island Bar

ref.

W
D

LIVING ROOM
15'-2" x 13'-9"

B. 1

FOYER

SHINGLES ONLY FOR
PORCH INCLUDED

FIRST LEVEL

BEDROOM 1
15'-6" x 13'-9"

Dressing

B. 3

Lin.

B. 2

HALL

BEDROOM 2
12'-0" x 11'-4"

BEDROOM 3
12'-3" x 10'-3"

SECOND LEVEL

BASEMENT
ALTERNATE

SERIES: 1-28 (28) TS
SIZE: 28'-0'' x 27'-6''
LIVABLE AREA: 1540 SQ. FT.

The Newport

MOD-U-KRAF®
BUILDING SYSTEMS

rng.

KITCHEN
8'-4" x 13'-9"

Island Bar

ref.

DINING
19'-8" x 13'-9"

Utility

D   W

B. 1

LIVING ROOM
18'-5" x 13'-9"

SHINGLES ONLY FOR
PORCH INCLUDED

FIRST LEVEL

BEDROOM 3
13'-3" x 10'-3"

BEDROOM 2
12'-5" x 13'-9"

Lin.

HALL

B. 2

BEDROOM 1
16'-0" x 13'-9"

Opt.

B. 3

SECOND LEVEL

BASEMENT
ALTERNATE

SERIES: 2-28 (28) TS
SIZE: 28'-0'' x 27'-6''
LIVABLE AREA: 1540 SQ. FT.

The Annandale

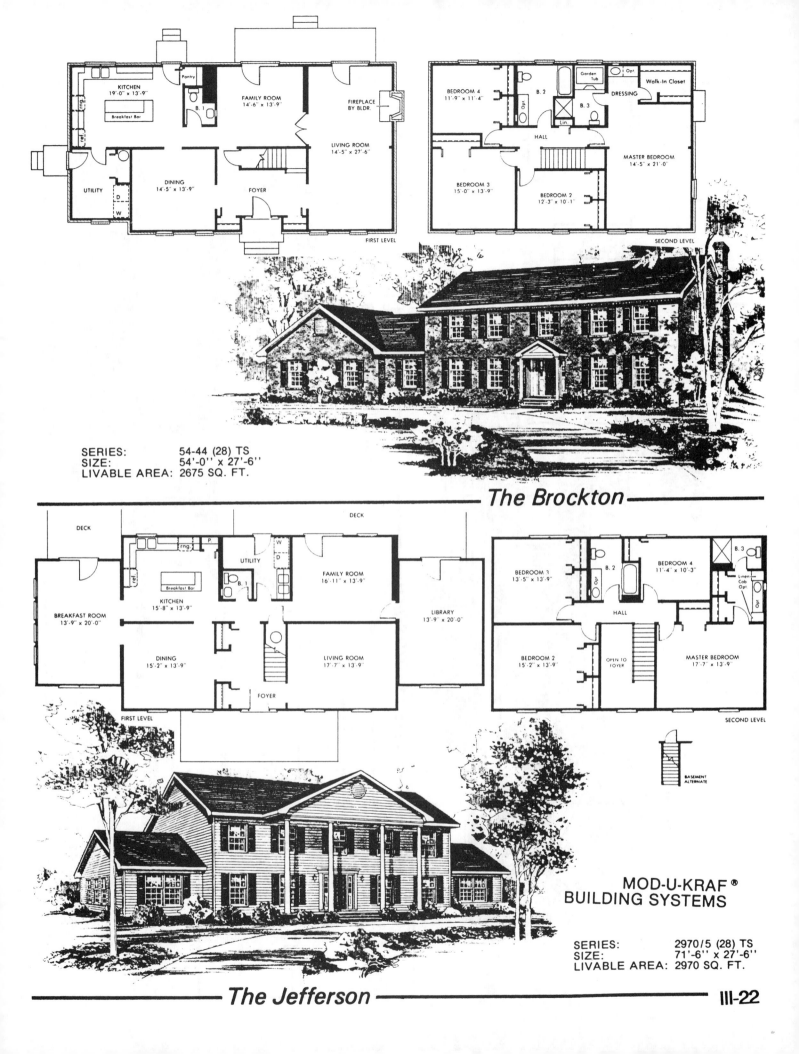

The Brockton

KITCHEN 19'-0" x 13'-9"
Breakfast Bar
Pantry
B. 1
FAMILY ROOM 14'-6" x 13'-9"
FIREPLACE BY BLDR.
rng.
ref.
LIVING ROOM 14'-5" x 27'-6"
UTILITY
DINING 14'-5" x 13'-9"
D W
FOYER

FIRST LEVEL

BEDROOM 4 11'-9" x 11'-4"
B. 2
Garden Tub
Opt.
Walk-In Closet
DRESSING
B. 3
Lin.
HALL
MASTER BEDROOM 14'-5" x 21'-0"
BEDROOM 3 15'-0" x 13'-9"
BEDROOM 2 12'-3" x 10'-1"

SECOND LEVEL

SERIES: 54-44 (28) TS
SIZE: 54'-0'' x 27'-6''
LIVABLE AREA: 2675 SQ. FT.

DECK
DECK
BREAKFAST ROOM 13'-9" x 20'-0"
rng.
P.
UTILITY
W D
KITCHEN 15'-8" x 13'-9"
Breakfast Bar
B. 1
FAMILY ROOM 16'-11" x 13'-9"
ref.
LIBRARY 13'-9" x 20'-0"
DINING 15'-2" x 13'-9"
LIVING ROOM 17'-7" x 13'-9"
FOYER

FIRST LEVEL

BEDROOM 3 13'-5" x 13'-9"
B. 2
Opt.
BEDROOM 4 11'-4" x 10'-3"
B. 3
Linen Cab. Opt.
Opt.
HALL
BEDROOM 2 15'-2" x 13'-9"
OPEN TO FOYER
MASTER BEDROOM 17'-7" x 13'-9"

SECOND LEVEL

BASEMENT ALTERNATE

**MOD-U-KRAF ®
BUILDING SYSTEMS**

SERIES: 2970/5 (28) TS
SIZE: 71'-6'' x 27'-6''
LIVABLE AREA: 2970 SQ. FT.

The Jefferson

III-22

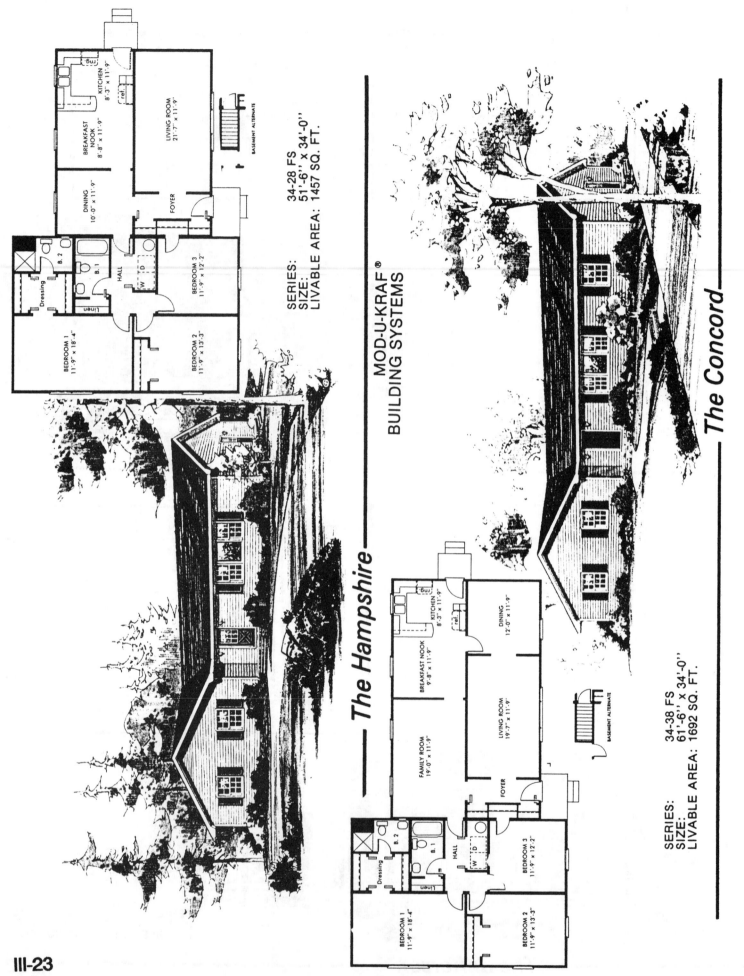

KITCHEN
8'-3" x 11'-9"

BREAKFAST NOOK
8'-8" x 11'-9"

DINING
10'-0" x 11'-9"

LIVING ROOM
21'-7" x 11'-9"

FOYER

B. 2

B. 1

Dressing

HALL

Linen

W   D

BEDROOM 1
11'-9" x 18'-4"

BEDROOM 3
11'-9" x 12'-2"

BEDROOM 2
11'-9" x 13'-3"

BASEMENT ALTERNATE

SERIES: 34-28 FS
SIZE: 51'-6'' x 34'-0''
LIVABLE AREA: 1457 SQ. FT.

— *The Hampshire* —

MOD-U-KRAF ®
BUILDING SYSTEMS

— *The Concord* —

KITCHEN
8'-3" x 11'-9"

BREAKFAST NOOK
9'-8" x 11'-9"

FAMILY ROOM
19'-0" x 11'-9"

DINING
12'-0" x 11'-9"

LIVING ROOM
19'-7" x 11'-9"

FOYER

B. 2

B. 1

Dressing

HALL

Linen

W   D

BEDROOM 1
11'-9" x 18'-4"

BEDROOM 3
11'-9" x 12'-2"

BEDROOM 2
11'-9" x 13'-3"

BASEMENT ALTERNATE

SERIES: 34-38 FS
SIZE: 61'-6'' x 34'-0''
LIVABLE AREA: 1692 SQ. FT.

III-23

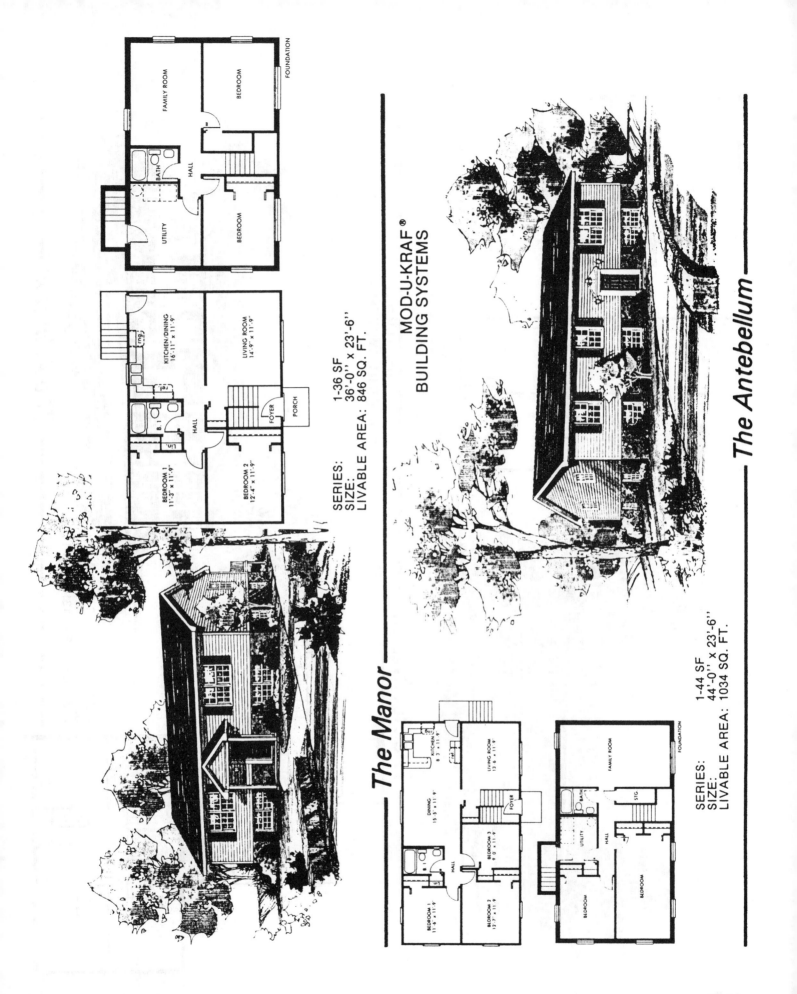

FAMILY ROOM

BEDROOM

FOUNDATION

BATH

HALL

UTILITY

BEDROOM

KITCHEN/DINING
16'-11" x 11'-9"

rng.

LIVING ROOM
14'-9" x 11'-9"

B.

HALL

FOYER

PORCH

BEDROOM 1
11'-3" x 11'-9"

BEDROOM 2
12'-4" x 11'-9"

MOD-U-KRAF ®
BUILDING SYSTEMS

SERIES: 1-36 SF
SIZE: 36'-0'' x 23'-6''
LIVABLE AREA: 846 SQ. FT.

The Manor

The Antebellum

KITCHEN
8'3 x 11'-9

DINING
15'-5 x 11'-9

LIVING ROOM
13'-6 x 11'-9

FOYER

HALL

BEDROOM 3
9'-0 x 11'-9

BEDROOM 1
11'-6 x 11'-9

BEDROOM 2
12'-7 x 11'-9

HALL

FAMILY ROOM

FOUNDATION

BATH

STG.

UTILITY

HALL

BEDROOM

BEDROOM

SERIES: 1-44 SF
SIZE: 44'-0'' x 23'-6''
LIVABLE AREA: 1034 SQ. FT.

III-24

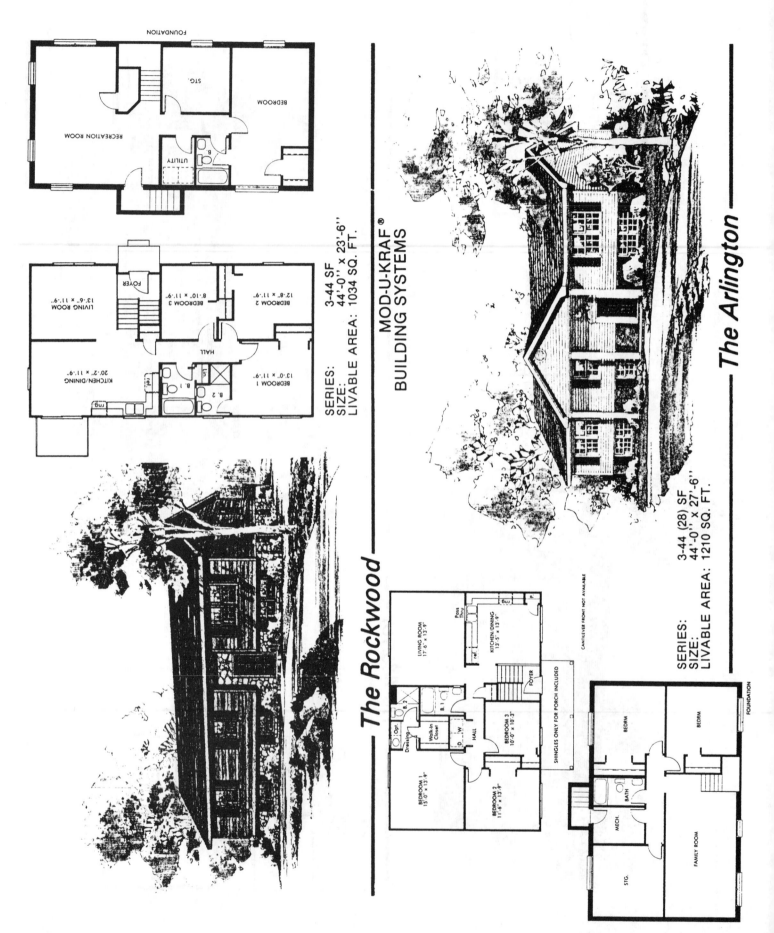

FOUNDATION

BEDROOM

RECREATION ROOM

UTILITY

STG.

LIVING ROOM
13'-6" x 11'-9"

BEDROOM 3
8'-10" x 11'-9"

BEDROOM 2
12'-8" x 11'-9"

FOYER

HALL

KITCHEN/DINING
20'-2" x 11'-9"

BEDROOM 1
13'-0" x 11'-9"

B.1

B.2

ref.

rng.

SERIES: 3-44 SF
SIZE: 44'-0" x 23'-6"
LIVABLE AREA: 1034 SQ. FT.

MOD-U-KRAF®
BUILDING SYSTEMS

The Arlington

The Rockwood

LIVING ROOM
17'-6 x 13'-9"

Pass
Thru

rng.

KITCHEN/DINING
13'-5" x 13'-9"

ref.

P.

FOYER

BEDROOM 1
15'-0" x 13'-9"

B.2

B.1

Dressing

Walk-In
Closet

Opt.

D

W

HALL

BEDROOM 2
11'-6" x 13'-9"

BEDROOM 3
10'-0" x 10'-3"

SHINGLES ONLY FOR PORCH INCLUDED

CANTILEVER FRONT NOT AVAILABLE

STG.

MECH.

BATH

FAMILY ROOM

BEDRM

BEDRM

FOUNDATION

SERIES: 3-44 (28) SF
SIZE: 44'-0" x 27'-6"
LIVABLE AREA: 1210 SQ. FT.

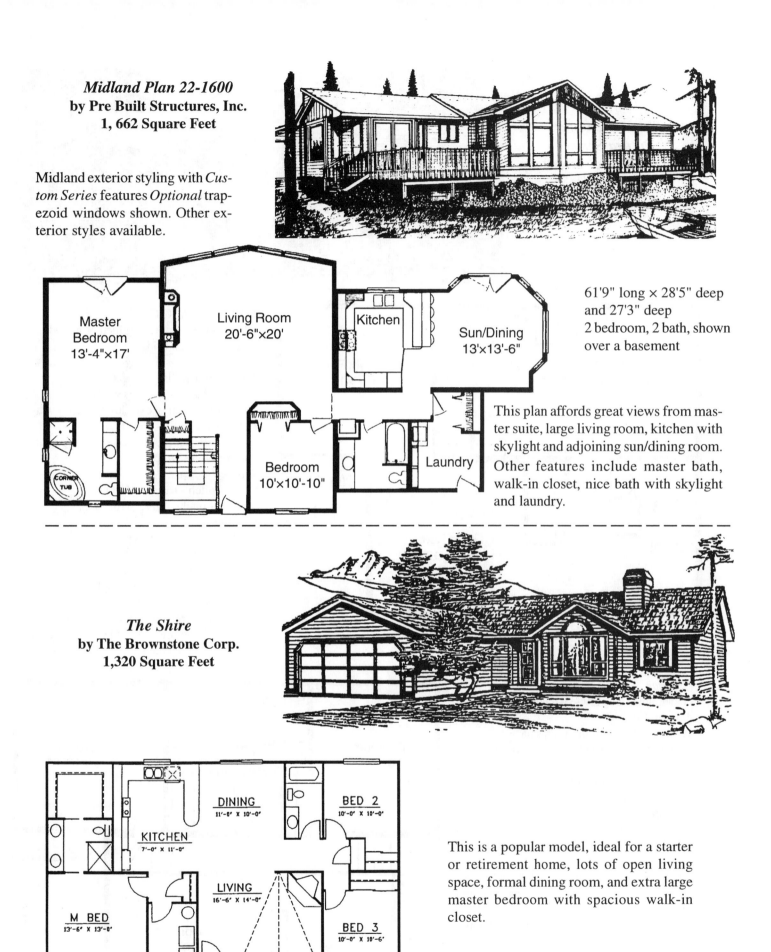

Midland Plan 22-1600
by Pre Built Structures, Inc.
1, 662 Square Feet

Midland exterior styling with *Custom Series* features *Optional* trapezoid windows shown. Other exterior styles available.

Master Bedroom 13'-4"×17'

Living Room 20'-6"×20'

Kitchen

Sun/Dining 13'×13'-6"

CORNER TUB

Bedroom 10'×10'-10"

Laundry

61'9" long × 28'5" deep and 27'3" deep
2 bedroom, 2 bath, shown over a basement

This plan affords great views from master suite, large living room, kitchen with skylight and adjoining sun/dining room. Other features include master bath, walk-in closet, nice bath with skylight and laundry.

The Shire
by The Brownstone Corp.
1,320 Square Feet

DINING 11'-0" X 10'-0"

BED 2 10'-0" X 10'-0"

KITCHEN 7'-0" X 11'-0"

LIVING 16'-6" X 14'-0"

M BED 13'-6" X 13'-0"

BED 3 10'-0" X 10'-6"

This is a popular model, ideal for a starter or retirement home, lots of open living space, formal dining room, and extra large master bedroom with spacious walk-in closet.

**The Manchester
Futura Series
by Future Home Technology
27' 6"×30'/38'
1,870 Square Feet**

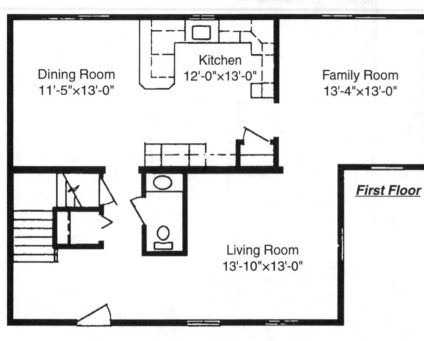

Dining Room
11'-5"×13'-0"

Kitchen
12'-0"×13'-0"

Family Room
13'-4"×13'-0"

Living Room
13'-10"×13'-0"

**First Floor**

**Floors**
2×10 joist - 16" O.C.
¾" T&G OSB flooring (glued & nailed)
solid block deck bridging

**Walls**
2×6 exterior walls - 16" O.C.
R-19 insulation - exterior walls
⁷/₁₆" OSB sheathing exterior & mating walls
2×4 interior walls - 16" O.C.
½" drywall - taped, bedded & primer coated
exterior house wrap

**Roof & Ceiling**
⁵/₁₂ roof pitch - trusses 16" O.C.
cape roof pitch - 12/12 - 16" O.C.
8' ceilings
R-30 insulation - batt type
⁵/₈" CDX plywood
30# felt paper
20-year fiberglass 3-tab shingles
10" front & rear overhangs
gable end overhangs (not on cape models)
½" drywall ceilings - 16" O.C. - taped, bedded
& primer coat painted

**Exterior**
clad double-hung low-e windows with screens
4/4 vinyl siding
vented soffit & aluminum fascia
insulated exterior entry doors with glass
exterior lights at each porch
door chimes at front door
wood slider (per print)
**Interior**
cut pile carpet & FHA-approved ½" pad in
living room, dining room, hall and all bedrooms
vinyl floor covering in kitchen & baths
six-panel colonial hollow core passage and
bi-fold doors painted white
colonial baseboard and casing painted white
trim inside all closets

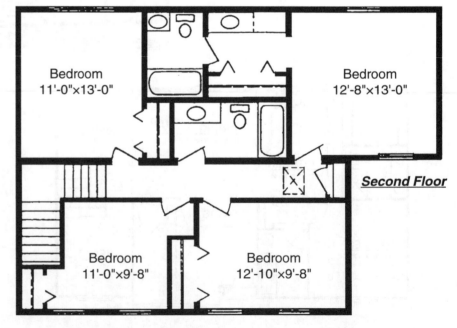

Bedroom
11'-0"×13'-0"

Bedroom
12'-8"×13'-0"

Bedroom
11'-0"×9'-8"

Bedroom
12'-10"×9'-8"

**Second Floor**

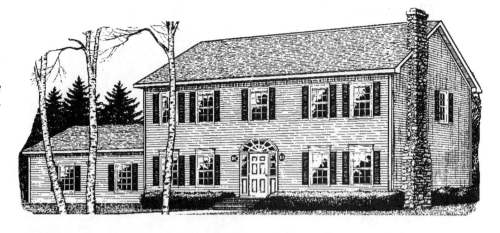

The MadisonFutura Series
by Future Home Technology
27' 6"×42"
2,310 Square Feet

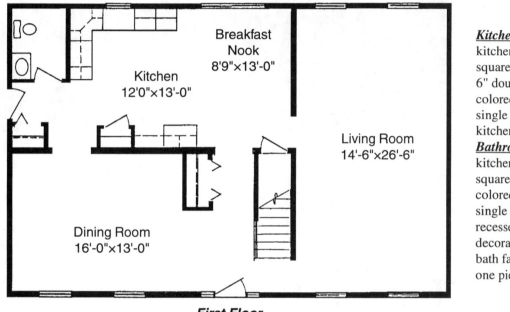

Breakfast Nook
8'9"×13'-0"

Kitchen
12'0"×13'-0"

Living Room
14'-6"×26'-6"

Dining Room
16'-0"×13'-0"

First Floor

Kitchen
kitchen Kompact richwood oak cabinets
square edge countertops
6" double bowl stainless steel sink
colored range hood — white or almond
single lever faucet
kitchen soffits or galley rail

Bathroom
kitchen Kompact richwood oak vanity
square edge countertops
colored steel enameled sink
single lever faucet
recessed medicine cabinet
decorator accessories
bath fan/light combination
one piece tub/shower unit

Plumbing
all plumbing stubbed through floor for
on-site connection
copper fresh water supply line
shut-offs on all sinks and water closet
schedule 40 ABS drain, waste & vent
lines
anti-scald devices on showers and/or
tub/shower

Electric
200 amp entrance panel box
circuit & receptacle for electric range
AC/DC smoke detector (as required by
model)
exterior weatherproof G.F.I. receptacle

Heat
baseboard electric heat with individual
wall-mounted thermostats or hot water
baseboard (stubbed through floor)

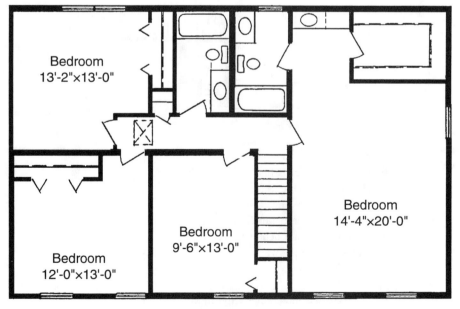

Bedroom
13'-2"×13'-0"

Bedroom
12'-0"×13'-0"

Bedroom
9'-6"×13'-0"

Bedroom
14'-4"×20'-0"

Second Floor

Chestnut Hill
Executive Series
by Haven Homes, Inc.
2,600 Square Feet

Standard Features

Floors

double floor construction glued & nailed —
½" plywood underlayment & 7/16" OSB
2×8 floor joists 16" O.C.
2×10 floor joists 16" O.C. on 27'6 wide units
metal cross bridging
double 2×10 perimeter box w/2 2×10 joists
double perimeter box (1) 2×10
(1) 2×8 w/2×8 joists
triple 2×10 under each half at center of house

Walls

½" sheetrock thru-out; taped and prime coated off white
sheetrock glued, foamed & nailed to studs
2×4 interior partitions except 2×3 at marriage wall
³/₈" plywood sheathing
sheathing locked to floor & plates

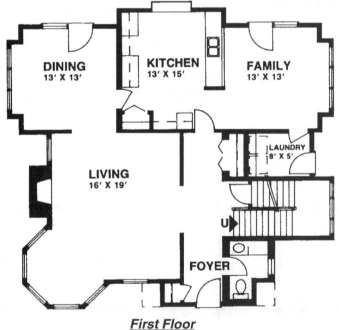

First Floor

sheathing glued 4' up walls
2×6 studs 24" O.C.;
optional items are — trim painted or stained, ½ plywood sheathing, 2×6 16" O.C. stud walls

Roofs

6/12 roof pitch
12/12 roof pitch on cape cods
optional roof pitches are available

Electrical

grounded electrical system
200 amp circuit breaker panelsmoke detectors (AC/DC)
ground fault circuits wired per National Electric Code
2 exterior G.F.I. receptacle
electric baseboard heat devices are all U.L. approved
doorbell at front entry

Second Floor

Doors

3/0 × 6/8 foam core metal clad — front door
2/8 × 6/8 foam core 9 lite crossbuck — secondary door
other door styles are available

Plumbing

single action faucets • reverse trap & water-saving toilet
50 gal energy saver hot water heater w/electric heat
3" main soil line — PVC • ½" water supply line — copper 1½"
fixture drain — PVC

Interior Floors

100% filament 26 oz. nylon carpet • vinyl in kitchen/bath
optional items — hardwood floors, slate, and ceramic tile

Portsmouth
Atlantic Series
by Haven Homes, Inc.
1,990 Square Feet

Door Hardware
exterior door hardware keyed alike
deadbolts are available
bathroom & master bedroom have
privacy locksets

Ventilation
vented aluminum soffit
continuous aluminum ridge vent

Heat
electric baseboard
optional items — hot air heat and
hot water baseboard heat

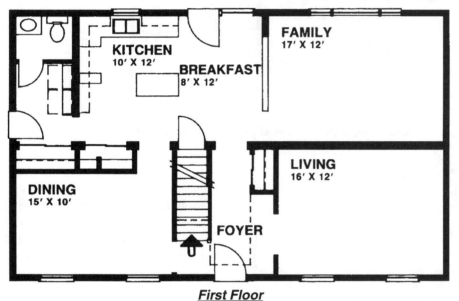

First Floor

Insulation
ceiling — R-38 fiberglass with vapor barrier
walls — R-19 fiberglass with vapor barrier
floors — R-19 fiberglass with vapor barrier
optional items — housewrap and ¾" rigid
foam insulation

Roof & Ceiling
2×6 16" O.C. roof rafter & ceiling joists
½" sheetrock (taped & prime coated off
white)
½" plywood roof sheathing
15# felt underlayment
25 year self seal fiberglass shingles
aluminum drip edge
optional items — cathedral ceilings (kitchen
soffits not included on cathedral ceilings)

Siding & Windows
Anderson Narrowline •shutter on front
aluminum fascia and soffit
optional items — windows per builder's
specs, window grilles

Lavatory Fixtures
fiberglass tub/shower • 1.6 gallon toilet
cultured marble countertops
combination fan/light,mirror, medicine
cabinet and light over mirror

Kitchen Fixtures
double bowl stainless steel sink w/fau-
cets & sink spray
vented kitchen range hood
post-formed Formica countertop
raised panel oak cabinets

Trim
finger jointed based, window and door trim
primed 6 panel Masonite interior doors

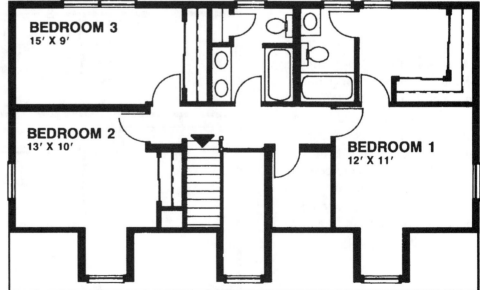

Second Floor

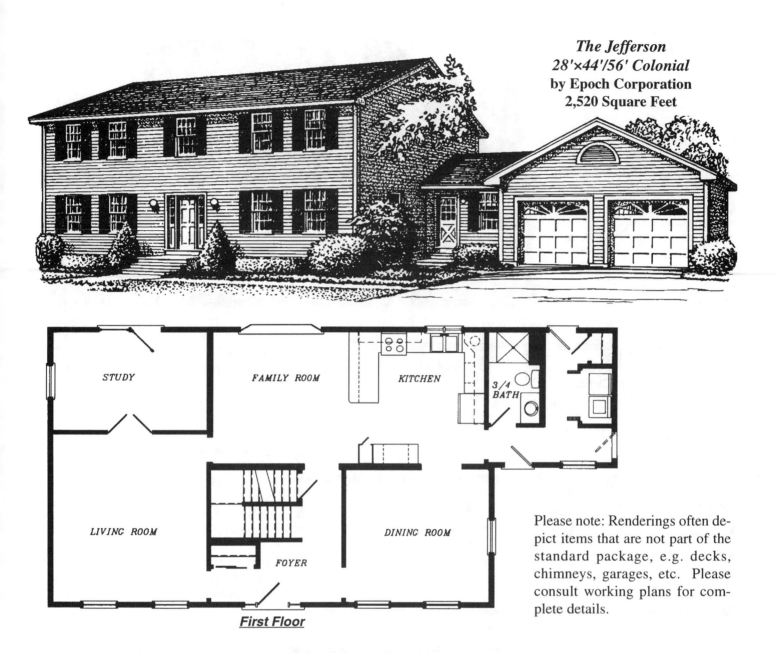

The Jefferson
28'×44'/56' Colonial
by Epoch Corporation
2,520 Square Feet

STUDY

FAMILY ROOM

KITCHEN

3/4 BATH

LIVING ROOM

FOYER

DINING ROOM

Please note: Renderings often depict items that are not part of the standard package, e.g. decks, chimneys, garages, etc. Please consult working plans for complete details.

First Floor

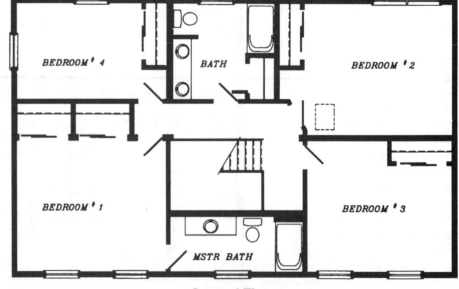

In the back of everyone's mind is the picture of the perfect house. On paper it's called the Jefferson!

As you can see, the Jefferson stands on its own. No words adequately describe this distinctive layout. We invite you to come to our factory and tour our design department. See for yourself how Epoch Corporation can take ideas and make them a reality.

BEDROOM #4

BATH

BEDROOM #2

BEDROOM #1

BEDROOM #3

MSTR BATH

Second Floor

The Bostonian
Plan 2901
by Crest Homes
1,968 Square Feet

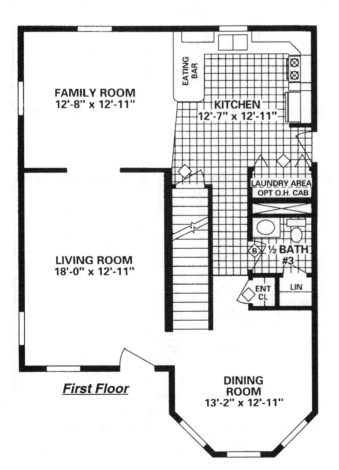

FAMILY ROOM
12'-8" x 12'-11"

EATING BAR

KITCHEN
12'-7" x 12'-11"

LAUNDRY AREA
OPT O.H. CAB

½ BATH #3

B

LIVING ROOM
18'-0" x 12'-11"

ENT CL

LIN

First Floor

DINING ROOM
13'-2" x 12'-11"

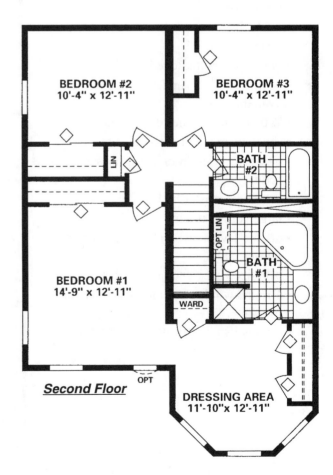

BEDROOM #2
10'-4" x 12'-11"

BEDROOM #3
10'-4" x 12'-11"

LIN

BATH #2

OPT LIN

BEDROOM #1
14'-9" x 12'-11"

BATH #1

WARD

Second Floor

OPT

DRESSING AREA
11'-10" x 12'-11"

III-32

The Savannah VII
B81001
Showcase Series
by Showcase Homes
2,420 Square Feet

- 28×44 - 2 story
- 4 bedrooms
- 2½ baths
- formal foyer
- large u-shaped kitchen
- both open plan and formal room plan available
- ½ bath with washer/dryer area
- spacious master bedroom suite
- generous walk-in closet in master bedroom
- luxurious master bath
- large garden tub in master bath
- double lavs in separate privacy areas in master bath
- oversized shower in master bath
- 4' round window over garden tub in master bath
- optional study off master bedroom

Breakfast Nook Kitchen Bath

Great Room

Dining Room

First Floor

Bedroom Bath Bath

Bedroom Bedroom Master Bedroom

Second Floor

The Tamarack IV
B77809
Showcase Series
by Showcase Homes
1,920 Square Feet

- 28×44 1½ story
- 1210 sq. ft. first floor
- 710 sq. ft. second floor
- 2 sliding wood patio doors
- 2 trapezoid windows
- vaulted ceiling in living room
- utility room with washer/dryer area
- 2 bedrooms on first floor
- large master bedroom on second floor
- loft overlooking living room
- u-shaped kitchen with snak bar
- oak stair rail and railing

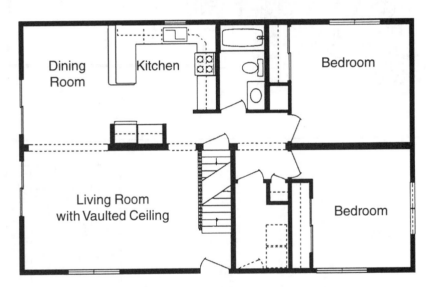

First Floor

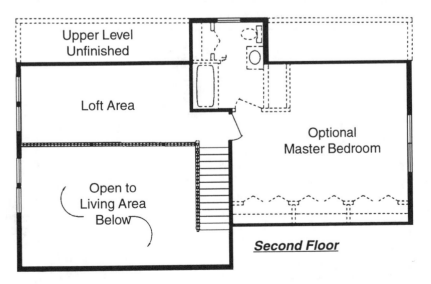

Second Floor

III-34

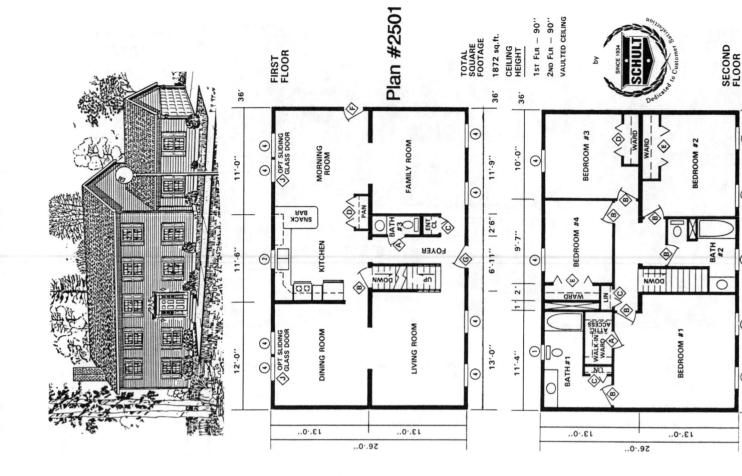

FIRST FLOOR

Plan #2501

TOTAL SQUARE FOOTAGE 1872 sq.ft.

CEILING HEIGHT
1ST FLR — 90''
2ND FLR — 90'' VAULTED CEILING

SECOND FLOOR

by SCHULT SINCE 1934 — Dedicated to Customer Satisfaction

First floor rooms: DINING ROOM, LIVING ROOM, KITCHEN, MORNING ROOM, FAMILY ROOM, SNACK BAR, FOYER, BATH #3, PAN, ENT CL, DOWN, UP, OPT SLIDING GLASS DOOR

Second floor rooms: BEDROOM #1, BEDROOM #2, BEDROOM #3, BEDROOM #4, BATH #1, BATH #2, WALK-IN WARD, WARD, LIN, ATTIC ACCESS, DOWN

Dimensions: 36', 12'-0", 11'-6", 11'-0", 13'-0", 26'-0", 11'-4", 9'-7", 6'-11", 2'-6", 11'-9", 10'-0", 9'-9", 1'-2"

STANDARD SPECIFICATIONS

EXTERIOR WALLS
2''x 6'' Studs 16'' O.C.
Double 2''x 6'' Top Plate
2''x 6'' Bottom Plate
7/16'' High Performance OSB Sheathing
Double 4'' Vinyl Woodgrain Siding (Blue, White, Gray, Beige or Ivory)
Wood Insulated Glass Windows with Screens (White) & Grids
36'' Steel Insulated Front Door
32'' Steel Insulated Rear Door
Raised Panel Shutters on Front Door Side of Home (White, Black, Brown, Burgundy, Blue or Green)
Exterior Light at Front and Rear Doors
Marriage Wall Fully Sheathed w/Structural Paneling

INTERIOR CONSTRUCTION
Interior Walls 16'' O.C.
Double 2''x 4'' Mating Walls 16'' O.C. — 1st Floor
Double 2''x 3'' Mating Walls 16'' O.C. — 2nd Floor
1/2'' Drywall Textured and Finished Painted (Antique White, Wedgewood, Apricot or Rose)
Decorator Vinyl Wall Covering — Kitchen & Baths
Linoleum Floor Covering — Entry Foyer, Kitchen, Utilities and Bath
Pre-Hung Raised White 6-Panel Passage Doors
Wood Raised 6-Panel Bi-Fold Wardrobe Doors
Deluxe Wire Vented Shelving

KITCHEN
NKCA Approved Cabinets (Oak, Cherry Stained or European)
Formica Self-Edged Countertop
Ceramic Backsplash
Pantry
Double Bowl Stainless Steel Sink
Vented Range Hood
Fluorescent Light Over Sink on Separate Switch
Recessed Fluorescent Ceiling Lights
Lazy Susan — Most Kitchens
Pull Out Center Shelf in Base Cabinets

BATH
One Piece 60'' Fiberglass Tub & Shower
Marble Countertop and Backsplash
Deluxe Vanity Cabinet
Large Lighted Mirror Over Vanity with Separate Cosmetic Box
Floor to Ceiling Linen Storage in Bath Area

HEATING
Electric Baseboard Heat with Individual Room Wall Mounted Thermostats Plus Toe Kick Heater in Kitchen and Bath
40 Gal. Electric Energy Savings Water Heater

PLUMBING
Copper Water Lines, Stubbed Through Floor
ABS Drain, Waste and Vent Lines
Shut-Off Valves on All Water Lines with Air Hammers
Single Lever Faucets

INSULATION
*R-22 Blown In Ceiling Insulation with Sprayed Vapor Barrier
*R-19 Fiberglass Kraft Backed In Sidewalls

ROOF AND CEILING
5/12 Roof Pitch
Roof Rafters 24'' O.C.
7/16'' High Performance OSB Roof Sheathing
Ply Dry Underlayment
Self-Sealing Asphalt Roof Shingles (White, Brown or Black)
Ridge Vent
12'' Overhang — Front, Rear and Gable Ends
Vented Soffits (White Only)
6'' Fascia (White Only)
Metal Drip Edge Entire House
5/8'' Textured Drywall Ceilings

ELECTRICAL
Electric Range Circuit & Receptacle
200 AMP Ent. Panel Dropped Below Floor
Smoke Detector
Ground Fault Interrupter for Outside & Bath Receptacles
Dining Room Chandelier

*The higher the R-Value, the greater the insulating power.

DOOR SCHEDULE

	WIDTH	HGT.	TYPE	REMARKS
A	2'-0"	6'-8"	HOLLOW-CORE	INTERIOR
B	2'-6"	6'-8"	HOLLOW-CORE	INTERIOR
C	2'-0"	6'-8"	BI-FOLD	INTERIOR
D	4'-0"	6'-8"	BI-FOLD	INTERIOR
E	5'-0"	6'-8"	BI-FOLD	INTERIOR
F	2'-8"	6'-8"	INSULATED	EXTERIOR
G	3'-0"	6'-8"	INSULATED	EXTERIOR
H	4'-2"	6'-8"	INSULATED	EXTERIOR (1) SIDELIGHT
I	5'-4"	6'-8"	INSULATED	EXTERIOR (2) SIDELIGHT
J	6'-0"	6'-8"	SLIDING	EXTERIOR GLASS DOOR

WINDOW SCHEDULE (*5)

	STANDARD			DELUXE		
	W	H	TYPE	W	H	TYPE
1	24	36	S.H.	24	34	D.H.
2	30	36	S.H.	28	34	D.H.
3	30	60	S.H.	30	54	D.H.
4	36	60	S.H.	36	54	D.H.
5	46	60	S.H.	46	54	D.H.
6	14	39	DECO GLASS	14	39	FIXED DECO
7	22		OCTAGON			

Square footage dimensions are based on exterior to exterior dimensions, and are nominal figures subject to industry standards. Room dimensions are nominal. Bedroom sizes may include wardrobes. Certain components of the running gear may be recycled.

See your housing consultant to select the options you desire, and to verify standard equipment and provide specific foundation dimensions.

30 Industrial Park Road / Milton, Pennsylvania 17847 / Phone (717) 742-8521

CERTIFIED NKCA CABINET

by SCHULT SINCE 1934

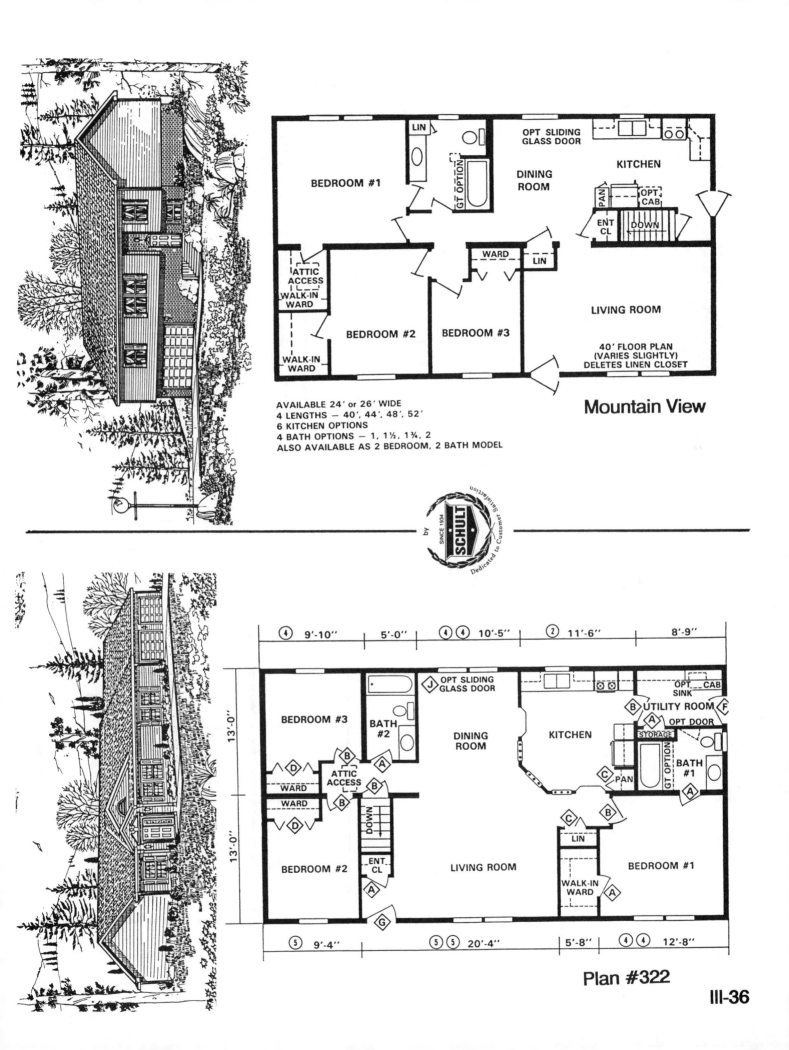

BEDROOM #1

LIN

OPT SLIDING GLASS DOOR

KITCHEN

GT OPTION

DINING ROOM

PAN

OPT CAB

ENT CL

DOWN

WARD

LIN

ATTIC ACCESS

WALK-IN WARD

BEDROOM #2

BEDROOM #3

WALK-IN WARD

LIVING ROOM

40' FLOOR PLAN
(VARIES SLIGHTLY)
DELETES LINEN CLOSET

AVAILABLE 24' or 26' WIDE
4 LENGTHS — 40', 44', 48', 52'
6 KITCHEN OPTIONS
4 BATH OPTIONS — 1, 1½, 1¾, 2
ALSO AVAILABLE AS 2 BEDROOM, 2 BATH MODEL

Mountain View

SINCE 1934
by SCHULT
Dedicated to Customer Satisfaction

| 4 9'-10'' | 5'-0'' | 4 4 10'-5'' | 2 11'-6'' | 8'-9'' |

13'-0''

BEDROOM #3

J OPT SLIDING GLASS DOOR

BATH #2

DINING ROOM

KITCHEN

OPT SINK

CAB

B UTILITY ROOM F

A OPT DOOR

STORAGE

D

B ATTIC ACCESS

B

C PAN

GT OPTION

BATH #1

WARD

B

A

WARD

D

DOWN

C

B

13'-0''

BEDROOM #2

ENT CL

A

LIVING ROOM

LIN

WALK-IN WARD

BEDROOM #1

A

G

| 5 9'-4'' | 5 5 20'-4'' | 5'-8'' | 4 4 12'-8'' |

Plan #322

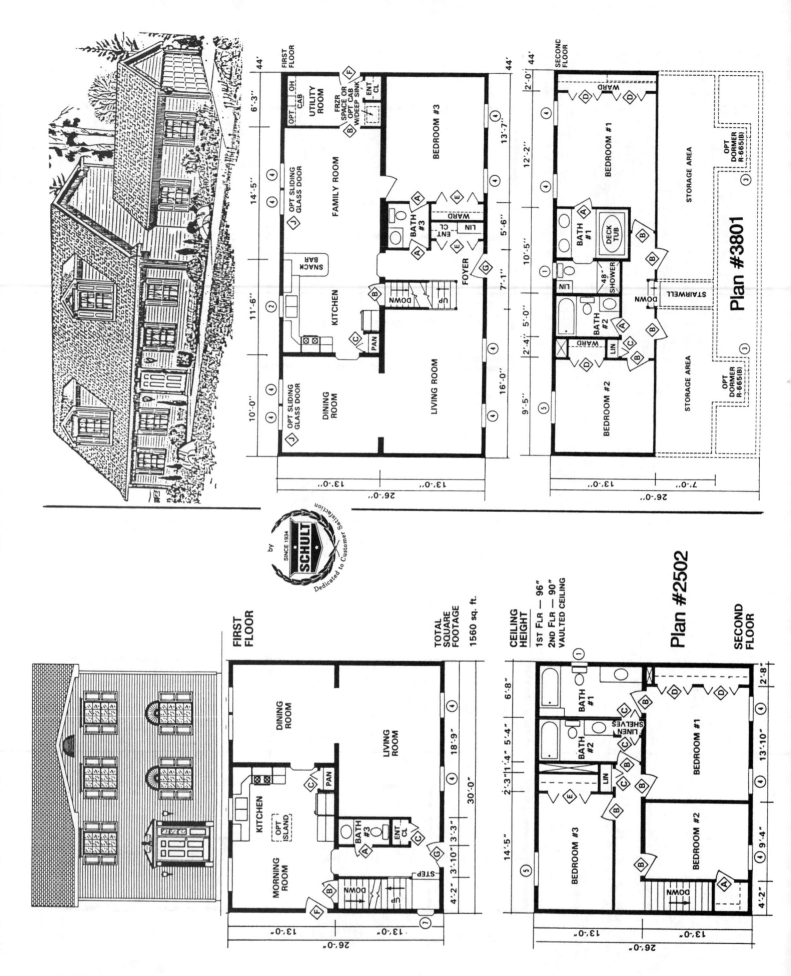

Plan #3801

Plan #2502

FIRST FLOOR

SECOND FLOOR

TOTAL SQUARE FOOTAGE 1560 sq. ft.

CEILING HEIGHT
1ST FLR — 96"
2ND FLR — 90"
VAULTED CEILING

The Cape

BEDROOM
12'1" x 19'4"

BATH

BEDROOM
13'6" x 9'5"

BEDROOM
10'7" x 9'5"

38'0"

26'0"

Second Floor

KITCHEN
12'0" x 11'

DINING
11'9" x 12'2"

LIVINGROOM
20'1" x 12'2"

BATH

BEDROOM#1
13'6" x 12'2"

BEDROOM#2
10'7" x 12'2"

50'0"

38'0"

26'0"

CG2650

CUSTOMIZED STRUCTURES INC.

The Split Style Home

BEDROOM#3
8'8" x 10'9"

BEDROOM#2
13'6" x 13'2"

BATH

DECK
12'0" x 20'0"

FAMILY ROOM
17'3" x 13'2"

LIVING ROOM
19'5" x 13'2"

KITCHEN
11'3" x 13'2"

BEDROOM#1
14'3" x 13'2"

MSTR BATH

56'0"

28'0"

SE2856

III-38

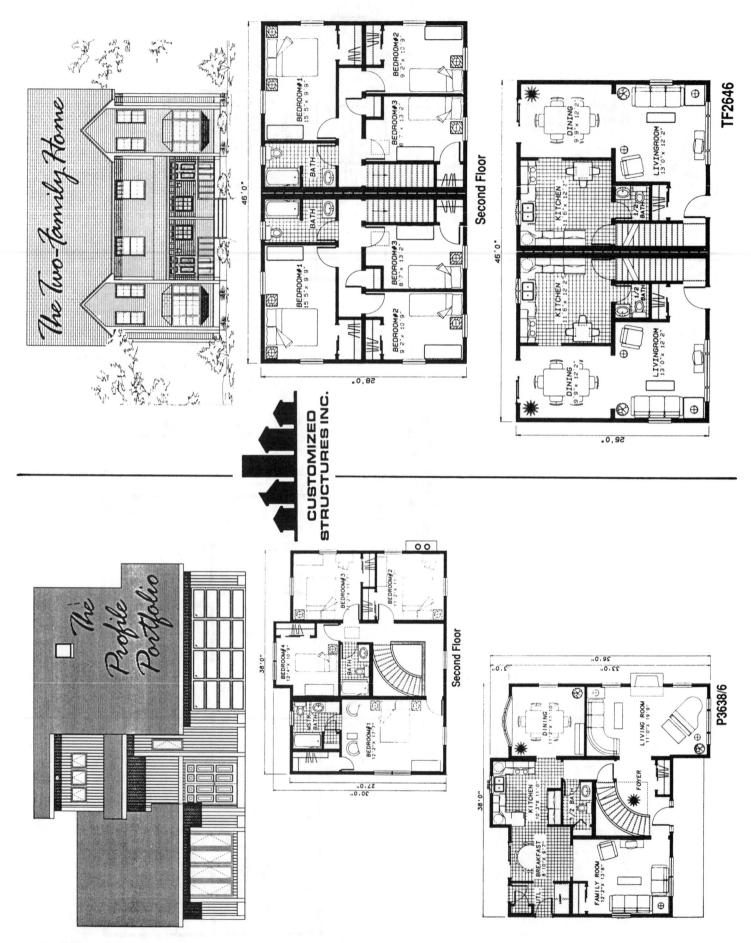

The Two-Family Home

BEDROOM #1
15'5" x 9'9"

BEDROOM #2
9'2" x 10'9"

BEDROOM #3
8'7" x 13'2"

BATH

BEDROOM #1
15'5" x 9'9"

BEDROOM #3
8'7" x 13'2"

BATH

BEDROOM #2
9'2" x 10'9"

Second Floor

46'0"

28'0"

TF2646

DINING
9'9" x 12'2"

LIVINGROOM
13'0" x 12'2"

KITCHEN
11'6" x 12'2"

1/2 BATH

KITCHEN
11'6" x 12'2"

1/2 BATH

LIVINGROOM
13'0" x 12'2"

DINING
9'9" x 12'2"

46'0"

26'0"

CUSTOMIZED STRUCTURES INC.

The Profile Portfolio

BEDROOM #3
12'2" x

BEDROOM #2
11'2" x 11'2"

BEDROOM #4
12'4" x 10'9"

BATH

MSTR. BATH

BEDROOM #1
12'2" x 17'2"

Second Floor

38'0"

27'0"

30'0"

DINING
11'2" x 11'10"

LIVING ROOM
11'0" x 19'9"

KITCHEN
10'3" x 11'0"

1/2 BATH

FOYER

BREAKFAST
8'10" x 9'7"

UTL.

FAMILY ROOM
12'2" x 13'6"

36'0"

33'0"

38'0"

P3638/6

III-39

The Two-Story Home

Second Floor

BEDROOM#3
10'1" x 8'9"

BEDROOM#2
8'10" x 8'9"

BEDROOM#1
13'5" x 12'2"

CLOSET

BATH

26'0"

24'0"

FAMILY ROOM
11'4" x 11'2"

KITCHEN
11'5" x 11'2"

UTIL RM

1/2 BATH

DINING ROOM
13'7" x 11'2"

LIVING ROOM
13'7" x 11'2"

FOYER

TS26/24-24/38

24'0"

38'0"

CUSTOMIZED STRUCTURES INC.

The Ranch

BEDROOM#2
12'0" x 13'2"

BEDROOM#1
12'10" x 13'2"

BEDROOM#3
12'0" x 11'5"

BATH

FAMILY/SUNROOM
w/ VAULTED CEILING
19'0" x 11'6"
(PANEL OPTION)

LIVING ROOM
w/ VAULTED CEILING
19'6" x 13'3"

FOYER

KITCHEN
13'3" x 13'2"

DINING
10'0" x 13'2"

DECK
8'0" x 24'0"
(PANEL OPTION)

GARAGE
20'0" x 26'0"
(PANEL OPTION)

LR2860

28'0"

12'0"

60'0"

20'0"

20'0"

20'0"

III-40

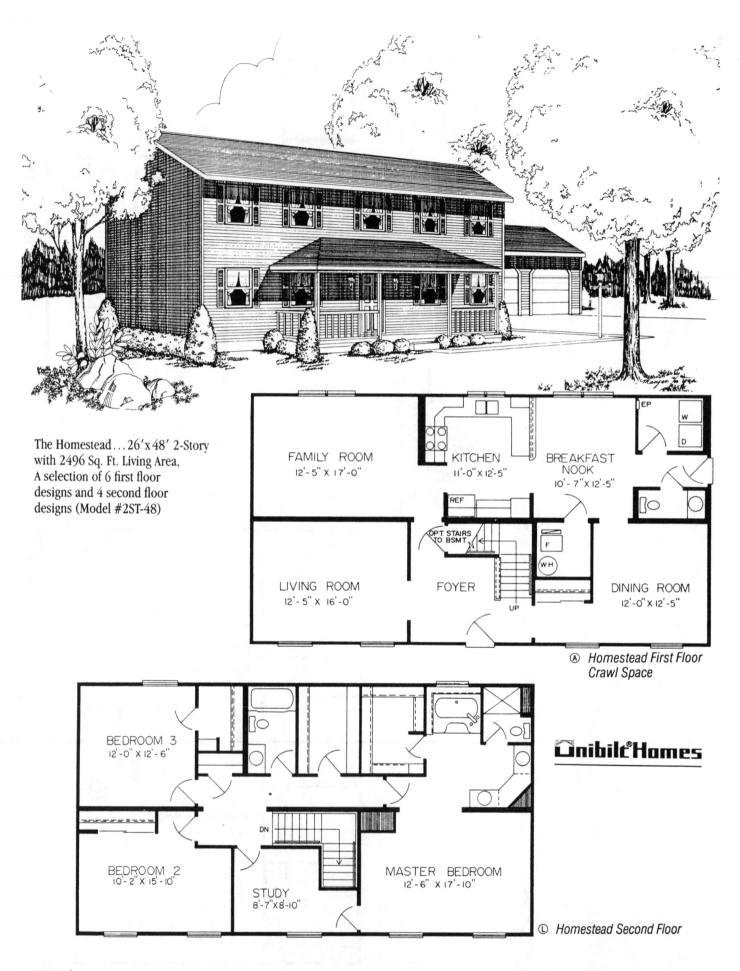

The Homestead...26'x48' 2-Story
with 2496 Sq. Ft. Living Area,
A selection of 6 first floor
designs and 4 second floor
designs (Model #2ST-48)

FAMILY ROOM
12'-5" X 17'-0"

KITCHEN
11'-0" X 12'-5"

BREAKFAST NOOK
10'-7" X 12'-5"

EP
W
D

REF

OPT. STAIRS TO BSMT.

F

WH

LIVING ROOM
12'-5" X 16'-0"

FOYER

UP

DINING ROOM
12'-0" X 12'-5"

(A) Homestead First Floor
Crawl Space

BEDROOM 3
12'-0" X 12'-6"

Unibilt® Homes

DN

BEDROOM 2
10'-2" X 15'-10"

STUDY
8'-7"X 8'-10"

MASTER BEDROOM
12'-6" X 17'-10"

(L) Homestead Second Floor

The Saratoga...26'x 40' 2-Story
with 2080 Sq. Ft. Living Area,
4 interchangeable designs for
a crawl space or basement.
(Model #2ST-40)

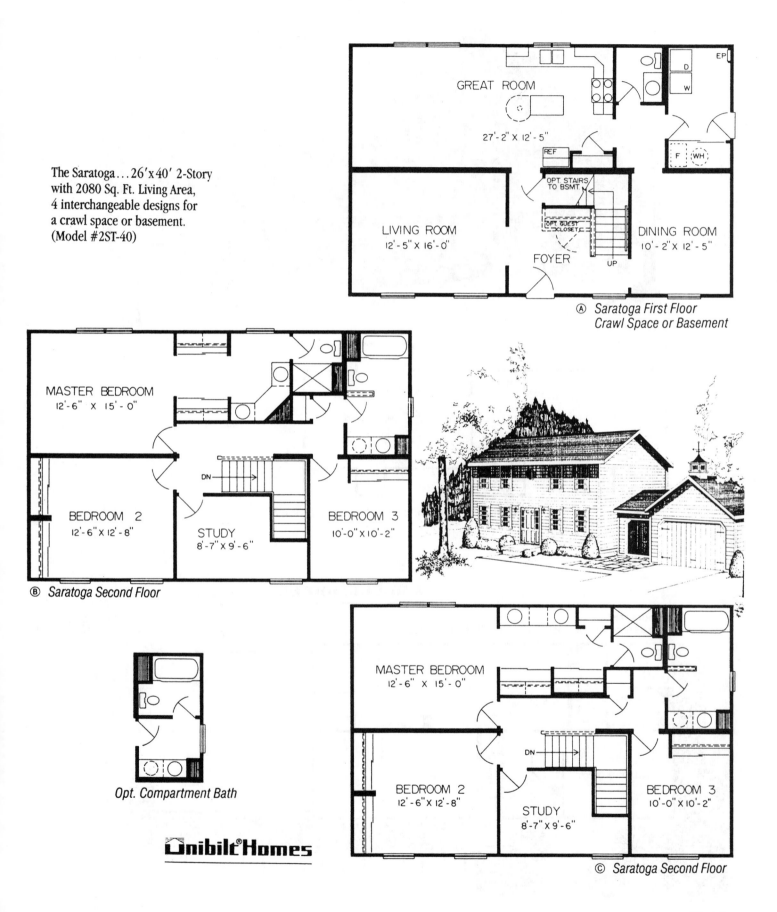

GREAT ROOM

27'-2" X 12'-5"

EP

D

W

REF

OPT. STAIRS TO BSMT.

F   WH

LIVING ROOM
12'-5" X 16'-0"

OPT. GUEST CLOSET

DINING ROOM
10'-2" X 12'-5"

FOYER   UP

Ⓐ Saratoga First Floor
Crawl Space or Basement

MASTER BEDROOM
12'-6" X 15'-0"

DN

BEDROOM 2
12'-6" X 12'-8"

STUDY
8'-7" X 9'-6"

BEDROOM 3
10'-0" X 10'-2"

Ⓑ Saratoga Second Floor

Opt. Compartment Bath

Unibilt®Homes

MASTER BEDROOM
12'-6" X 15'-0"

DN

BEDROOM 2
12'-6" X 12'-8"

STUDY
8'-7" X 9'-6"

BEDROOM 3
10'-0" X 10'-2"

Ⓒ Saratoga Second Floor

III-42

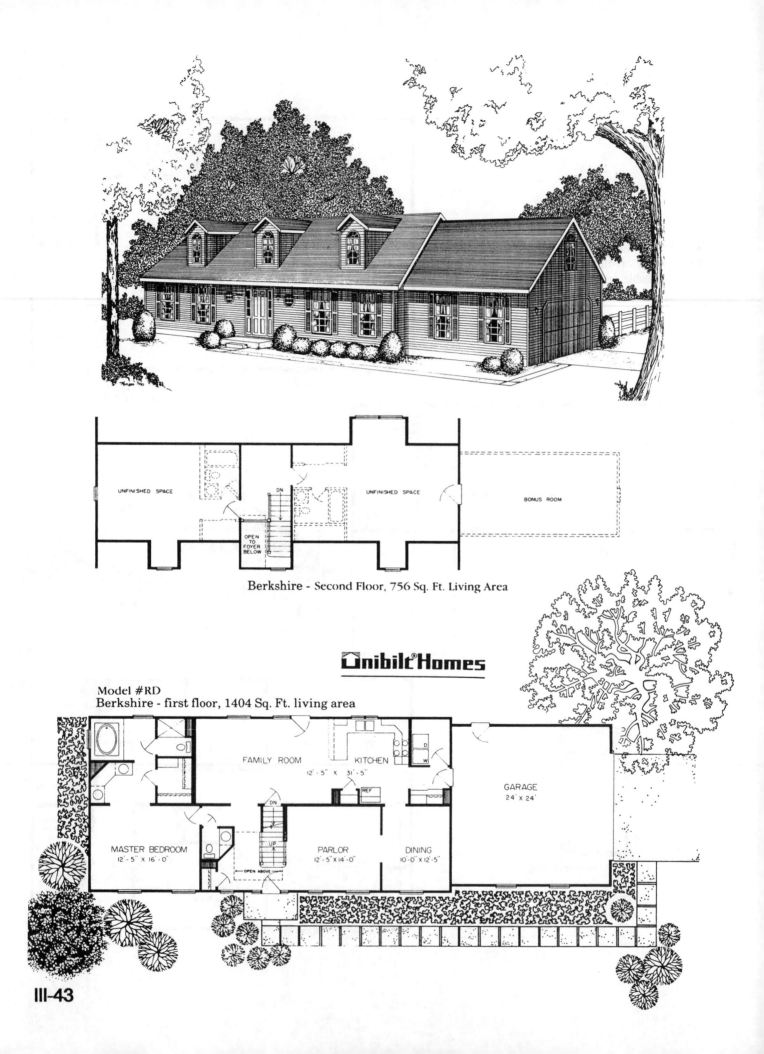

Berkshire - Second Floor, 756 Sq. Ft. Living Area

UNFINISHED SPACE

DN

OPEN TO FOYER BELOW

UNFINISHED SPACE

BONUS ROOM

Unibilt Homes

Model #RD
Berkshire - first floor, 1404 Sq. Ft. living area

MASTER BEDROOM
12'-5" X 16'-0"

FAMILY ROOM
12'-5" X 31'-5"

KITCHEN

REF

D
W

DN

UP

OPEN ABOVE

PARLOR
12'-5" X 14'-0"

DINING
10'-0" X 12'-5"

GARAGE
24' X 24'

BEDROOM 3
12'-0" x 12'-6"

BEDROOM 2
10'-2" x 15'-10"

STUDY
8'-7" x 8'-10"

MASTER BEDROOM
12'-6" x 17'-10"

Homestead - second floor, 1248 Sq. Ft. living area

Unibilt Homes

Model #2ST-48
Homestead - first floor, 1248 Sq. Ft. living area

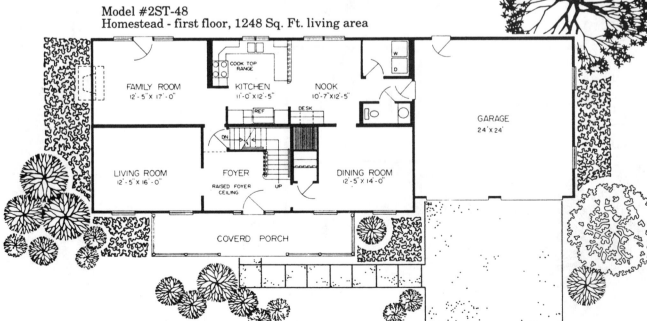

FAMILY ROOM
12'-5" x 17'-0"

KITCHEN
11'-0" x 12'-5"

COOK TOP RANGE

NOOK
10'-7" x 12'-5"

W
D

GARAGE
24' x 24'

REF

DESK

DN

LIVING ROOM
12'-5" x 16'-0"

FOYER

RAISED FOYER CEILING

UP

DINING ROOM
12'-5" x 14'-0"

COVERD PORCH

III-44

The Designer Series
by Unibilt® Homes

BEDROOM 1
12'-6" X 14'-1"

BEDROOM 2
11'-8" X 12'-6"

BEDROOM 3
8'-8" X 14'-9"

DN

Greenbrier Second Floor, 884 Sq. Ft. Living Area

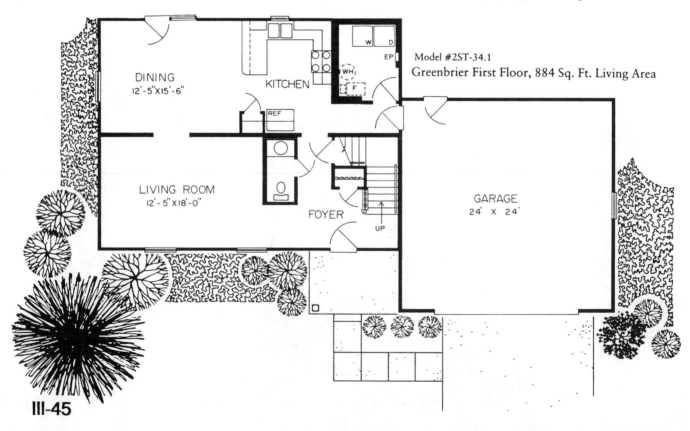

DINING
12'-5" X 15'-6"

KITCHEN

W   D

EP

WH

F

REF

LIVING ROOM
12'-5" X 18'-0"

FOYER

UP

Model #2ST-34.1
Greenbrier First Floor, 884 Sq. Ft. Living Area

GARAGE
24' X 24'

III-45

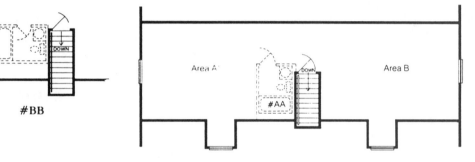

#BB

Area A

Area B

#AA

DOWN

Cape Cod - second floor, unfinished space for future growth

Unibilt® Homes

Model #F-1
Cape Cod - first floor, 1248 Sq. Ft. living area

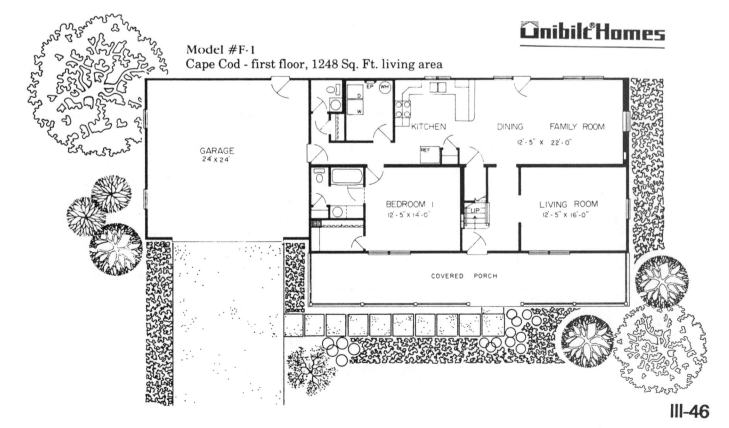

GARAGE
24' x 24'

KITCHEN

DINING   FAMILY ROOM
12'-5" x 22'-0"

REF

BEDROOM 1
12'-5" x 14'-0"

UP

LIVING ROOM
12'-5" x 16'-0"

COVERED   PORCH

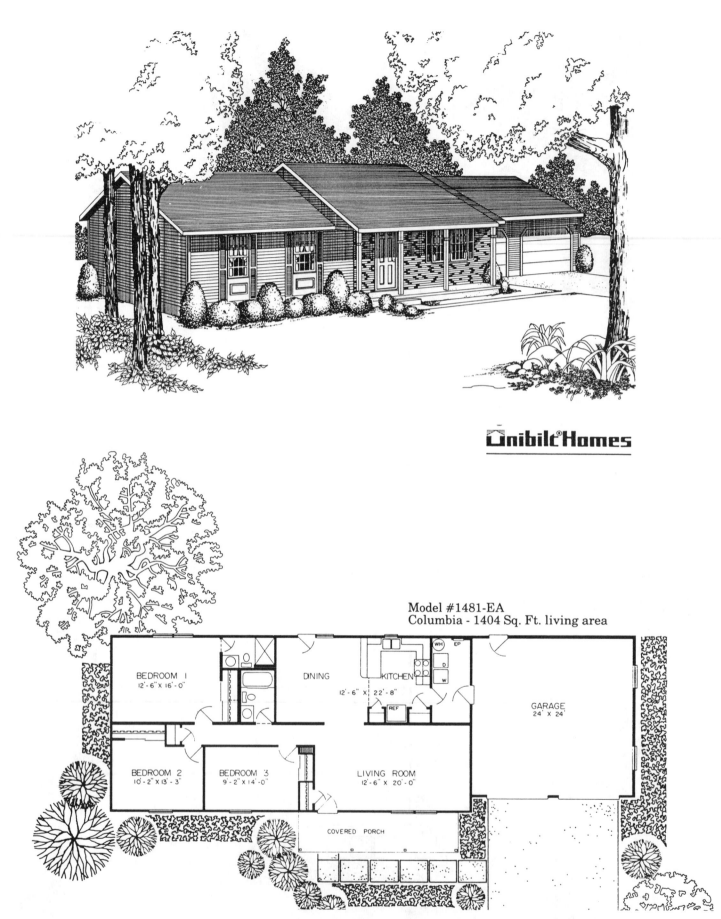

Unibilt Homes

Model #1481-EA
Columbia - 1404 Sq. Ft. living area

BEDROOM 1
12'-6" X 16'-0"

DINING

KITCHEN
12'-6" X 22'-8"

WH   EP

D

W

REF

GARAGE
24' X 24'

BEDROOM 2
10'-2" X 13'-3"

BEDROOM 3
9'-2" X 14'-0"

LIVING ROOM
12'-6" X 20'-0"

COVERED PORCH

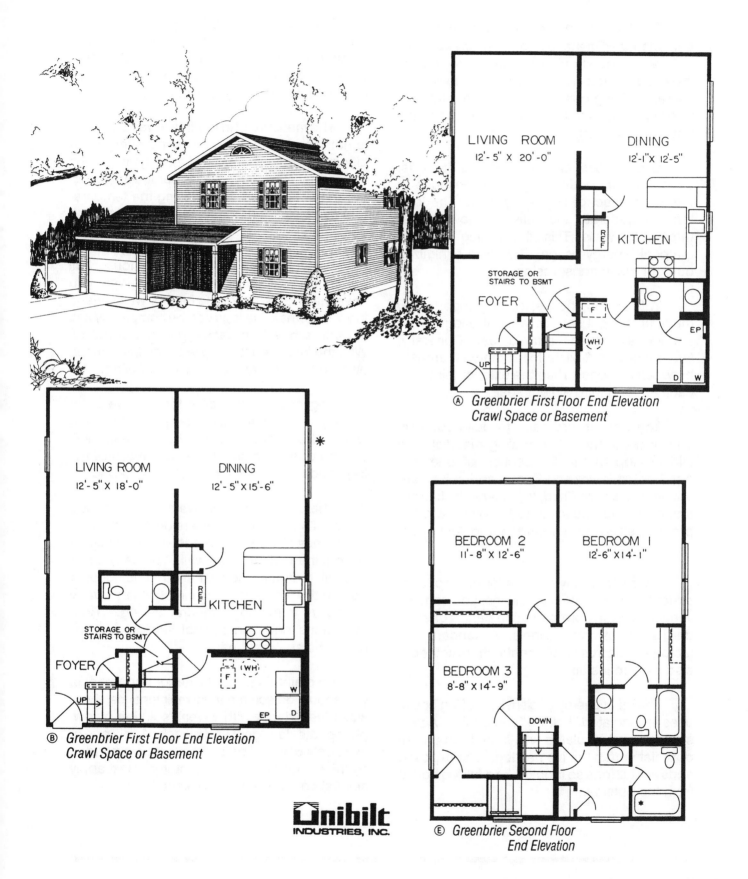

LIVING ROOM
12'-5" X 20'-0"

DINING
12'-1"X 12'-5"

REF

KITCHEN

STORAGE OR
STAIRS TO BSMT

FOYER

F

WH

EP

UP

D   W

Ⓐ *Greenbrier First Floor End Elevation
Crawl Space or Basement*

LIVING ROOM
12'-5" X 18'-0"

DINING
12'-5" X15'-6"

REF

KITCHEN

STORAGE OR
STAIRS TO BSMT

FOYER

F   WH

UP

EP

W   D

Ⓑ *Greenbrier First Floor End Elevation
Crawl Space or Basement*

BEDROOM 2
11'-8" X 12'-6"

BEDROOM 1
12'-6" X14'-1"

BEDROOM 3
8'-8" X 14'-9"

DOWN

Ⓔ *Greenbrier Second Floor
End Elevation*

Unibilt
INDUSTRIES, INC.

III-48

Modern log houses are very attractive and energy efficient. Since many are sold in a "kit form", you should be able to do much of the construction work yourself and lower the overall building costs. These are available in sizes up to 3,000 square feet and some utilize passive solar heating.

Log houses can have low utility bills, especially air-conditioning costs, because of the mass effect of the heavy logs. The logs tend to moderate and delay the flow of heat through the walls. This "thermal lag" reduces the peak energy usage. This also minimizes outdoor noise transmission.

With a full log house, it is very important to make an airtight seal between the logs. You should have at least a triple seal. Generally, two strips of a flexible foam material are laid between the logs. Then the exterior joints are caulked for a third airtight seal.

Log houses are easy to build yourself. The gaskets and other sealing materials are laid on top of the flat section of one log. Another log is set on top of it and spikes are driven in to secure them together. The kits are made for each specific house plan, with the properly-sized logs for window and door openings.

There are many options for the roof construction. For cathedral ceilings, you can use ventilated foam core insulation panels or standard stress-skin wall panels. A standard roof factory-made truss roof construction method is also easy to install.

The most energy-efficient type of log house uses an insulated "half log" wall design. A 2x6-studded and insulated wall is built on the indoor flat surface of the half log. The exposed ends are full logs so it looks like a full log house from the outside.

The six inches of fiberglass insulation, foam board sheathing, and logs yield a wall insulation value of R-30. The ceiling is insulated to R-40. Many kits also include super energy-efficient heat mirror type windows.

The measure of insulating R-value of walls is not the only factor concerning energy efficiency. The heavy mass of the logs improves the energy efficiency. This is particularly effective in the summer. By delaying the temperature rise inside the house, the air-conditioning costs can be reduced.

Depending on the type of log house wall construction, solid or insulated half-logs, you have many options for the interior wall surface in your rooms. The logs can be completely flat, flat with a bevel on each log edge, or round. With the insulated half log wall, the interior can also be finished with drywall or paneling.

Log houses are ideal for passive solar heating. You can install large south-facing windows and skylights which are a natural fit with an open design. The heavy mass of the logs adds to the solar heat storage capacity.

There are some passive solar heated log house kits available. They are designed so the sun shines through the windows and skylights on to a thermal masonry wall. You can build a special masonry downshaft that is located behind the fireplace. This circulates the warm air down from the cathedral ceiling. Roof overhangs and sun control skylight shades block the summer heat.

To maintain a good exterior appearance, you should do some annual maintenance. First, wash the exterior with a weak solution of low-phosphate detergent and bleach. Apply one or two coats of wood preservative recommended by the log house kit manufacturer. Next apply several coats of water repellent.

MANUFACTURERS OF LOG AND SOLID CEDAR HOUSES

AIR-LOCK-LOG COMPANY, INC., P.O. Box 2506, Las Vegas, NM 87701
(800) 786-0525 (505) 425-8888
ALTA INDUSTRIES, LTD., Route 30, Box 88, Halcottsville, NY 12438
(800) 926-2582 (914) 586-3336
AMERLINK, P.O. Box 669, Battleboro, NC 27809
(800) 872-4254 (919) 977-2545
APPALACHIAN LOG HOMES, INC., 113212 Station West Dr., Knoxville, TN 37922
(615) 966-6440
APPALACHIAN LOG STRUCTURES, INC., P.O. Box 614, Ripley, WV 25271
(800) 458-9990 (304) 372-6410
ASPERLINE, RD #1, Box 240, Route 150, Lock Haven, PA 17745
(800) 428-4663 (717) 748-1880
AUTHENTIC LOG HOMES, Box 1288, Laramie, WY 82070
(307) 742-3786
B K CYPRESS LOG HOMES, INC., P.O. Box 191, Bronson, FL 32621
(800) 553-1564 (352) 486-2470
BEAVER MOUNTAIN LOG HOMES, INC., RD 1, Box 32, Hancock, NY 13783
(800) 233-2770 (607) 467-2700
BRENTWOOD LOG HOMES, 1716 Henry G Lane, Maryville, TN 37801
(615) 982-3788
CEDAR FOREST PRODUCTS COMPANY, 107 W. Colden St., Polo, IL 61064
(815) 946-3994
COLONIAL STRUCTURES, 1946 Union Cross Rd., Winston-Salem, NC 27107
(910) 785-0111
GARLAND LOG HOMES, P.O. Box 12, Victor, MT 59875
(800) 642-3837 (406) 642-3095
GASTINEAU LOG HOMES, INC., Route 2, Box 248, New Bloomfield, MO 65063
(800) 654-9253 (314) 896-5122
GREATWOOD LOG HOMES, INC., P.O. Box 707, Elkhart Lake, WI 53020
(800) 588-5812 (414) 876-3378
HEARTHSTONE, INC., 1630 E. Hwy 25/70, Dandridge, TN 37725
(800) 743-2784 (615) 397-9425
HERITAGE LOG HOMES, INC., P.O. Box 610, Gatlinburg, TN 37738
(800) 456-4663 (615) 436-9331
HIAWATHA LOG HOMES, INC., P.O. Box 8, Munising, MI 49862
(800) 876-8100 (906) 387-4121
HOLLAND LOG HOMES, 13352 Van Buren, Holland, MI 49424
(616) 399-9627
HONEST ABE LOG HOMES, INC., 3855 Clay County Hwy., Moss, TN 38575
(800) 231-3695 (615) 258-3648
JIM BARNA LOG SYSTEMS, P.O. Box 4529, Oneida, TN 37841
(800) 962-4734 (615) 569-8559

MANUFACTURERS OF LOG AND SOLID CEDAR HOUSES - contd.

KATAHDIN FOREST PRODUCTS, P.O. Box 145, Oakfield, ME 04763
(207) 757-8278

KUHNS BROS. LOG HOMES, INC., RD#2, Box 406A, Lewisburg, PA 17837
(800) 346-7903 (717) 568-1422

LINCOLN LOGS, LTD., Riverside Drive, Chestertown, NY 12817
(800) 833-2461 (518) 494-4777

LINDAL CEDAR HOMES, P.O.Box 24426, Seattle, WA 98124
(800) 426-0536 (206) 725-0900

LINWOOD HOMES, 7220 Pacific Hwy. E., Tacoma, WA 98424
(800) 451-4888

LODGE LOGS BY MACGREGOR, INC., 3200 Gowen Road, Boise, ID 83705
(800) 533-2450 (208) 336-2450

LOG CABIN HOMES, LTD., P.O. Drawer 1457, Rocky Mount, NC 27802
(800) 562-2246 (919) 977-7785

LOG STRUCTURES, P.O. Box 470009, Lake Monroe, FL 32747
(800) 835-3881 (407) 321-5647

LOK-N-LOGS, INC., P.O. Box 677, Sherburne, NY 13460
(800) 343-8928 (607) 674-4447

MAJESTIC LOG HOMES, INC., P.O. Box 772, Ft. Collins, CO 80522
(800) 279-5647 (303) 224-4857

MAPLE ISLAND LOG HOMES, 2387 Bayne Rd., Twin Lake, MI 49457
(800) 748-0137 (616) 821-2151

MODEL LOG HOMES, 75777 Gallatin Road, Gallatin Gateway, MT 59730
(800) 235-4321 (406) 763-4411

MOOSE CREEK LOG HOMES, P.O. Box 204, Turner, ME 04282
(207) 224-7497

MONTANA-IDAHO LOG CORPORATION, 1069 North US 93, Victor, MT 59875
(406) 961-3092 (406) 961-3093 FAX

MOUNTAIN ST. LOG HOMES INC., Rt. 2, Box 6AA, Ireland, WV 26376
(304) 452-8228

NATIONAL LOG HOMES, INC., Box 2370, Missoula, MT 59806
(406) 542-8809

NATURAL BLDG. SYSTEMS, INC., 35 Old Rte. 12 North, W. Moreland, NH 03467
(800) 598-7830 (603) 399-7725

NEVILLE LOG HOMES, 2036 Hwy. 93 North, Victor, MT 59875
(800) 635-7911 (406) 642-3091

NORTH STAR TIMBER, W3516 Labelle Rd., Powers, MI 49874
(906) 497-5020

NORTHEASTERN LOG HOMES, INC., P.O. Box 46, Kenduskeag, ME 04450
(800) 624-2797 (207) 884-7000

OLD MILL LOG HOMES, HC 89, Box 115B, Pocono Summit, PA 18346
(717) 646-1445

ORIGINAL OLD TIMER LOG HOMES, 1901 Logue Rd., Mount Juliet, TN 37122
(800) 321-5647 (615) 443-0085

MANUFACTURERS OF LOG AND SOLID CEDAR HOUSES - contd.

PAN ABODE, 4350 Lake Washington Blvd. N., Renton, WA 98056
(800) 782-2633 (206) 255-8260

PIONEER LOG SYSTEMS, INC., P.O. Box 226, Kingston Springs, TN 37082
(615) 952-5647

PRECISION CRAFT LOG STRUCTURES, 711 East Broadway, Meridian, ID 83642
(800) 729-1320 (208) 887-1020

RAPID RIVER RUSTIC, INC., P.O. Box 10, Rapid River, MI 49878
(800) 422-3327 (906) 474-6427

REAL LOG HOMES, P.O. Box 202, Hartland, VT 05048
(800) 732-5564 (802) 436-2121

ROCKY MOUNTAIN LOG HOMES, 1883 Highway 93 S., Hamilton, MT 59840
(406) 363-5680

SATTERWHITE LOG HOMES, Route 2, Box 256A, Longview, TX 75605
(800) 777-7288 (903) 663-1729

SOUTHLAND LOG HOMES, INC., P.O. Box 1668, Irmo, SC 29063
(800) 845-3555 (803) 781-5100

STONEMILL LOG HOMES, 7015 Stonemill Rd., Knoxville, TN 37919
(423) 693-4833

TENNESSEE LOG HOMES, P.O. Box 865, Athens, TN 37371
(800) 251-9218 (615) 745-8993

TIMBER LOG BUILDING SYSTEMS, 639 Old Hartford Rd., Colchester, CT 06415
(800) 533-5906 (203) 537-2393

TOWN & COUNTRY CEDAR HOMES, 4772 US 131 S., Petoskey, MI 49770
(616) 347-4360

TRAVERSE BAY LOG HOMES, 6446 M-72, Traverse City, MI 49694
(616) 947-1881

TRUE NORTH LOG HOMES, Box 2169, Bracebridge, Ont., Canada P1l 1W1
(705) 645-3096

WARD LOG HOMES, P.O. Box 72, Houlton, ME 04730
(800) 341-1566 (207) 532-6531

WHOLESALE LOG HOMES, INC., P.O. Box 177, Hillsborough, NC 27278
(919) 732-9286

WILDERNESS LOG HOMES, P.O. Box 902, Plymouth, WI 53073
(800) 237-8564 (414) 893-8416

WISCONSIN LOG HOMES, INC., P.O. Box 11005, Green Bay, WI 54307
(800) 678-3010 (414) 434-3010

WOODKREST CUSTOM HOMES, 3175 Johnson Ave., Memphis, TN 38112
(901) 324-0152

YELLOWSTONE LOG HOMES, 280 N. Yellowstone Road, Rigby, ID 83442
(208) 745-8108 (208) 745-8110

STANDARD PACKAGE MATERIAL LISTS

COMPLETE STANDARD INSULOG™ PACKAGE MATERIAL:

EXTERIOR WALL STRUCTURE MATERIAL:

- Handcrafted INSULOG™ corners w/partners
- Handcrafted INSULOG™ exterior
- 2"x6" pre-cut studs, sole/top plates
- 1" Tuff-R™ Sheathing
- Vapor barrier
- Batt insulation
- 2" nominal window headers
- Metal corner wind bracing
- Steel prehung 9 lite crossbuck 1¾" exterior door
- Wood crossbuck combination storm/screen door
- 2" nominal door headers & ceiling joists
- All nails, fasteners, special hardware
- Draw knife, caulk gun and tan caulk
- High performance glass casement windows, aluminum clad w/screen

INTERIOR PARTITION MATERIAL:

- 2"x4" pre-cut studs, sole/top plate
- 2" nominal door headers

STANDARD ROOF SYSTEM MATERIAL:

- All 2" nominal roof framing
- 12" batt insulation for horizontal ceiling area
- ½" OSB sheathing
- 15# roof felt
- Seal-down shingles
- "D" edging
- Gutter apron
- Fascia trim
- Continuous ridge & soffit vents
- Knotty pine soffits

CATHEDRAL CEILING ROOF SYSTEM MATERIAL (if applicable):

- 2"x12" roof rafters
- 9" batt insulation
- ½" OSB sheathing
- 15# felt
- Seal-down shingles
- "D" edging
- Gutter apron
- Fascia trim
- Knotty pine tongue & groove ceiling paneling
- Handcrafted log rafters
- Handcrafted log tie beams
- Continuous ridge and soffit vents
- Knotty pine soffits
- 1" Tuff-R™ sheathing inside

LOFT/SECOND FLOOR MATERIAL (if applicable):

- Handcrafted log posts and railings (in loft package only)
- 2" nominal joists, skirt joists and girders
- ½" OSB sheathing
- Wood bridging
- Joist hangers

PORCH/DECK MATERIAL (if applicable):

- Handcrafted log posts
- Handcrafted log rafters (where applicable)
- Handcrafted log railings (where applicable)
- Handcrafted log porch headers (where applicable)
- Knotty pine tongue and groove roof paneling
- 15# felt
- Seal-down shingles
- 2"x6" pressure treated framing and deck lumber
- ½" OSB sheathing

DORMER MATERIAL (if applicable):

- Handcrafted INSULOG™ corners or quarter round log corner post and INSULOG™ exterior components
- 2" nominal sole/top plates
- 1" Tuff-R™ sheathing
- 2" nominal pre-cut studs
- Batt insulation
- Vapor barrier
- 2" nominal window headers
- Additional roof material as required
- No logs on interior of dormer
- High performance glass casement windows, aluminum clad w/screen

SUBFLOORING MATERIAL:

- 2" nominal joists, skirt joists and girders
- ½" OSB sheathing
- Sill insulation
- Joist hangers
- Wood bridging
- 2" nominal treated sole plate
- Stair stringers, risers and treads (conventional)
- INSULOG™ corners w/partners and INSULOG™ to cover skirt joists

INSULOG™ ATTACHED GARAGE MATERIALS (if applicable):

- All materials for garage construction are same as standard package with 2x4 wall construction and standard roof (excluding 4 mil vapor barrier and insulation, and ½" Celotex sheathing in lieu of 1" Tuff-R™). The common wall between house and garage does not include logs.

COMPLETE STANDARD FULL LOG PACKAGE MATERIAL:

EXTERIOR WALL STRUCTURE MATERIAL:

- Handcrafted pre-mitered full log corners
- Handcrafted pre-mitered ledger logs and ledger corners
- Handcrafted wall logs
- ⅜" closed cell backer rod insulation
- 12" helically turned steel spikes
- 1"x1"x⅛" angle iron window splines
- 2"x6" window framing and top plate
- Steel prehung 9 lite crossbuck 1¾" exterior door
- Wood crossbuck combination storm/screen door
- 2" nominal door headers & ceiling joists
- All nails, fasteners, special hardware
- Draw knife, caulk gun and tan caulk
- Gable end wall w/INSULOG™ exterior and interior
- 2"x4" studs and plates, 3½" insulation wall, 1" Tuff-R™ sheathing, vapor barrier and 2" nominal headers
- High performance glass casement windows, aluminum clad w/screen

INTERIOR PARTITION MATERIALS INCLUDE:
Same as INSULOG™

STANDARD ROOF SYSTEM:
Same as INSULOG™

SUBFLOORING MATERIAL:
Same as INSULOG™

SECOND FLOOR MATERIAL (if applicable):
Same as INSULOG™

CATHEDRAL CEILING (if applicable):
Same as INSULOG™

LOFT/SECOND FLOOR (if applicable):
Same as INSULOG™

PORCH/DECK (if applicable):
Same as INSULOG™

DORMER (if applicable):
Same as INSULOG™

ATTACHED GARAGE MATERIALS (if applicable):

- All materials for garage construction are same as standard package with standard roof (excluding 4 mil vapor barrier and insulation, and ½ Celotex sheathing in lieu of 1" Tuff-R™ for gable ends).

OPTIONAL MATERIAL:

INTERIOR PINE LOGS:
- Handcrafted interior pine logs for inside perimeter walls.

INTERIOR KNOTTY PINE
- Interior knotty pine tongue and groove for inside perimeter walls. (See dealer for specific area of coverage.)

Wilderness™
Log Homes

Buckhorn

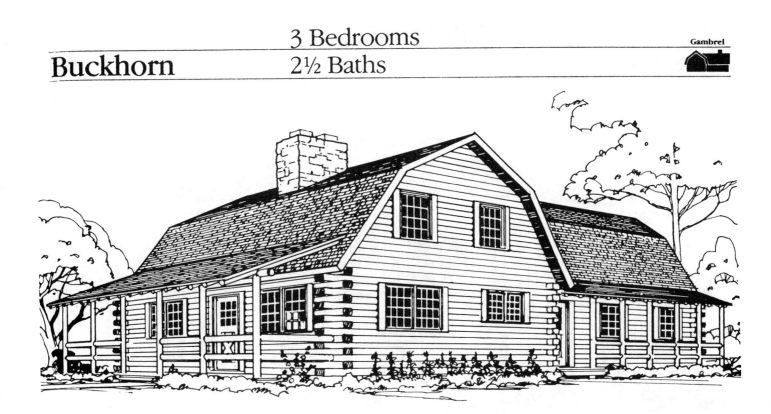

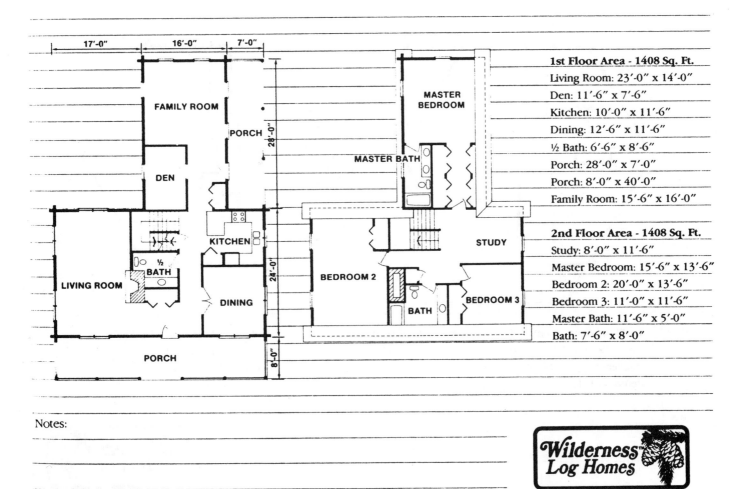

1st Floor Area - 1408 Sq. Ft.

Living Room: 23'-0" x 14'-0"

Den: 11'-6" x 7'-6"

Kitchen: 10'-0" x 11'-6"

Dining: 12'-6" x 11'-6"

½ Bath: 6'-6" x 8'-6"

Porch: 28'-0" x 7'-0"

Porch: 8'-0" x 40'-0"

Family Room: 15'-6" x 16'-0"

2nd Floor Area - 1408 Sq. Ft.

Study: 8'-0" x 11'-6"

Master Bedroom: 15'-6" x 13'-6"

Bedroom 2: 20'-0" x 13'-6"

Bedroom 3: 11'-0" x 11'-6"

Master Bath: 11'-6" x 5'-0"

Bath: 7'-6" x 8'-0"

Notes:

Wilderness Log Homes

3 Bedrooms
Hogan
2 Baths

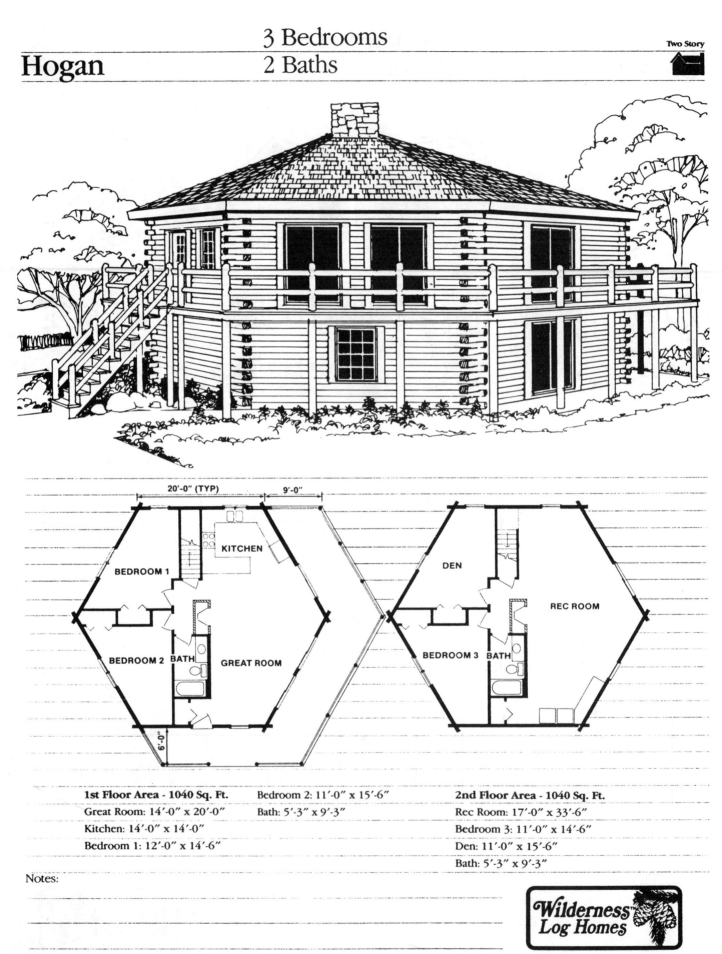

1st Floor Area - 1040 Sq. Ft.

Great Room: 14'-0" x 20'-0"

Kitchen: 14'-0" x 14'-0"

Bedroom 1: 12'-0" x 14'-6"

Bedroom 2: 11'-0" x 15'-6"

Bath: 5'-3" x 9'-3"

2nd Floor Area - 1040 Sq. Ft.

Rec Room: 17'-0" x 33'-6"

Bedroom 3: 11'-0" x 14'-6"

Den: 11'-0" x 15'-6"

Bath: 5'-3" x 9'-3"

Notes:

Wilderness Log Homes

Heritage

5 Bedrooms
2 Baths

Gambrel

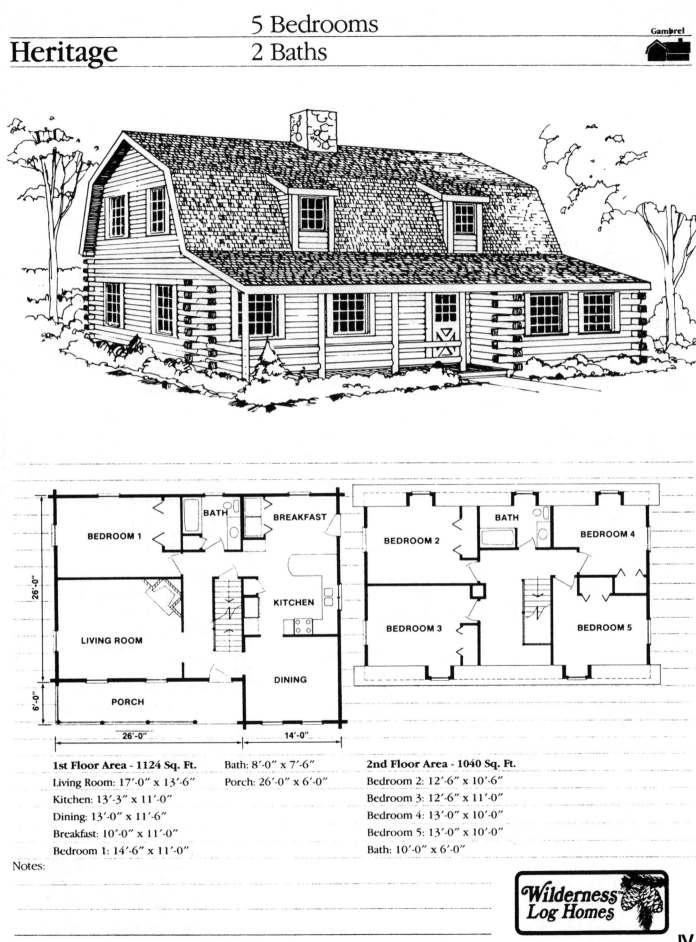

1st Floor Area - 1124 Sq. Ft.

Living Room: 17'-0" x 13'-6"

Kitchen: 13'-3" x 11'-0"

Dining: 13'-0" x 11'-6"

Breakfast: 10'-0" x 11'-0"

Bedroom 1: 14'-6" x 11'-0"

Bath: 8'-0" x 7'-6"

Porch: 26'-0" x 6'-0"

2nd Floor Area - 1040 Sq. Ft.

Bedroom 2: 12'-6" x 10'-6"

Bedroom 3: 12'-6" x 11'-0"

Bedroom 4: 13'-0" x 10'-0"

Bedroom 5: 13'-0" x 10'-0"

Bath: 10'-0" x 6'-0"

Notes:

Wilderness Log Homes

IV-8

5 Bedrooms
2½ Baths

Two Story

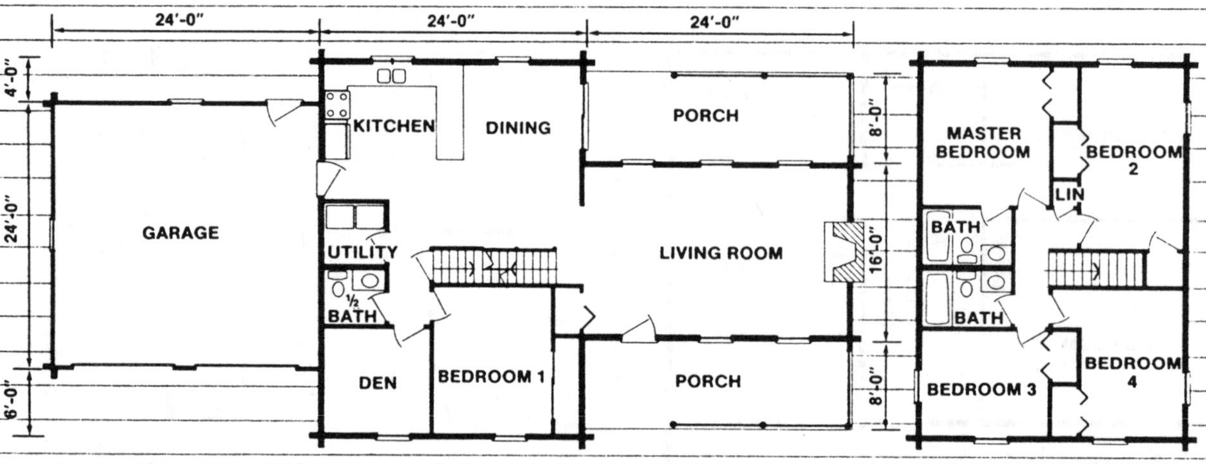

Garage Floor Area - 576 Sq. Ft.	Bedroom 1: 10'-6" x 13'-0"	2nd Floor Area - 544 Sq. Ft.
Garage: 23'-8" x 23'-4"	Den: 9'-6" x 9'-6"	Master Bedroom: 11'-3" x 12'-6"
	½ Bath: 5'-6" x 5'-0"	Bedroom 2: 9'-0" x 16'-0"
1st Floor Area - 1200 Sq. Ft.	Utility: 5'-6" x 5'-6"	Bedroom 3: 11'-3" x 9'-3"
Living Room: 23'-6" x 15'-0"	Porch: 24'-0" x 8'-0"	Bedroom 4: 9'-0" x 13'-0"
Kitchen: 12'-6" x 12'-0"	Porch: 24'-0" x 8'-0"	Bath: 8'-0" x 5'-0"
Dining: 10'-6" x 12'-6"		Bath: 8'-0" x 5'-0"

Notes:

Wilderness Log Homes

IV-9

Williamsburg

3 Bedrooms
2½ Baths

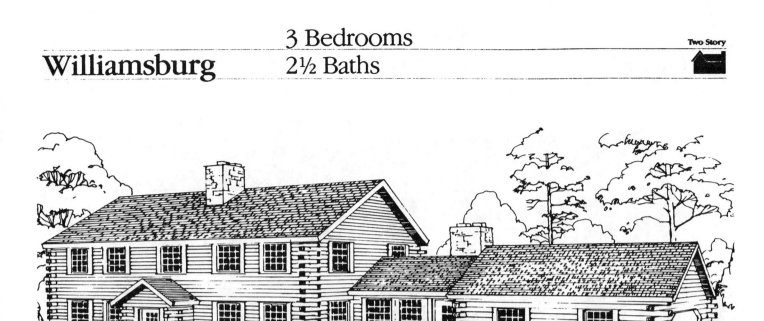

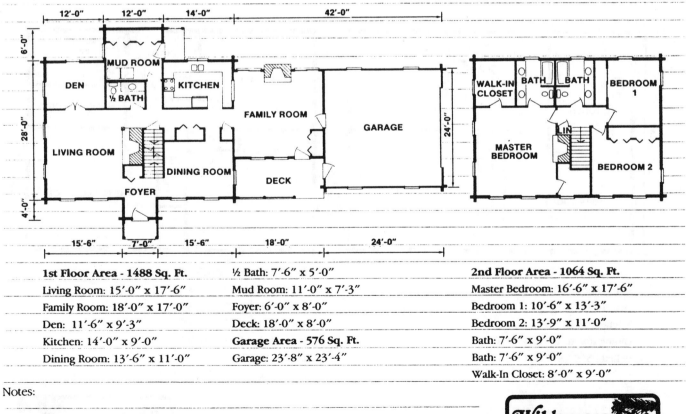

1st Floor Area - 1488 Sq. Ft.

Living Room: 15'-0" x 17'-6"

Family Room: 18'-0" x 17'-0"

Den: 11'-6" x 9'-3"

Kitchen: 14'-0" x 9'-0"

Dining Room: 13'-6" x 11'-0"

½ Bath: 7'-6" x 5'-0"

Mud Room: 11'-0" x 7'-3"

Foyer: 6'-0" x 8'-0"

Deck: 18'-0" x 8'-0"

Garage Area - 576 Sq. Ft.

Garage: 23'-8" x 23'-4"

2nd Floor Area - 1064 Sq. Ft.

Master Bedroom: 16'-6" x 17'-6"

Bedroom 1: 10'-6" x 13'-3"

Bedroom 2: 13'-9" x 11'-0"

Bath: 7'-6" x 9'-0"

Bath: 7'-6" x 9'-0"

Walk-In Closet: 8'-0" x 9'-0"

Notes:

Larkspur

3 Bedrooms
2½ Baths

34'-0"

26'-0"

KITCHEN

½ BATH

DEN

DINING ROOM

LIVING ROOM

BEDROOM 1

BATH

LIN.

MASTER BATH

WALK-IN CLOSET

LIN.

BEDROOM 2

MASTER BEDROOM

1st Floor Area - 884 Sq. Ft.

Living Room: 14'-6" x 13'-6"

Den: 10'-9" x 11'-0"

Kitchen: 9'-3" x 13'-6"

Dining Room: 14'-6" x 11'-0"

½ Bath: 5'-0" x 7'-3"

2nd Floor Area - 884 Sq. Ft.

Master Bedroom: 14'-6" x 13'-6"

Bedroom 1: 10'-9" x 11'-0"

Bedroom 2: 14'-6" x 11'-0"

Master Bath: 11'-0" x 6'-0"

Bath: 8'-0" x 7'-6"

Walk-in Closet: 11'-0" x 4'-9"

Notes:

Wilderness Log Homes

Burlington

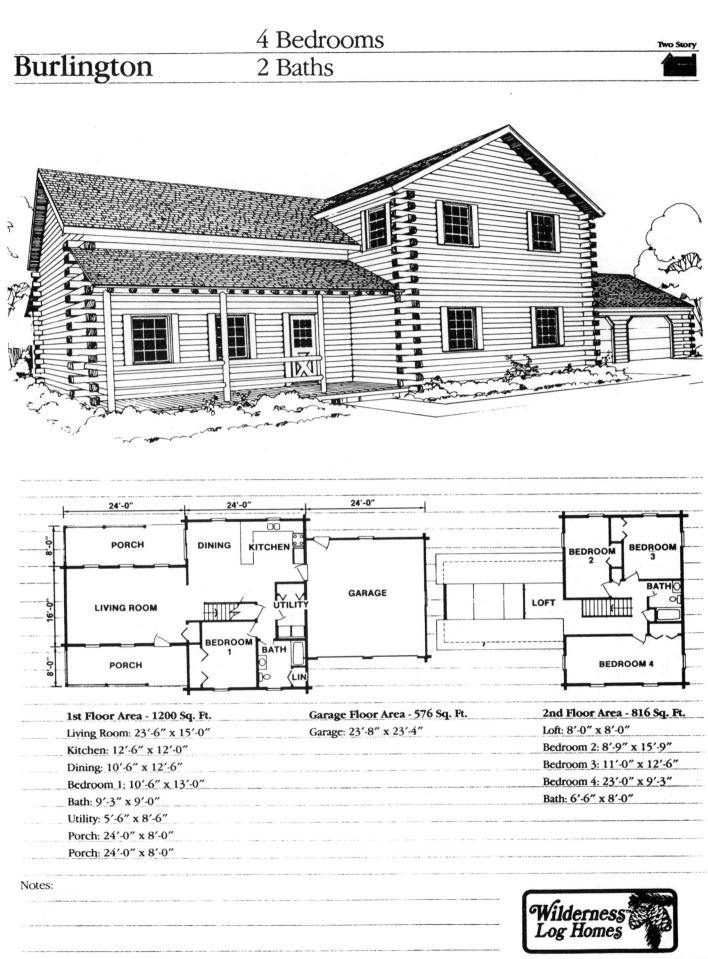

24'-0"	24'-0"	24'-0"

PORCH · **DINING** · **KITCHEN** · **GARAGE** · **BEDROOM 2** · **BEDROOM 3**

LIVING ROOM · **UTILITY** · **LOFT** · **BATH**

BEDROOM 1 · **BATH** · **LIN** · **PORCH** · **BEDROOM 4**

1st Floor Area - 1200 Sq. Ft.

Living Room: 23'-6" x 15'-0"

Kitchen: 12'-6" x 12'-0"

Dining: 10'-6" x 12'-6"

Bedroom 1: 10'-6" x 13'-0"

Bath: 9'-3" x 9'-0"

Utility: 5'-6" x 8'-6"

Porch: 24'-0" x 8'-0"

Porch: 24'-0" x 8'-0"

Garage Floor Area - 576 Sq. Ft.

Garage: 23'-8" x 23'-4"

2nd Floor Area - 816 Sq. Ft.

Loft: 8'-0" x 8'-0"

Bedroom 2: 8'-9" x 15'-9"

Bedroom 3: 11'-0" x 12'-6"

Bedroom 4: 23'-0" x 9'-3"

Bath: 6'-6" x 8'-0"

Notes:

Wilderness Log Homes

Franklin

5 Bedrooms
2½ Baths

Solar

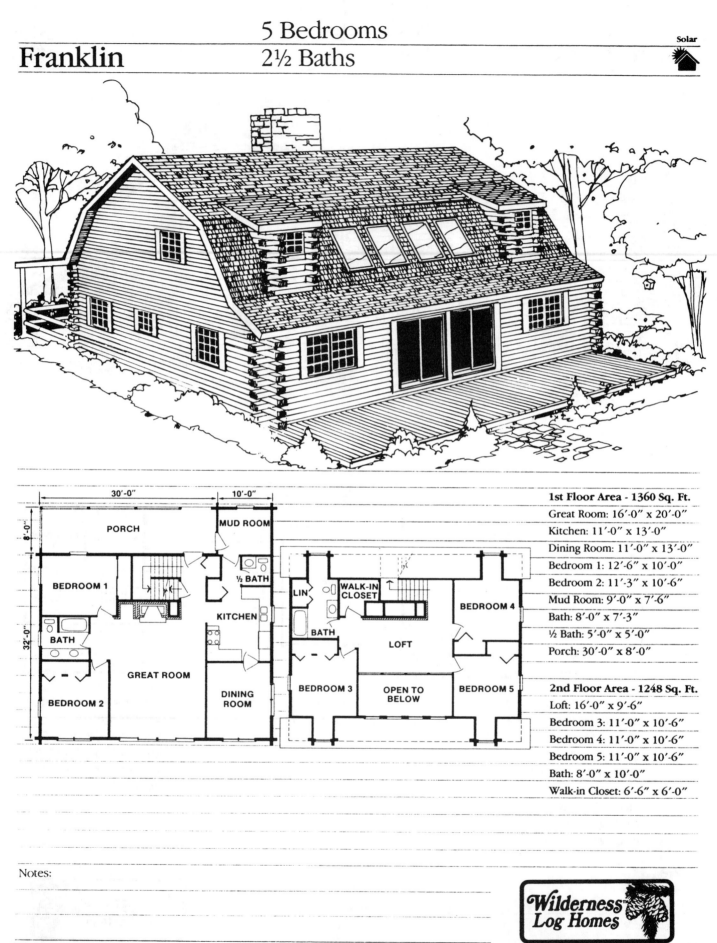

30'-0" **10'-0"**

8'-0"

PORCH

MUD ROOM

BEDROOM 1

½ BATH

KITCHEN

32'-0"

BATH

GREAT ROOM

DINING ROOM

BEDROOM 2

LIN

WALK-IN CLOSET

BEDROOM 4

BATH

LOFT

BEDROOM 3

OPEN TO BELOW

BEDROOM 5

1st Floor Area - 1360 Sq. Ft.

Great Room: 16'-0" x 20'-0"

Kitchen: 11'-0" x 13'-0"

Dining Room: 11'-0" x 13'-0"

Bedroom 1: 12'-6" x 10'-0"

Bedroom 2: 11'-3" x 10'-6"

Mud Room: 9'-0" x 7'-6"

Bath: 8'-0" x 7'-3"

½ Bath: 5'-0" x 5'-0"

Porch: 30'-0" x 8'-0"

2nd Floor Area - 1248 Sq. Ft.

Loft: 16'-0" x 9'-6"

Bedroom 3: 11'-0" x 10'-6"

Bedroom 4: 11'-0" x 10'-6"

Bedroom 5: 11'-0" x 10'-6"

Bath: 8'-0" x 10'-0"

Walk-in Closet: 6'-6" x 6'-0"

Notes:

Wilderness Log Homes

Winchester

3 Bedrooms
2 Baths

American

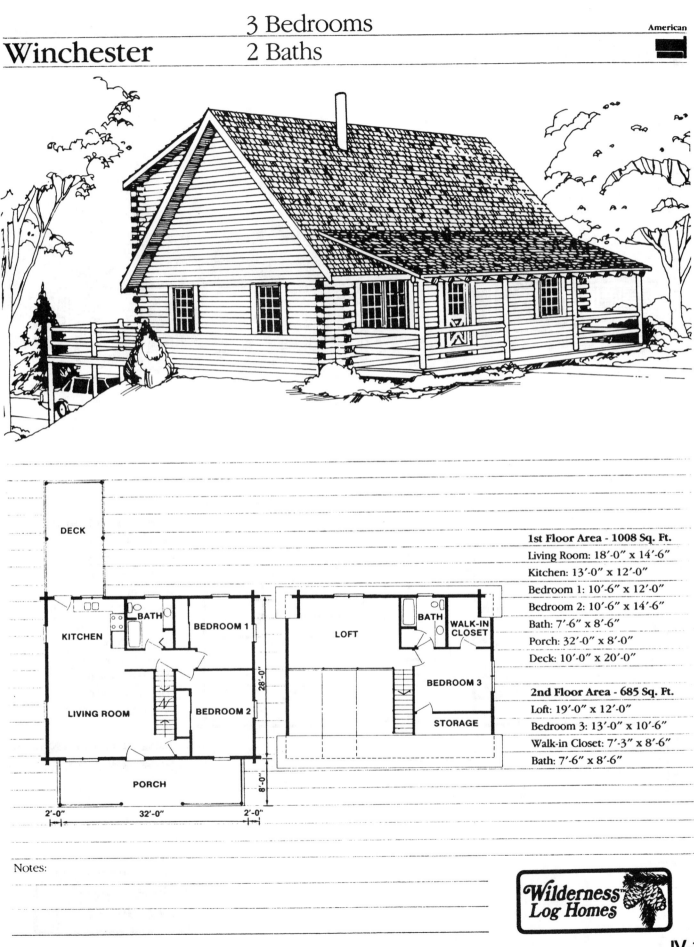

1st Floor Area - 1008 Sq. Ft.

Living Room: 18'-0" x 14'-6"

Kitchen: 13'-0" x 12'-0"

Bedroom 1: 10'-6" x 12'-0"

Bedroom 2: 10'-6" x 14'-6"

Bath: 7'-6" x 8'-6"

Porch: 32'-0" x 8'-0"

Deck: 10'-0" x 20'-0"

2nd Floor Area - 685 Sq. Ft.

Loft: 19'-0" x 12'-0"

Bedroom 3: 13'-0" x 10'-6"

Walk-in Closet: 7'-3" x 8'-6"

Bath: 7'-6" x 8'-6"

Notes:

Wilderness Log Homes

IV-14

Springfield

3 Bedrooms
2 Baths

Solar

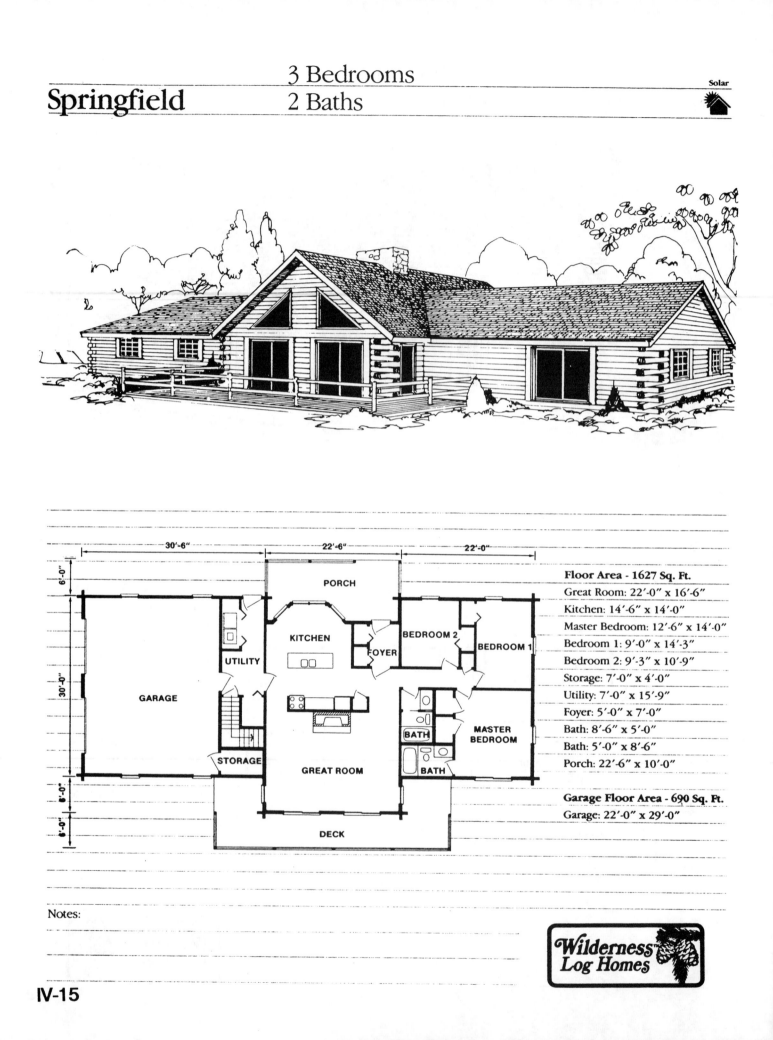

Floor Area - 1627 Sq. Ft.

Great Room: 22'-0" x 16'-6"

Kitchen: 14'-6" x 14'-0"

Master Bedroom: 12'-6" x 14'-0"

Bedroom 1: 9'-0" x 14'-3"

Bedroom 2: 9'-3" x 10'-9"

Storage: 7'-0" x 4'-0"

Utility: 7'-0" x 15'-9"

Foyer: 5'-0" x 7'-0"

Bath: 8'-6" x 5'-0"

Bath: 5'-0" x 8'-6"

Porch: 22'-6" x 10'-0"

Garage Floor Area - 690 Sq. Ft.

Garage: 22'-0" x 29'-0"

Notes:

Richmond

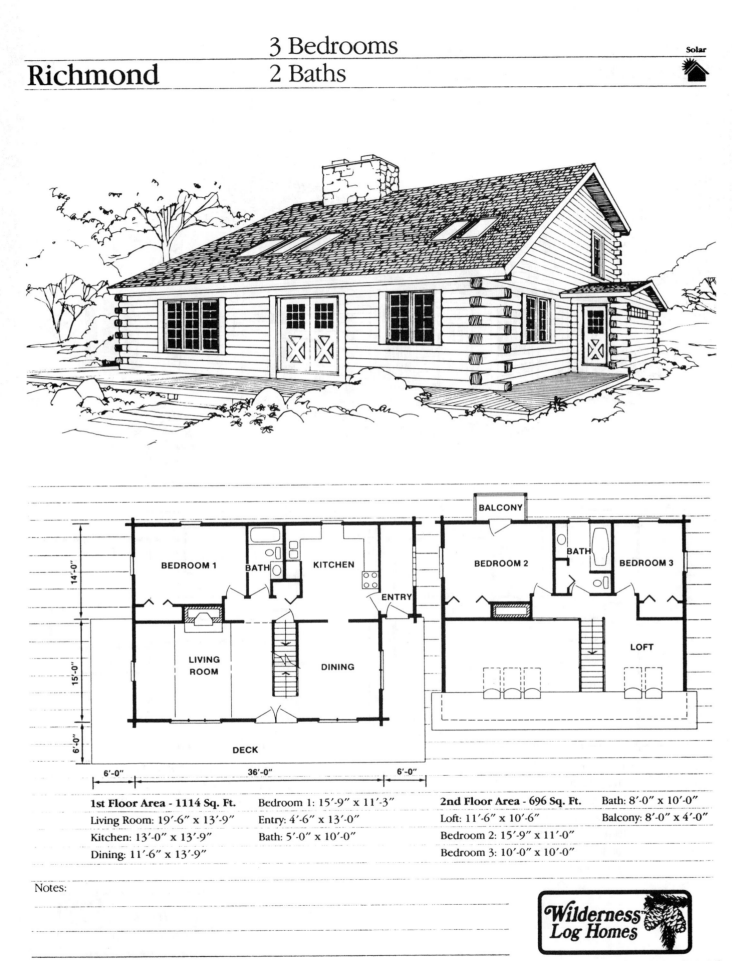

3 Bedrooms

2 Baths

Solar

BALCONY

BEDROOM 1   BATH   KITCHEN

ENTRY

BEDROOM 2   BATH   BEDROOM 3

14'-0"

LIVING ROOM   DINING

LOFT

15'-0"

6'-0"

DECK

6'-0"   36'-0"   6'-0"

1st Floor Area - 1114 Sq. Ft.

Living Room: 19'-6" x 13'-9"

Kitchen: 13'-0" x 13'-9"

Dining: 11'-6" x 13'-9"

Bedroom 1: 15'-9" x 11'-3"

Entry: 4'-6" x 13'-0"

Bath: 5'-0" x 10'-0"

2nd Floor Area - 696 Sq. Ft.

Loft: 11'-6" x 10'-6"

Bedroom 2: 15'-9" x 11'-0"

Bedroom 3: 10'-0" x 10'-0"

Bath: 8'-0" x 10'-0"

Balcony: 8'-0" x 4'-0"

Notes:

Wilderness Log Homes

IV-16

Cedarton

2 Baths

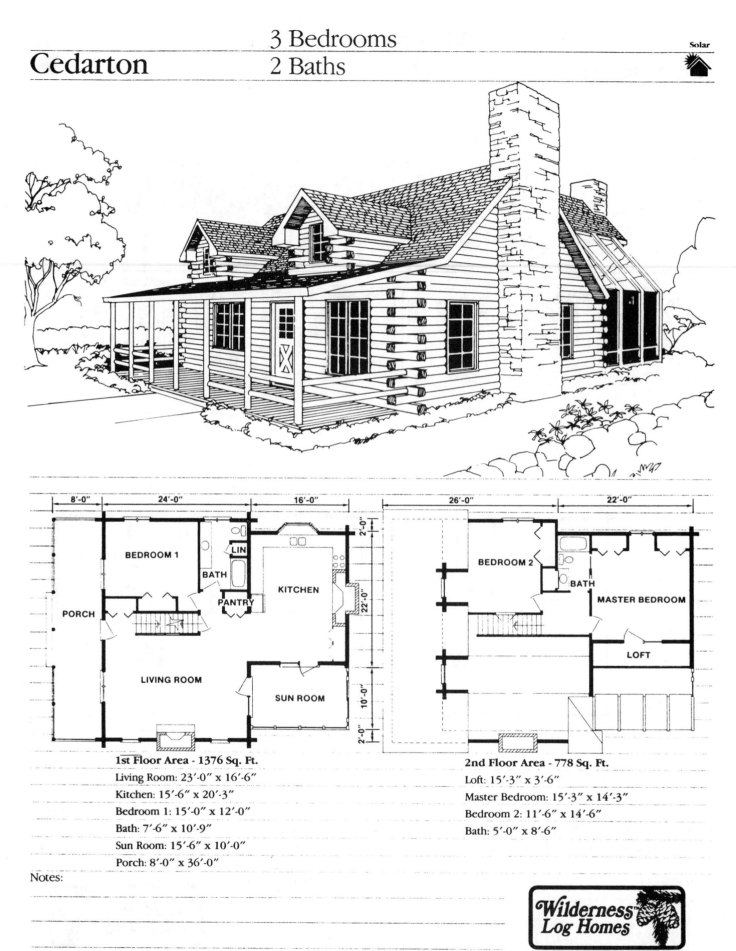

1st Floor Area - 1376 Sq. Ft.

Living Room: 23'-0" x 16'-6"

Kitchen: 15'-6" x 20'-3"

Bedroom 1: 15'-0" x 12'-0"

Bath: 7'-6" x 10'-9"

Sun Room: 15'-6" x 10'-0"

Porch: 8'-0" x 36'-0"

2nd Floor Area - 778 Sq. Ft.

Loft: 15'-3" x 3'-6"

Master Bedroom: 15'-3" x 14'-3"

Bedroom 2: 11'-6" x 14'-6"

Bath: 5'-0" x 8'-6"

Notes:

Wilderness Log Homes

Hamilton

3 Bedrooms
2 Baths

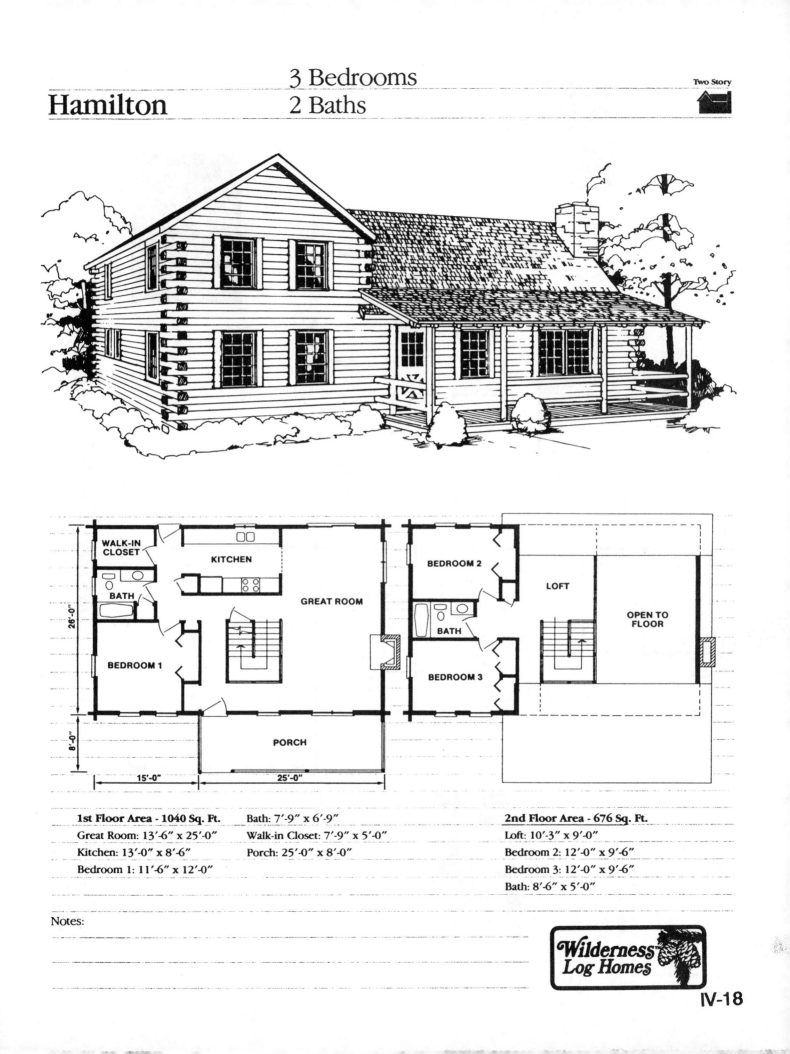

1st Floor Area - 1040 Sq. Ft.

Great Room: 13'-6" x 25'-0"	Bath: 7'-9" x 6'-9"
Kitchen: 13'-0" x 8'-6"	Walk-in Closet: 7'-9" x 5'-0"
Bedroom 1: 11'-6" x 12'-0"	Porch: 25'-0" x 8'-0"

2nd Floor Area - 676 Sq. Ft.

Loft: 10'-3" x 9'-0"

Bedroom 2: 12'-0" x 9'-6"

Bedroom 3: 12'-0" x 9'-6"

Bath: 8'-6" x 5'-0"

Notes:

Wilderness Log Homes

IV-18

INTERNATIONAL SERIES

TOKYO

- **■** 3 Bedrooms
- **■■** 2 Bathrooms
- **■■■** 2627 sq. ft.
- Overall Size: 66' x 56'
- Photos of Internationals are shown on pages 50-51.

Deck (Optional)

Living
20'0" x 21'4"

Dining
15'0" x 10'8"

Entry

Deck (Optional)

Closet

Down

Family
16'0" x 19'0"

Kitchen
16'0" x 13'0"

Pantry

Deck (Optional)

Master Bedroom Suite
24'0" x 26'0"

Closet

Closet

Linen

Bath

Bath

W   D

Closet   Utility

Closet   Closet

Linen

Dressing

Closet

Bedroom 3
10'8" x 16'0"

Closet

Bedroom 2
17'0" x 14'0"

3-Car Garage
32'0" x 26'6"
(Optional)

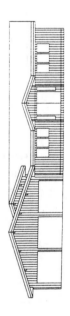

The owners virtually doubled their living space with a walkout daylight basement.

Lavish use of decks extends living out-of-doors. Western red cedar is used in Lindal decking, rails and framing.

This lovely ranch style home, with its low profile, has a covered entry with double doors and an optional 3-car garage.

▲ Lindal Cedar Homes

SIGNATURE SERIES

HALLMARK

- 3 Bedrooms
- 2 1/2 Bathrooms
- Master bedroom on first floor
- 2325 sq. ft.
- First Floor: 1513 sq. ft.
- Other Floor: 812 sq. ft.
- Overall Size: 50' x 35'

Photos of Signatures are
shown on pages 52-53.

Shading indicates skylight or sunroom.

First Floor

A Velux® skylight is a
valuable addition over
the entry, in a long
corridor or a small
bathroom – or
anywhere you want.

Varying roof pitches, a covered entry,
vertical glass and skylights give this
finely detailed home visual appeal.

The home opens to the deck
and its wonderful view,
with a sunwall positioned
over sliding glass doors.

Second Floor

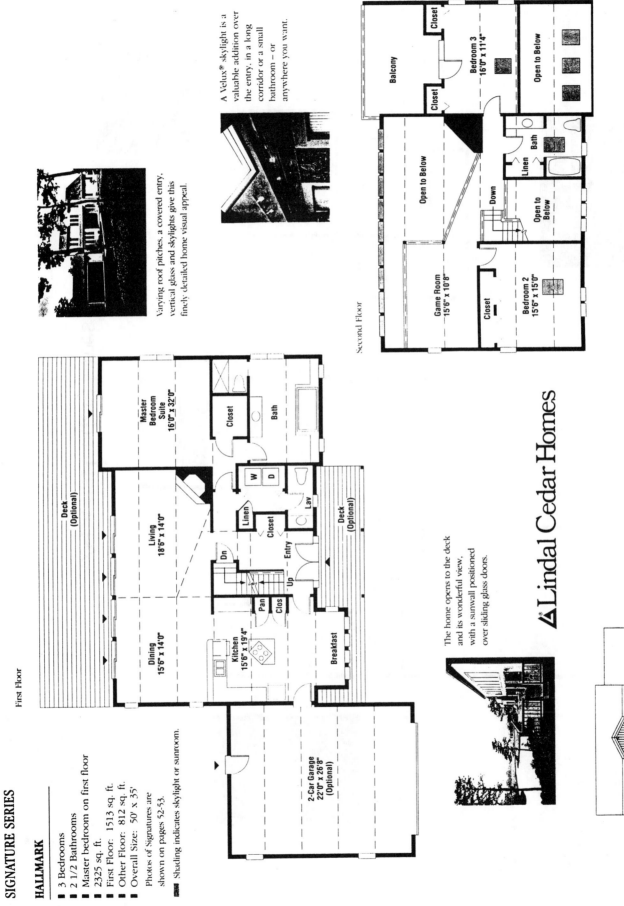

Second Floor

- Balcony
- Closet
- Closet
- Bedroom 3 16'0" x 11'4"
- Open to Below
- Open to Below
- Bath
- Linen
- Down
- Open to Below
- Game Room 15'6" x 10'8"
- Closet
- Bedroom 2 15'6" x 15'0"

First Floor

- Deck (Optional)
- Master Bedroom Suite 16'0" x 32'0"
- Closet
- Bath
- Living 18'6" x 14'0"
- Linen
- W D
- Closet
- Lav
- Dining 15'6" x 14'0"
- Kitchen 15'6" x 19'4"
- Pan Clos
- Dn
- Up
- Entry
- Deck (Optional)
- Breakfast
- 2-Car Garage 22'0" x 26'8" (Optional)

△ Lindal Cedar Homes

IV-20

CONTINENTAL SERIES

BAVARIA

- 2+ Bedrooms
- 2 3/4 Bathrooms
- Master bedroom on second floor
- 2166 sq. ft.
- First floor: 1399 sq. ft.
- Other floor: 767 sq. ft.
- Overall Size: 43' x 44'

Photos of Continentals are shown on pages 48-49.

■ Shading indicates skylight or sunroom.

This is the back or view side of the home. The formal entry and garage are on the other side.

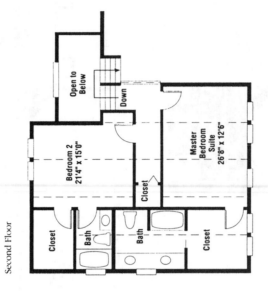

Second Floor

Closet

Bath

Bath

Closet

Closet

Bedroom 2
21'4" x 15'0"

Closet

Down

Open to Below

Master Bedroom Suite
26'8" x 12'6"

From the family room off the kitchen/dining area, it's four steps down to the more formal and separate living room.

First Floor

2-Car Garage
21'4" x 22'0"

W D

Utility
10'8" x 7'6"

Down

Bath

Entry

Closet

Up

Closet

Study
9'6" x 13'0"

Down

Kitchen
10'8" x 12'0"

Dining
12'0" x 16'0"

Family
20'0" x 15'0"

Breakfast

Deck (Optional)

Living
16'0" x 16'0"

Down

Deck (Optional)

Down

▲ Lindal Cedar Homes

In this plan, the living room projects on the right and the breakfast room on the left.

IV-21

MASTERPIECE SERIES

MICHELANGELO

- 4 Bedrooms
- 2 1/2 Bathrooms
- Master bedroom on first floor
- 3020 sq. ft.
- First Floor: 2148 sq. ft.
- Other Floor: 872 sq. ft.
- Overall Size: 69' x 46'

Photos of Masterpieces are shown on pages 60-61.

■ Shading indicates skylight or sunroom.

This detail shows the underside of the second floor with wood ceiling planks, glu-laminated beams and posts flush with the drywall.

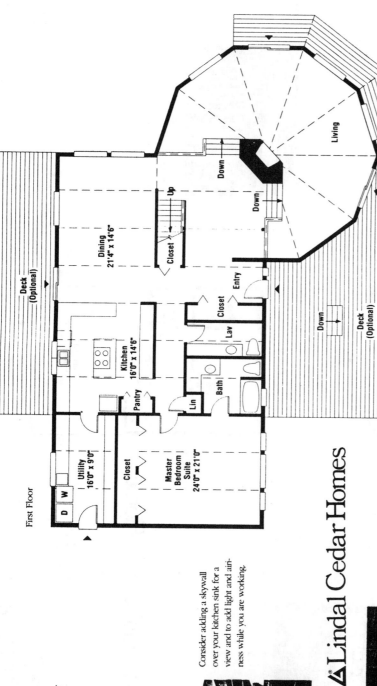

First Floor

Deck (Optional)

Dining 21'4" x 14'6"

Up

Down

Down

Closet

Kitchen 16'0" x 14'6"

Pantry

Lav

Lin

Bath

Entry

Closet

Living

Down

Deck (Optional)

Utility 16'0" x 9'0"

Closet

Master Bedroom Suite 24'0" x 21'0"

D   W

Consider adding a skywall over your kitchen sink for a view and to add light and airiness while you are working.

Large windows and sliding glass doors punctuate the sides of the pavilion.

▲Lindal Cedar Homes

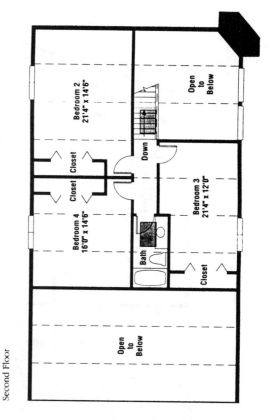

Second Floor

Bedroom 2 21'4" x 14'6"

Closet Closet

Open to Below

Down

Bedroom 4 16'0" x 14'6"

Bath

Bedroom 3 21'4" x 12'0"

Closet

Open to Below

PROW STAR SERIES

SEA VISTA

- 3 Bedrooms
- 2 Bathrooms
- Master bedroom on second floor
- 1834 sq. ft.
- First Floor: 1453 sq. ft.
- Other Floor: 381 sq. ft.
- Overall Size: 60' x 36'

Photos of Prow Stars are shown on pages 64-71.

Shading indicates skylight or sunroom.

The Sea Vista is a 4-module, 2-story prow with 1-story wings swept back on both sides, and a rear entry on the right. Here's a detail of the wood-lined roof overhang on the prow.

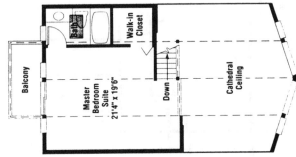

This detail shows the 2x2 rails and 2x4 top rail in our all-cedar deck package.

First Floor

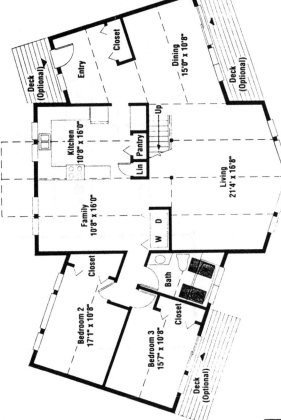

Deck (Optional)

Entry

Closet

Dining 15'0" x 10'8"

Deck (Optional)

Kitchen 10'8" x 16'0"

Up

Lin Pantry

Living 21'4" x 16'8"

Family 10'8" x 16'0"

W D

Bath

Closet

Bedroom 2 17'1" x 10'8"

Bedroom 3 15'7" x 10'8"

Closet

Deck (Optional)

Second Floor

Balcony

Bath

Walk-in Closet

Master Bedroom Suite 21'4" x 19'6"

Down

Cathedral Ceiling

Prows are a popular choice for framing panoramic views.

◢ Lindal Cedar Homes

PROW STAR SERIES

OMNI VISTA

- 3 Bedrooms
- 3 Bathrooms
- Master bedroom on second floor
- 2021 sq. ft.
- First Floor: 1672 sq. ft.
- Other Floor: 349 sq. ft.
- Overall Size: 59' x 36'

Photos of Prow Stars are shown on pages 64-71.

Shading indicates skylight or sunroom.

In the dining room, a mirrored backwall enlarges the room visually. The owners deleted the door to the garage.

First Floor

Deck (Optional)

Bedroom 3
16'6" x 12'8"

Closet

Bath

Bath

Lin

Closet

Bedroom 2
17'0" x 14'0"

Utility
8'6" x 11'0"

W   D

Deck (Optional)

Family
12'4" x 16'0"

Entry

Closet

Covered

Kitchen
10'8" x 14'8"

Closet

Up

Living
21'4" x 17'0"

Dining
10'8" x 18'0"

Deck (Optional)

2-Car Garage
20'0" x 26'8"
(Optional)

Drywall provides a counter-foil to the richness of the A.I.T.C. certified glu-laminated beams and the windows framed in clear cedar.

Lindal Cedar Homes

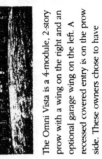

The Omni Vista is a 4-module, 2-story prow with a wing on the right and an optional garage wing on the left. A recessed covered entry is on the prow side. These owners chose to have their garage open to the side rather than to the front.

Second Floor

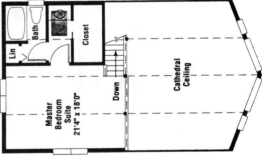

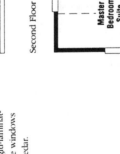

Bath

Lin

Closet

Master Bedroom Suite
21'4" x 18'0"

Down

Cathedral Ceiling

The Century features an optional 3-bay sunroom off the breakfast area.

This detail shows the bird's mouth joinery in a Straight Eave.

A SunCurve style could be substituted.

There are cantilevered balconies off both floors. A garage is built into the basement.

CENTENNIAL SERIES

CENTURY

- 3 Bedrooms
- 2 1/2 Bathrooms
- Master bedroom on second floor
- 3427 sq. ft.
- First Floor: 1775 sq. ft.
- Other Floor: 1652 sq. ft.
- Overall Size: 61' x 37'

Photos of Centennials are shown on pages 58-59.

Shading indicates skylight or sunroom.

IV-25

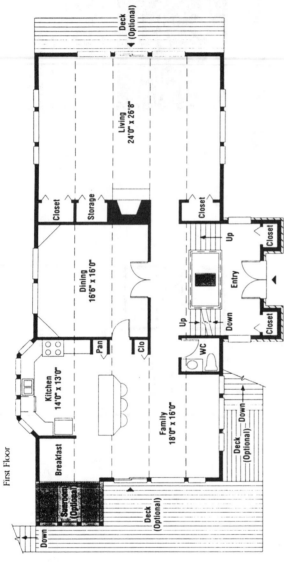

First Floor

- Closet
- Storage
- Living 24'0" x 26'8"
- Deck (Optional)
- Dining 16'6" x 16'0"
- Kitchen 14'0" x 13'0"
- Breakfast
- Sunroom (Optional)
- Pan
- Clo
- Family 18'0" x 16'0"
- Deck (Optional)
- WC
- Closet
- Entry
- Up
- Down
- Closet
- Deck (Optional)
- Down

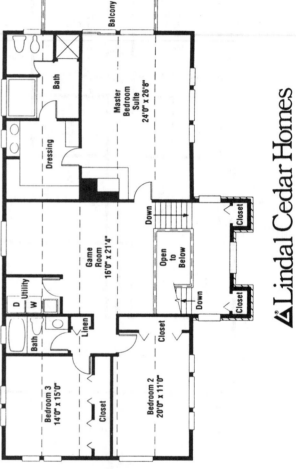

Second Floor

- Bath
- Dressing
- Balcony
- Master Bedroom Suite 24'0" x 26'8"
- Utility
- D / W
- Bath
- Linen
- Bedroom 3 14'0" x 15'0"
- Game Room 16'0" x 21'4"
- Open to Below
- Down
- Closet
- Bedroom 2 20'0" x 11'0"
- Closet
- Closet
- Closet

This home features a split entry. Stairs lead upstairs to two floors of living space, and down to a full basement.

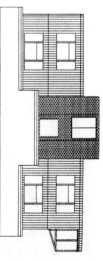

Lindal Cedar Homes

TOWN & COUNTRY SERIES

FAIRLANE

- 4+ Bedrooms
- 3 Bathrooms
- Master bedroom on second floor

3388 sq. ft.

- First Floor: 1796 sq. ft.
- Other Floor: 1592 sq. ft.
- Overall Size: 51' x 37'

Photos of Town & Countries are shown on pages 56-57.

Shading indicates skylight or sunroom.

A 7-bay sunroom off the living room is optional. Simple rail borders the deck.

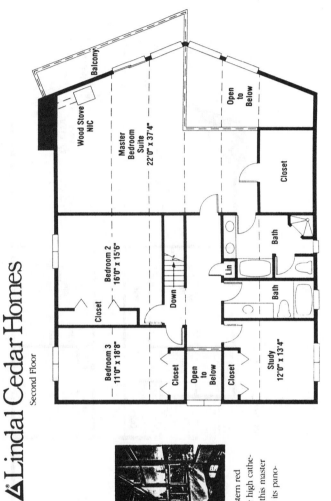

First Floor

Sunroom (Optional)

Deck (Optional)

Living 22'0" x 18'8"

Family 14'0" x 18'8"

Dining 9'0" x 18'8"

TV Room 11'0" x 15'6"

Closet

Up

Storage

Kitchen 16'0" x 13'6"

Bath

Bedroom 4 11'0" x 15'6"

Closet

Closet

Entry

Pantry

Utility 8'0" x 12'0"

D W WH

2-Car Garage 24'0" x 21'4" (Optional)

Deck (Optional)

Lindal Cedar Homes

Second Floor

Balcony

Wood Stove NIC

Master Bedroom Suite 22'0" x 37'4"

Open to Below

Closet

Bedroom 2 16'0" x 15'6"

Lin

Bath

Down

Closet

Bath

Bedroom 3 11'0" x 18'8"

Closet

Open to Below

Closet

Study 12'0" x 13'4"

Although this home presents a private facade to the street, it opens up up with a prow front to the view.

Luxurious Western red cedar lines the high cathedral ceiling of this master bedroom with its panoramic view.

You can top your home with different roofs, among them:

1. Justus standard solid plank roof. R-38.

2. Lindal standard cavity roof. R-33.

3. Lindal Polar Cap 3 cavity roof. R-63. Optional.

TOWN & COUNTRY SERIES

FAIRWAY

■ 4+ Bedrooms
■ 3 Bathrooms
■ Master bedroom on second floor
■ 2826 sq. ft.
■ First Floor: 1461 sq. ft.
■ Other Floor: 1365 sq. ft.
■ Overall Size: 50' x 32'

Photos of Town & Countries are shown on pages 56-57.

IV-27

First Floor

Deck (Optional)

Closet

Study 14'6" x 12'6"

Living 22'0" x 16'0"

Bath

Up

Storage

Kitchen 14'6" x 11'8"

Dining 12'0" x 16'0"

Family 9'6" x 16'0"

Deck (Optional)

Closet

Entry

Pantry

Lin

Closet

Utility 13'0" x 11'8"

D W

2-Car Garage 23'0" x 21'4" (Optional)

Second Floor

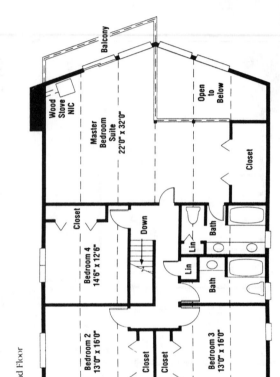

Wood Stove NIC

Balcony

Closet

Bedroom 4 14'6" x 12'6"

Master Bedroom Suite 22'0" x 32'0"

Down

Lin

Bath

Open to Below

Bedroom 2 13'0" x 16'0"

Closet

Closet

Lin

Bath

Closet

Bedroom 3 13'0" x 16'0"

This photo highlights the beauty of architectural grade glu-laminated beams and wood ceiling planks.

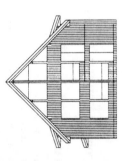

⚠ Lindal Cedar Homes

EMBASSY SERIES

DIPLOMAT

- 4 Bedrooms
- 3 1/2 Bathrooms
- Master bedroom on first floor
- 4420 sq. ft.
- First Floor: 3148 sq. ft.

- Other Floor: 1272 sq. ft.
- Overall Size: 72' x 51'
- Photos of Embassies are shown on pages 54-55.
- ■ Shading indicates skylight or sunroom.

Most Lindal homes come with wide overhangs. Here, the absence of eaves is reminiscent of saltbox design.

First Floor

Second Floor

△ Lindal Cedar Homes

IV-28

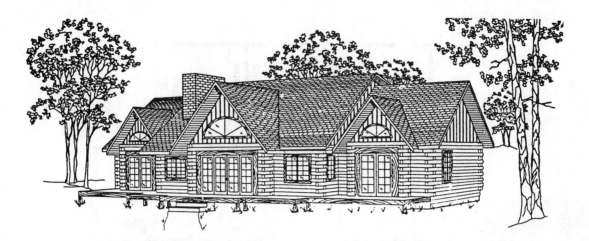

The Richmond A

First Floor Plan

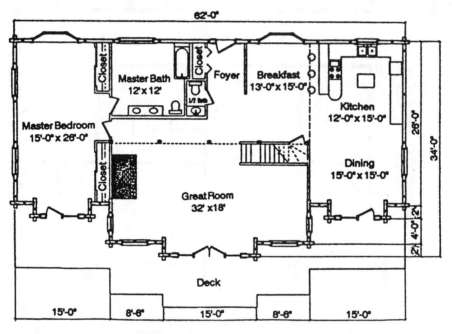

62'-0"

Closet

Master Bath
12' x 12'

Closet

Foyer

Breakfast
13'-0" x 15'-0"

Kitchen
12'-0" x 15'-0"

28'-0"

34'-0"

Master Bedroom
15'-0" x 26'-0"

Closet

Dining
15'-0" x 15'-0"

Great Room
32' x 18'

2' 4'-0" 2'

Deck

15'-0"   8'-6"   15'-0"   8'-6"   15'-0"

Second Floor Plan   Appalachian Log Structures

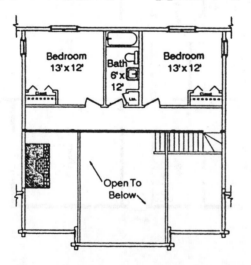

Bedroom
13' x 12'

Bath
6' x 12'

Bedroom
13' x 12'

Open To
Below

IV-29

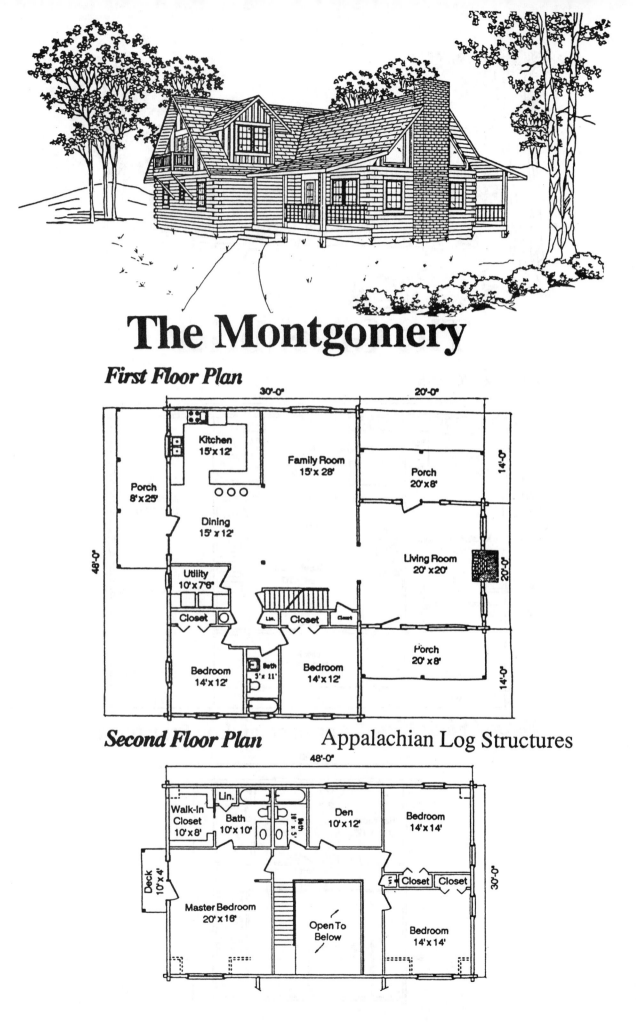

The Montgomery

First Floor Plan

- 30'-0"
- 20'-0"
- Kitchen 15' x 12'
- Family Room 15' x 28'
- Porch 20' x 8'
- 14'-0"
- Porch 8' x 25'
- Dining 15' x 12'
- Living Room 20' x 20'
- 48'-0"
- 20'-0"
- Utility 10' x 7'6"
- Closet
- Closet
- Closet
- Porch 20' x 8'
- Bedroom 14' x 12'
- Bath 5' x 11'
- Bedroom 14' x 12'
- 14'-0"

Second Floor Plan

Appalachian Log Structures

- 48'-0"
- Lin.
- Walk-In Closet 10' x 8'
- Bath 10' x 10'
- Bath 13' x 5'
- Den 10' x 12'
- Bedroom 14' x 14'
- Deck 10' x 4'
- Closet
- Closet
- 30'-0"
- Master Bedroom 20' x 16'
- Open To Below
- Bedroom 14' x 14'

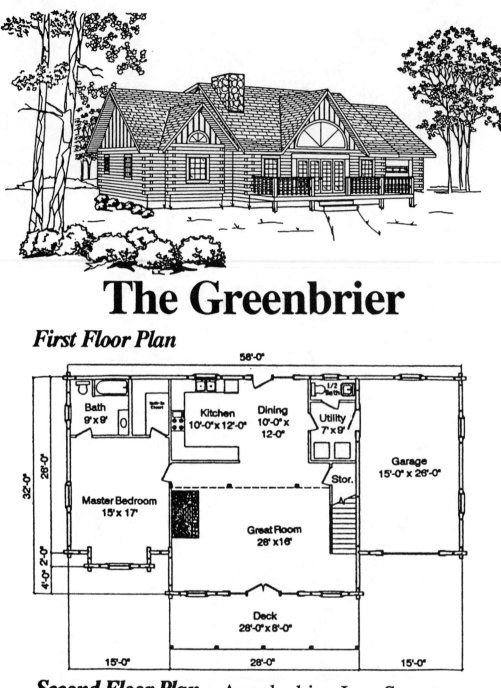

The Greenbrier

First Floor Plan

56'-0"

Bath
8' x 9'

Kitchen
10'-0" x 12'-0"

Dining
10'-0" x 12'-0"

1/2 Bath

Utility
7' x 9'

Garage
15'-0" x 26'-0"

28'-0"

32'-0"

Master Bedroom
15' x 17'

Stor.

Great Room
28' x16'

4'-0" 2'-0"

Deck
28'-0" x 8'-0"

15'-0" 28'-0" 15'-0"

Second Floor Plan   Appalachian Log Structures

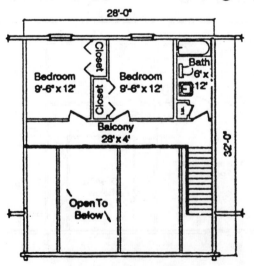

28'-0"

Bedroom
9'-6" x 12'

Closet
Closet

Bedroom
9'-6" x 12'

Bath
6' x 12'

Balcony
28' x 4'

32'-0"

Open To
Below

The Berkeley

First Floor Plan

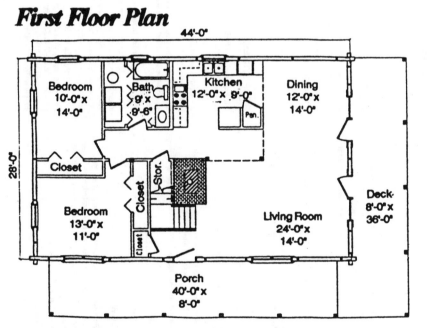

44'-0"

Bedroom
10'-0" x
14'-0"

Bath
9' x
9'-6"

Kitchen
12'-0" x 8'-0"

Dining
12'-0" x
14'-0"

28'-0"

Closet

Closet

Stor.

Bedroom
13'-0" x
11'-0"

Closet

Living Room
24'-0" x
14'-0"

Deck
8'-0" x
36'-0"

Porch
40'-0" x
8'-0"

Second Floor Plan   Appalachian Log Structures

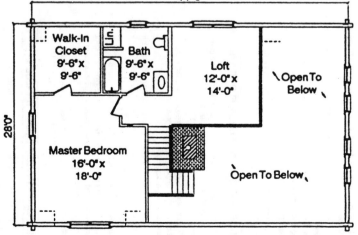

44'-0"

Walk-In
Closet
9'-6" x
9'-6"

Bath
9'-6" x
9'-6"

Loft
12'-0" x
14'-0"

Open To
Below

28'0"

Master Bedroom
16'-0" x
18'-0"

Open To Below

Contemporary Post and Beam Specifications

PAN ABODE

SINCE 1952
CUSTOM CEDAR HOMES

IB-1-90

Subject to change without notice.

■ Options are not included in base price.

FLOOR SYSTEM

1. Floor beams are 4 x 10 No. 2 and Better at 6'0" center lines.

2. Floor framing is 2 x 6 No. 2 and Better, kiln-dried floor joists at 16" center lines.

3. Subfloor is ¾" tongue and groove underlayment grade plywood, which is to be nailed and glued.

■ Fiberglass batt insulation — (R-11) or (R-19).

■ Exposed glue laminated beams for homes on a basement, i.e. walkout or daylight.

LOFT AND SECOND FLOOR, FLOOR SYSTEM

4. Exposed floor beams are architectural grade glue laminated at 6'0" center lines, sized as required by engineering.

5. Finished ceiling between exposed glue laminated beams is ⅝" drywall, which is purchased locally and not included in package price.

6. Framing above beams is 2 x 6 No. 2 and Better, kiln-dried joists at 16" center lines.

7. Subfloor is ¾" tongue and groove underlayment grade plywood, which is to be nailed and glued.

■ Exposed ceiling 1 x 6 tongue and groove tight knot kiln-dried cedar, ½ x 4 clear cedar, or pine random lengths to replace drywall ceiling.

■ Fiberglass batt insulation used to reduce sound transfer between floors is either (R-11) or (R-19).

EXTERIOR WALL SYSTEM, R VALUE 21

8. Studs are 2 x 6 Hem Fir No. 2 and Better, kiln-dried at 24" center lines.

9. Sheathing is ½" CDX plywood.

10. Moisture barrier is Tyvek.

11. Exterior siding is resaw 1 x 6 tight knot kiln-dried cedar (ship lap or T&G pattern) in random lengths applied vertically.

12. Interior finish is ½" drywall, which is purchased locally and not included in package price.

13. Fiberglass batt insulation is (R-19).

■ Exterior siding Pan Abode Pattern 1 x 6 tight knot kiln-dried cedar in random lengths applied horizontally.

■ Interior finish ½" x 4 tongue and groove clear cedar kiln-dried random lengths to replace interior drywall.

■ Interior finish 1 x 6 Pan Abode Pattern tight knot kiln-dried cedar in random lengths applied horizontally to replace interior drywall.

INTERIOR TRIM

20. Cedar casing for all windows and door frames.

21. Cedar moulding to finish between roof boards and interior walls. Cedar base.

INTERIOR DOORS

22. Doors are oak solid core, prehung, complete with Schlage hardware.

23. Closet doors are bi-fold hollow core oak with frame and hardware.

■ Raised panel doors.

■ Raised panel, mirrored, or louvered bi-fold closet doors.

ROOF SYSTEM

24. Exposed roof beams are architectural grade glue laminated at 6'0" center lines, sized as required by engineering.

25. Beams are supported by No. 1 Fir or glue laminated posts, sized as required.

26. Exposed ceiling roof boards are 2 x 6 select tongue and groove kiln-dried white wood decking over exposed beams.

Two standard roof insulation choices are available.

27a. Roof Insulation System is a sandwich consisting of alternate layers of 2" rigid foam insulation and ½" CDX. This equates to (R-33). Many states allow an additional 20% insulation value because this is a continuous insulation system with no framing penetration. (R-39).

27b. A Vented Cavity Roof System with 2 x 10 rafters at 24" center lines, with 2½" rigid foam insulation (R-18) plus 5½" dense fiberglass batt insulation (R-21) between rafters and ½" CDX plywood roof sheathing. Ridge vent is supplied. Total (R-41).

■ Vented Cavity Roof System with 2 x 6 rafters at 24" center lines, above 2 x 6 select tongue and groove wood decking with 2 layers of rigid foam insulation between rafters and ½" CDX plywood roof sheathing. Ridge vent is supplied. Total (R=30.6).

■ A cavity-type roof system consisting of 2 x 12 and 2 x 2 rafters at 24" center lines above 2 x 6 select tongue and groove kiln-dried white wood or cedar decking over architectural grade glue laminated beams. The roof is insulated with (R-38) fiberglass batt between the rafters which allows air movement above insulation. Ridge venting is supplied.

■ A cavity-type roof system consisting of 2 x 12 and 2 x 2 rafters at 24" center lines above our standard glue laminated roof beams with 2 layers R-21 dense fiberglass batt insulation = (R-42) between rafters. Interior of roof to be finished with ⅝" drywall which is purchased locally and not included in package price or with 1 x 6 cedar, ½ x 4 clear cedar, or 1 x 6 pine ceiling boards, roof finish can vary by room. Continuous ridge vent is supplied.

■ Western Red Cedar roof T & G decking.

ROOF COVERING

28. Fiberglass composition shingles, 20-year warranty, dark brown color with 15-lb. felt included.

■ Premium composition shingles.

■ Cedar shakes.

■ Tile.

■ Metal.

DECKS & RAILINGS

■ Decks are Western Red Cedar 2 x 4s No. 2 and Better decking with 2 x 2 cedar rail and 2 x 4 top rails. All framing is pressure treated or sun wood, maximum spacing 24" centers.

■ Decks utilizing "all weather wood" or treated lumber are also available.

GARAGES

■ All garages are optional, even those shown on standard models. For complete specifications, see garage pricer.

STAINS & FINISHES

■ Sikkens or equivalent.

ADDITIONAL INFORMATION

■ Pan Abode's Post & Beam standard architectural plans are designed on a 6' module; however, our architects can deviate from this model to match customer's designs or to provide "total custom" plans.

■ The following items are not included in our standard building: foundation, heating system, plumbing, electrical, cabinets, floor coverings, metal framing connectors, permits, special engineering, and any other items not specified.

■ Pan Abode buildings are designed for various snow and wind loads. Pan Abode must be notified of all local snow loads, wind loads, and heat loss requirements prior to purchase of a house package. In some cases these items can change the cost of the home.

EXTERIOR DOORS

14. Raised panel doors, prehung in frames with Schlage lock.

15. Sliding glass doors are wood framed with "insulated" glass and bronze anodized aluminum screens.

■ Doors with side lights, French doors, metal insulated doors.

■ Sliding glass doors with Low "E" glass.

■ Garage doors.

WINDOWS

16. Windows are wood framed with "insulated" glass and screens. All opening windows are "A" rated; wood sliders, awning, or casement with roto hardware as detailed on blueprints.

17. Extension jambs are cedar.

■ Garden windows.

■ Sun rooms.

■ Low "E" insulated glass windows.

■ Roof windows by Velux.

INTERIOR PARTITIONS

18. Studs are 2 x 4 Hem Fir No. 2 and Better, kiln-dried at 24" on center.

19. Interior finish is ½" drywall, which is purchased locally and not included in package price.

■ Interior finish 1 x 6 tongue and groove V-Groove tight knot kiln-dried cedar or pine, random lengths applied vertically or horizontally to replace interior drywall.

PAN ABODE

4350 Lake Washington Blvd. N.   Renton, Washington 98056   (206) 255-8260

SOLAR CAVALIER 3100

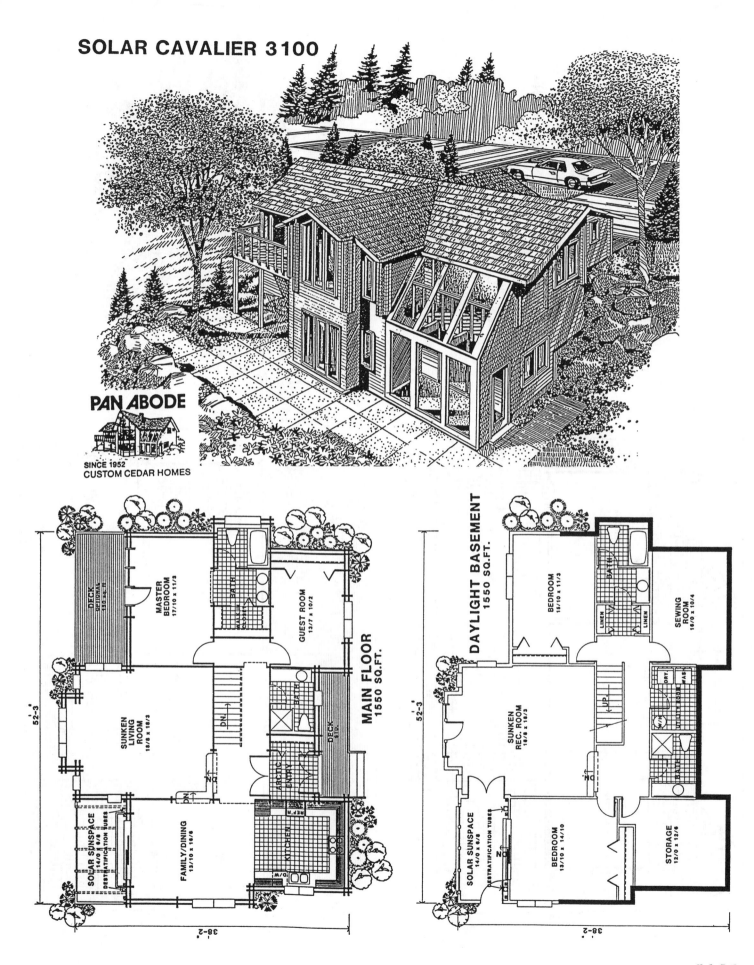

PAN ABODE

SINCE 1952
CUSTOM CEDAR HOMES

MAIN FLOOR
1550 SQ.FT.

DECK OPTIONAL 130 sq. ft.

MASTER BEDROOM
17/10 x 11/3

GUEST ROOM
13/7 x 10/2

BATH

WALK-IN CLOSET

SUNKEN LIVING ROOM
16/8 x 18/3

BATH

DN

DECK

ENTRY

SOLAR SUNSPACE
14/0 x 6/8
DESTRATIFICATION TUBES

FAMILY/DINING
13/10 x 18/6

KITCHEN

REF.

W/D

DN

52-3

38-2

DAYLIGHT BASEMENT
1550 SQ.FT.

BEDROOM
16/10 x 11/3

BATH

LINEN

LINEN

SEWING ROOM
16/0 x 10/4

SUNKEN REC. ROOM
16/8 x 18/3

UP

DRY

WASH

UTILITY ROOM

W/H

SOLAR SUNSPACE
14/0 x 6/8
DESTRATIFICATION TUBES

BEDROOM
13/10 x 14/10

STORAGE
13/0 x 12/6

DN

52-3

38-2

IV-34

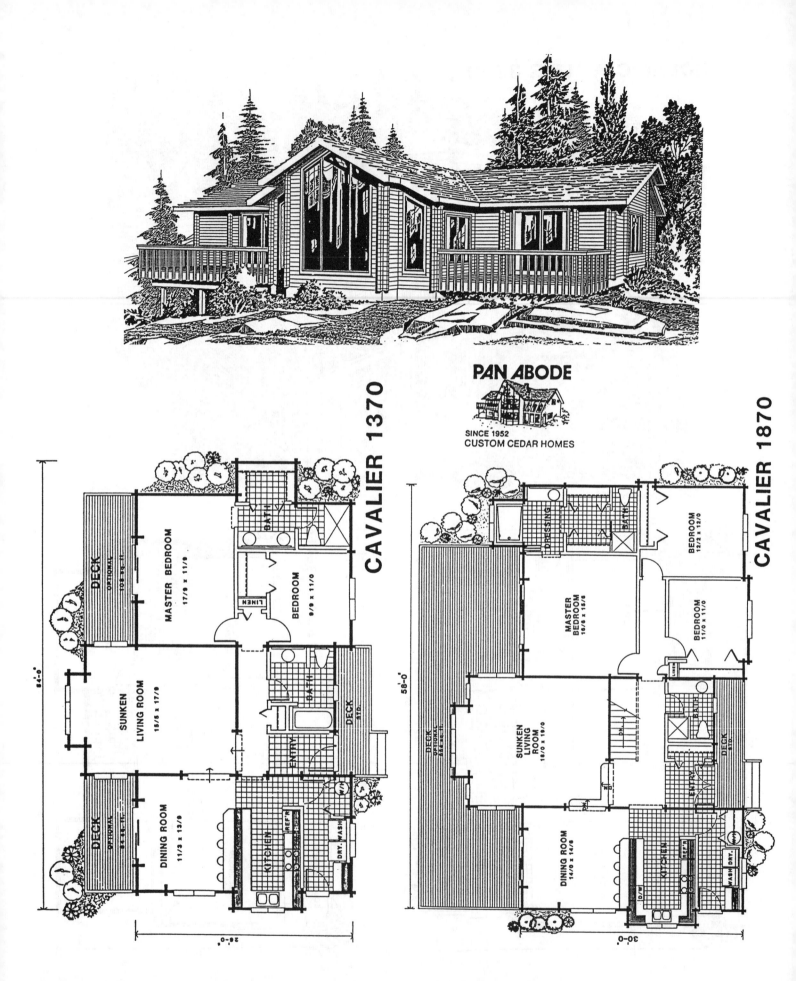

PAN ABODE

SINCE 1952
CUSTOM CEDAR HOMES

CAVALIER 1370

CAVALIER 1870

Cavalier 1370 floor plan labels:

DECK OPTIONAL 108 sq. ft.

MASTER BEDROOM 17/3 x 11/9

BATH

BEDROOM 9/9 x 11/0

LINEN

SUNKEN LIVING ROOM 15/5 x 17/9

BATH

DECK STD.

ENTRY

DECK OPTIONAL 81 sq. ft.

DINING ROOM 11/3 x 13/9

KITCHEN

REF'R

DRY. WASH.

84'-0"

26'-0"

Cavalier 1870 floor plan labels:

DRESSING

BATH

BEDROOM 12/3 x 12/0

MASTER BEDROOM 16/6 x 15/9

BEDROOM 11/0 x 11/0

LINEN

DECK OPTIONAL 344 sq. ft.

SUNKEN LIVING ROOM 18/0 x 19/0

BATH

DECK STD.

ENTRY

DN

UP

DINING ROOM 14/0 x 14/6

KITCHEN

REF'R

D/W

WASH DRY.

58'-0"

30'-0"

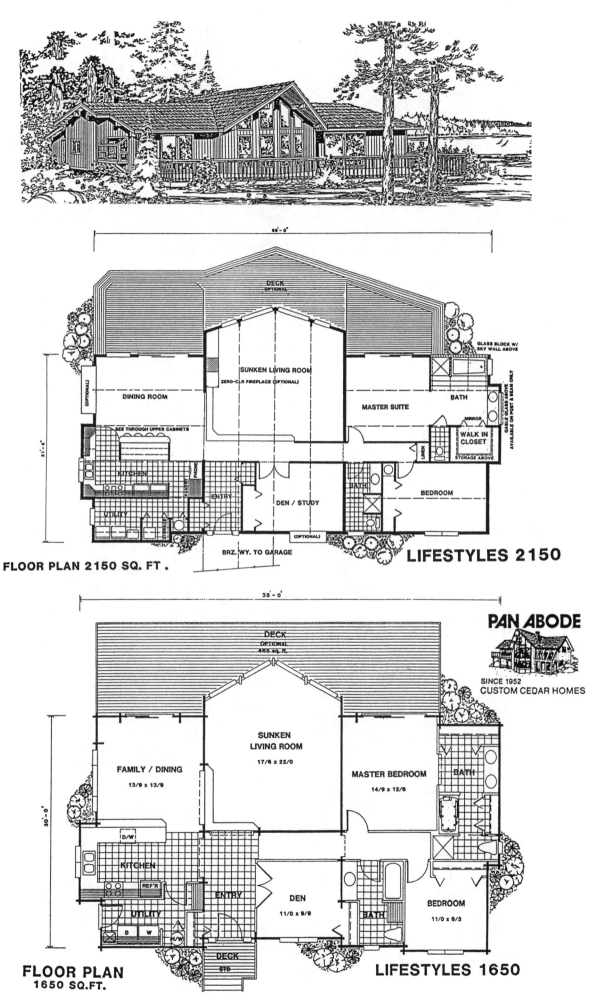

DECK
OPTIONAL

SUNKEN LIVING ROOM

ZERO-CLR FIREPLACE (OPTIONAL)

GLASS BLOCK W/
SKY WALL ABOVE

DINING ROOM

MASTER SUITE

BATH

GABLE GLASS ABOVE
AVAILABLE ON POST & BEAM ONLY

SEE THROUGH UPPER CABINETS

MIRROR

WALK IN
CLOSET

KITCHEN

PANTRY

PHONE

LINEN

STORAGE ABOVE

UTILITY

STORAGE

ENTRY

DEN / STUDY

BATH

BEDROOM

(OPTIONAL)

BRZ. WY. TO GARAGE

FLOOR PLAN 2150 SQ. FT .

LIFESTYLES 2150

PAN ABODE

SINCE 1952
CUSTOM CEDAR HOMES

DECK
OPTIONAL
455 sq. ft.

SUNKEN
LIVING ROOM
17/6 x 22/0

FAMILY / DINING
13/9 x 13/9

MASTER BEDROOM
14/9 x 12/6

BATH

D/W

KITCHEN

REF'R

ENTRY

DEN
11/0 x 9/9

BEDROOM
11/0 x 9/3

UTILITY

D   W

H/W

BATH

DECK
STD

FLOOR PLAN
1650 SQ.FT.

LIFESTYLES 1650

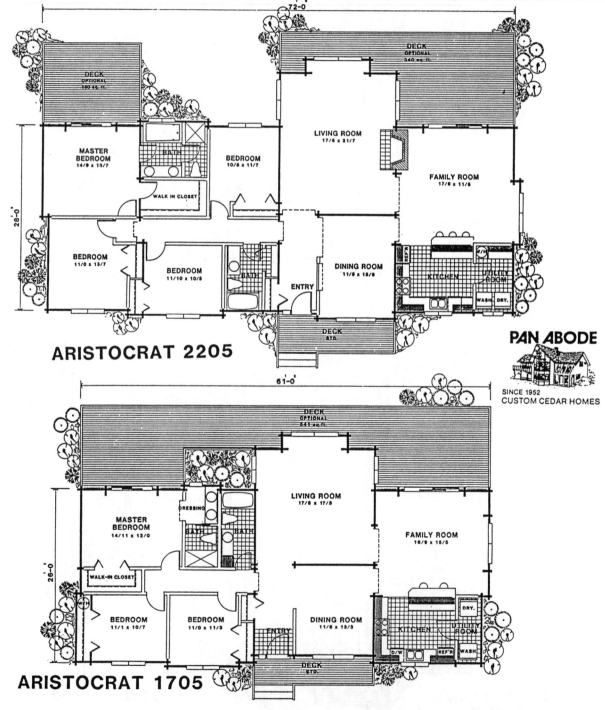

ARISTOCRAT 2205

DECK
OPTIONAL
180 sq. ft.

DECK
OPTIONAL
340 sq. ft.

72'-0"

28'-0"

MASTER
BEDROOM
14/9 x 13/7

BATH

BEDROOM
10/5 x 11/7

LIVING ROOM
17/5 x 21/7

FAMILY ROOM
17/9 x 11/5

WALK IN CLOSET

BEDROOM
11/0 x 13/7

BEDROOM
11/10 x 10/5

BATH

ENTRY

DINING ROOM
11/5 x 15/5

KITCHEN

UTILITY
ROOM

REF'R

WASH. DRY.

DECK
STD.

ARISTOCRAT 1705

PAN ABODE

SINCE 1952
CUSTOM CEDAR HOMES

61'-0"

DECK
OPTIONAL
541 sq. ft.

26'-0"

MASTER
BEDROOM
14/11 x 12/0

DRESSING

BATH

BATH

LIVING ROOM
17/5 x 17/5

FAMILY ROOM
16/9 x 15/5

WALK-IN CLOSET

BEDROOM
11/1 x 10/7

BEDROOM
11/0 x 11/3

ENTRY

DINING ROOM
11/5 x 13/3

KITCHEN

UTILITY
ROOM

DRY.

D/W

REF'R

WASH

DECK
STD.

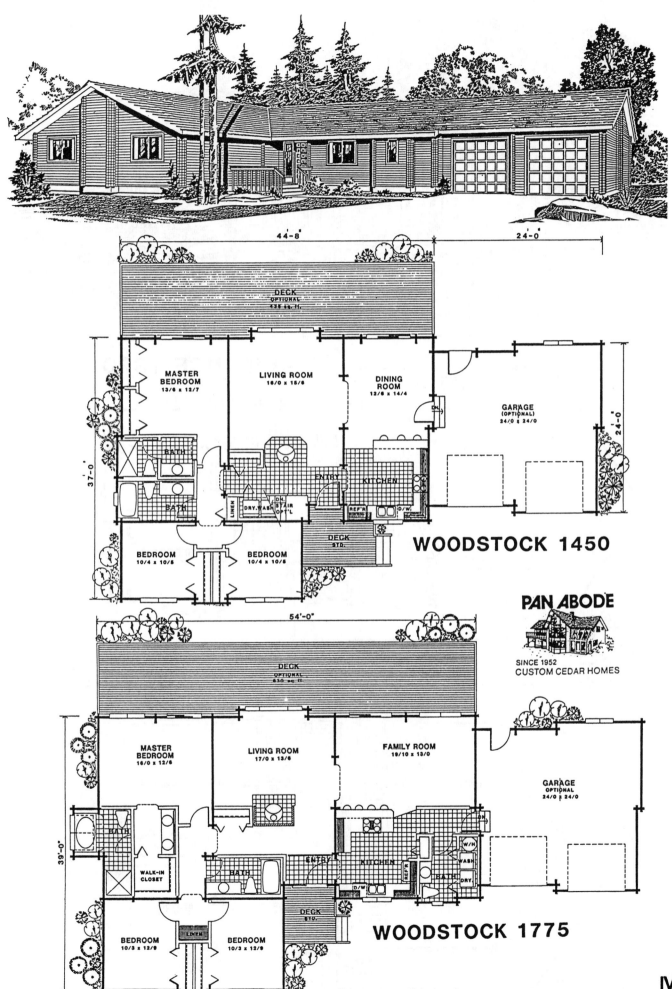

44'-8" 24'-0"

DECK
OPTIONAL
435 sq. ft.

MASTER
BEDROOM
13/6 x 12/7

LIVING ROOM
16/0 x 15/6

DINING
ROOM
12/6 x 14/4

GARAGE
(OPTIONAL)
24/0 x 24/0

37'-0" 24'-0"

BATH

BATH

LINEN

DRY. WASH

DN.
STAIR
OPT'L

ENTRY

KITCHEN

REF'R

D/W

DECK
STD.

BEDROOM
10/4 x 10/8

BEDROOM
10/4 x 10/8

WOODSTOCK 1450

PAN ABODE

SINCE 1952
CUSTOM CEDAR HOMES

54'-0"

DECK
OPTIONAL
830 sq. ft.

MASTER
BEDROOM
16/0 x 12/6

LIVING ROOM
17/0 x 13/6

FAMILY ROOM
19/10 x 13/0

GARAGE
OPTIONAL
24/0 x 24/0

39'-0"

BATH

WALK-IN
CLOSET

BATH

ENTRY

KITCHEN

REF'R

W/H

WASH

DRY

BATH

D/W

DECK
STD.

LINEN

BEDROOM
10/3 x 12/9

BEDROOM
10/3 x 12/9

WOODSTOCK 1775

IV-38

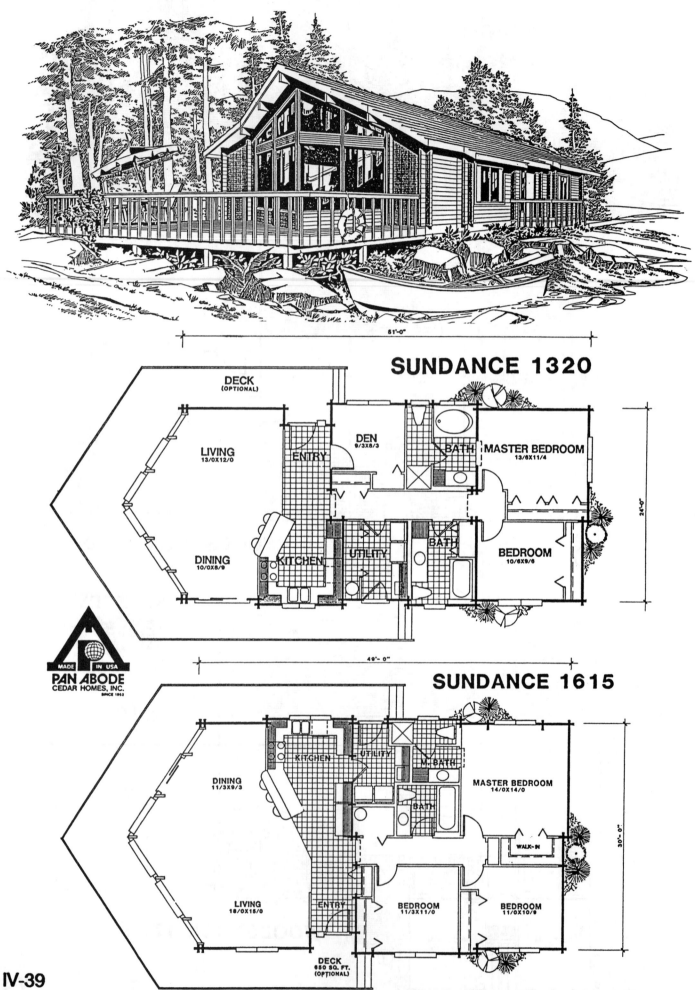

51'-0"

SUNDANCE 1320

DECK
(OPTIONAL)

LIVING
13/0X12/0

DEN
9/3X8/3

BATH

MASTER BEDROOM
13/6X11/4

ENTRY

DINING
10/0X8/9

KITCHEN

UTILITY

BATH

BEDROOM
10/6X9/6

24'-0"

PAN ABODE
CEDAR HOMES, INC.
SINCE 1952
MADE IN USA

49'- 0"

SUNDANCE 1615

KITCHEN

UTILITY

M. BATH

MASTER BEDROOM
14/0X14/0

DINING
11/3X9/3

BATH

30'-0"

WALK-IN

LIVING
18/0X15/0

ENTRY

BEDROOM
11/3X11/0

BEDROOM
11/0X10/9

DECK
650 SQ. FT.
(OPTIONAL)

IV-39

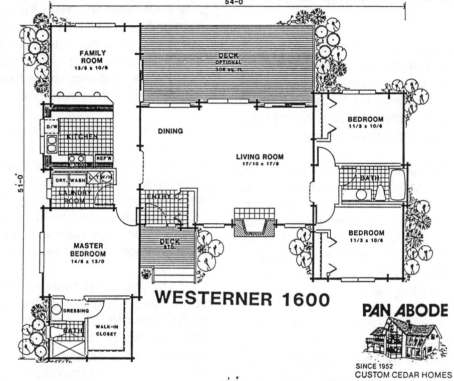

54-0

FAMILY ROOM
13/6 x 10/6

DECK
OPTIONAL
308 sq. ft.

51-0

KITCHEN

D/W

REF'R

DRY. WASH W/H

LAUNDRY ROOM

DINING

ENTRY

LIVING ROOM
17/10 x 17/6

BEDROOM
11/3 x 10/6

BATH

BEDROOM
11/3 x 10/6

DECK
STD.

MASTER BEDROOM
14/6 x 13/0

BATH

DRESSING

WALK-IN CLOSET

WESTERNER 1600

PAN ABODE

SINCE 1952
CUSTOM CEDAR HOMES

68-0

BEDROOM
14/8 x 10/6

DECK
OPTIONAL
425 sq. ft.

LIVING ROOM
18/5 x 17/10

44-0

BEDROOM
12/4 x 10/3

FAMILY ROOM
13/0 x 18/5

KITCHEN

D/W

DINING ROOM
12/3 x 14/0

STORAGE

W/H

UTILITY ROOM

DRY. WASH

ENTRY

BATH

BATH

WALK-IN CLOSET

DRESSING

BATH

DECK
STD.

BEDROOM
13/2 x 10/2

MASTER BEDROOM
18/5 x 13/10

WESTERNER 2195

One of the most energy efficient and easiest kits to build are geodesic dome houses. These are very unique and attractive homes, with the standard kits ranging in floor space from about 900 square feet to more than 3,000 square feet with five bedrooms. For even more space and interesting appearance, you can cluster several smaller kits together into one house.

There are four inherent characteristics of a dome house that make it extremely miserly on heating and cooling costs. You can expect your utility bills to be as much as 40 percent less than for a similarly-constructed and insulated conventional rectangular house.

First, with the basic rounded exterior shape of a dome house, there is about 30 percent less outside wall area than for a conventional rectangular house of the same floor space. Since the amount of heat loss (or heat gain in the summer) is directly related to the amount of exterior wall area, you can expect a substantial savings on your utility bills.

Second, the air inside of a dome house circulates naturally, so the heated air doesn't end up at the ceiling as in a rectangular house. The air tends to flow up the sloped side walls, collide in the center, and then drift down to the living area where you are. Therefore, you can have high ceilings and open lofts without the typical energy efficiency penalty.

Installing many operable (opening) skylights also can improve energy efficiency in a dome house. In the summer, with the high ceilings, you can open the skylights for natural venting. The hot air rises up and out the skylights. This draws cooler air in near the ground.

Third, the rounded exterior shape gives less resistance to wind flowing past it. This reduces pressure differences on the exterior of the home, so there is less air infiltration (leakage) into it. With a traditional rectangular house, the pressure differences from side to side can be significant.

Fourth, a unique feature of a geodesic dome design is that there are no interior support walls needed. With the sloping outside walls and fewer interior obstructions, you can add many windows and skylights to provide more natural lighting. This holds down your electric bills, and reduce the heat buildup from electric lights in the summer.

Several workers can usually enclose the entire shell of a dome home in two weekends. In many of the kits, the construction members in the kit are pre-cut and color-coded. You can also select many options such as 2 x 6 studs for extra insulation thickness, special skylights, and entrance extensions to individualize the style and add more open areas.

The basic structure uses heavy-duty steel connectors. The 2x4 or 2x6 lumber framing struts slide into the connector and you secure them with bolts. The struts and the connectors form the basic framing structure for the geodesic dome. The connectors are also color-coded so you put the right ones in the right locations. Then you nail in studs, add insulation and cover with sheathing.

Dome home kits are usually available in two basic designs - a 3/8 sphere and a 5/8 sphere. With a 3/8-sphere dome design, the first side wall panels starting from the ground are already slanting slightly. It is basically the shape of the top 3/8 of a sphere.

With a 5/8-sphere dome design, there is an additional level of vertical side wall panels with 3/8 dome mounted on top. Either the 3/8 or 5/8-dome can be built over a vertical riser wall for additional height.

MANUFACTURERS OF GEODESIC DOME HOUSES

AMERICAN INGENUITY, INC., 8777 Holiday Springs Rd., Rockledge, FL 32955
(800) 241-2447 (407) 639-8777

DOMES AMERICA, 6345 W. Joliet Rd., Countryside, IL 60525
(312) 579-9400

GEODESIC DOMES, 10290 Davison Rd., Davison, MI 48423
(800) 854-9977 (810) 653-2383

GEODESIC DOMES & HOMES, P.O. Box 575, Whitehouse, TX 75791
(903) 839-2000

GEODOMES WOODWORK, P.O. Box 4141, Riverside, CA 92514
(909) 787-8800

HERITAGE MFG. CO., 5852 Orebank Rd., Kingsport, TN 37664
(423) 288-7141

MONOLITHIC CONSTRUCTORS INC., P.O. Box 479, Italy, TX 76651
(800) 608-0001 (21) 483-7423

NATURAL SPACE DOMES, 37955 Bridge Rd., N. Branch, MN 55056
(800) 733-7107 (612) 674-4292

OREGON DOME, INC., 3215 Meadow Ln., Eugene, OR 97402
(541) 689-3443

SEMISPHERES, 1505 Webster St., Richmond, VA 23220
(804) 643-3184

TIMBERLINE GEODESIC, 2015 Blake St., Berkeley, CA 94704
(800) 366-3466 (510) 849-4481

WINDOW DORMERS:
Single 1st floor windows, not within an entryway, are located in window dormers above any riser panel in the 34', 40', 45', & 48'. You can place 2nd floor window dormers in any of 5 locations in the 34', 40', 45', & 48'.

SKYLIGHTS:
You may place skylights in any room and even group them for dramatic results. Skylight panels are available in clear, tinted, reflective, or low-E glass to suit your climate and direction of orientation. Each skylight comes installed in the panel and provides over 8 square feet of glass.

CUPOLAS:
You may choose to include a cupola at the peak of your dome. It provides indirect light, excellent ventilation, and additional headroom for a loft.

GARAGE ENTRYWAYS:
Overhead doors up to 14' wide are placed in garage entryways spanning 3 riser wall panels.

2ND FLOOR DOOR DORMERS:
Pair a 2nd floor door dormer with a standard entryway to create an upstairs balcony in the 40', 45', & 48'.

1ST FLOOR DOOR DORMERS:
Single doors, not in an entryway, are located in a 1st floor door dormer. They may replace almost any riser wall panel on the ground floor. Utilize them for a separate outside entrance for a kitchen, laundry, or guest room.

HIGH PROFILE ENTRYWAYS:
You might want a high profile entryway for a dynamic entry or taller glass features.

ENTRYWAYS:
Bring French doors, sliding glass doors, and banks of windows into your home with entryways. Spanning the width of 2 riser wall panels, structural entryways may be in as many as 5 first floor locations.

MODIFIED STOCK PLANS:

Modifying a Stock Plan that is close to your dream dome allows you to adapt a plan to your needs. While it does incur a charge, it is much less than the expenditure of custom design work.

Any of the Stock Plans may be modified to provide for such structural changes as:
- building a mirror image
- rearranging rooms, moving walls, or adding closets
- combining the first floor from one plan with the second floor of another
- adding or subtracting entryways, door and window dormers, or balconies
- adding bathrooms
- adding a full or partial basement
- fortifying a floor structure to accommodate special furnishings such as a waterbed, hot tub, or weight room

We will be happy to quote a price for blueprints and a building kit for your Modified Stock Plan once we review your sketches or Floor Planner.

CUSTOM PLANS:

If you are seeking more than what is reflected in the following pages, then perhaps you will want to go a step further to a Custom Plan. It will encompass all your thoughts for the perfect dome and will be drawn by our design team especially for you, yet at a reasonable cost.

Using our state-of-the-art computer aided drafting system, our CAD technician will translate your concept into a set of blueprints. We will work from any combination of ideas as you express them:
- completed floor planner kit
- rough sketches
- list of items to include
- written descriptions
- telephone conversations

Often this personal service will include communication with your area building officials to assure the acceptance of your Custom Plan for issuance of a permit.

The cost of the blueprints for your Custom Plan, as well as the cost of the building kit, can be ascertained after review of your concept.

DESIGN FACTORS:

All plans may be built on your choice of foundation including:
- concrete slab
- raised, stem wall, or pier foundation
- full or partial basement

When planning the location of entryways, door dormers, balconies and window dormers please note their selective locations.

When planning room sizes for your second floor, remember that the headroom decreases as it approaches the knee wall.

GARAGE AND BASEMENT PLANS:

We have included several Stock Plans for garages which may be linked to any dome where indicated, or may be built separately.

Since every building site is different, Basement Plans usually necessitate a Custom Plan. We have included several Stock Plans with basements to show you how they may be utilized.

LINKS AND EXTENSIONS:

If you are planning a complex of domes, you will join the plans together at entryways to form a link. The link will vary in width according to the size of the domes' entryways and can vary in length from 2 feet to 10 feet.

While many companies offer the alternatives of large links and room extensions to the dome, American Ingenuity feels they are not in your best interest. Among the reasons:
- When floorspace is increased using an extension or link, the exposed surface area is greater than for the square footage within a dome. This results in less energy efficiency and a higher cost per square foot.
- Construction is more involved and time consuming.
- The overall scale, relationship between elements, and proportion of the home are adversely affected.
- The visual impact of the design is lessened.

We recommend simply moving up to the next larger size dome or arranging your space differently to increase the efficiency of your design. It will save time, energy, and money.

AMERICAN INGENUITY

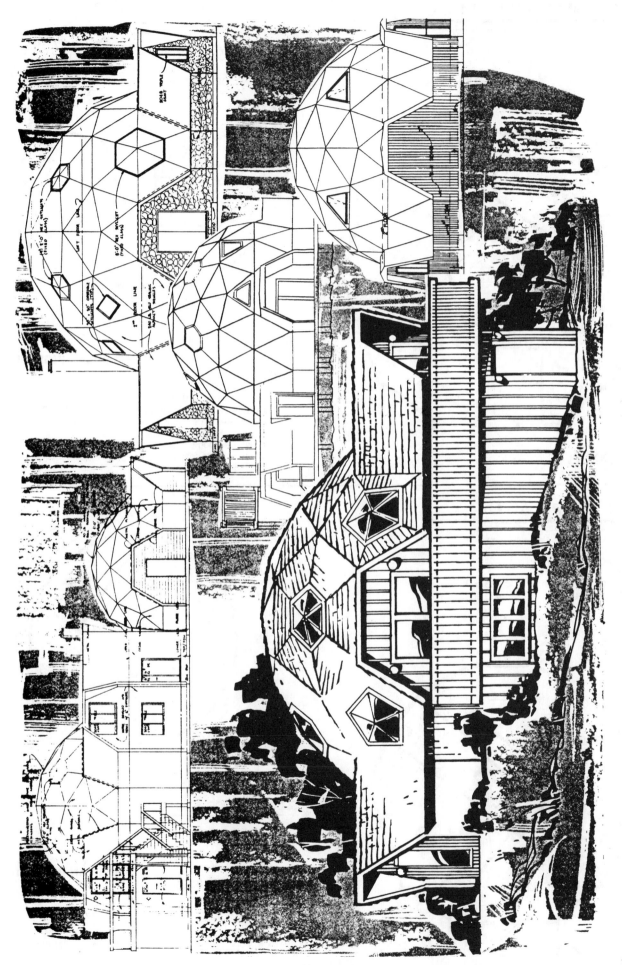

V-4

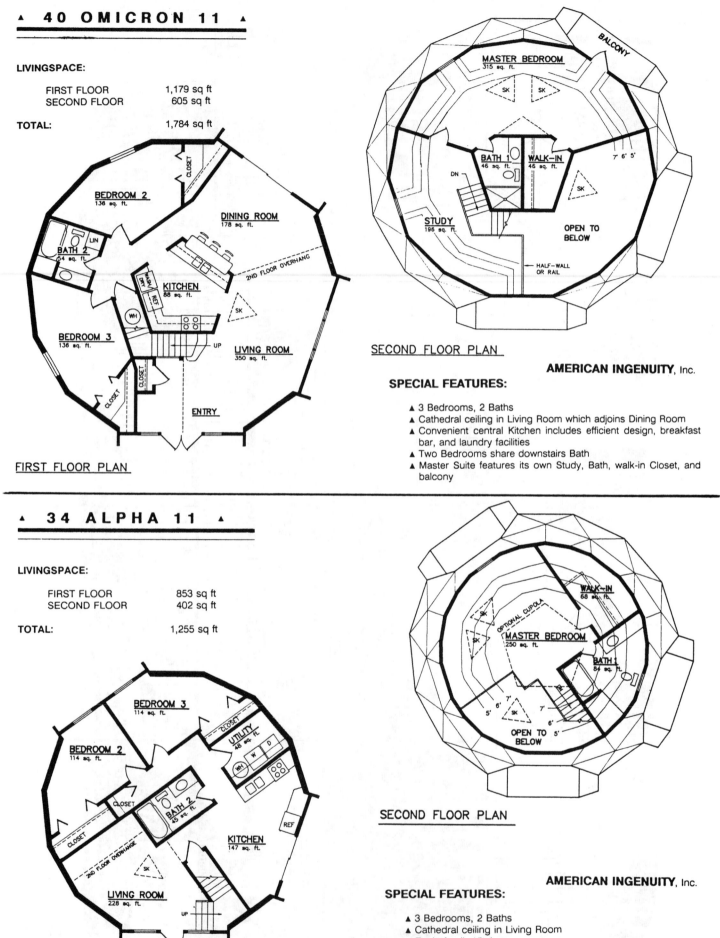

▲ 40 OMICRON 11 ▲

LIVINGSPACE:

FIRST FLOOR	1,179 sq ft
SECOND FLOOR	605 sq ft

TOTAL: 1,784 sq ft

BEDROOM 2 136 sq. ft.

DINING ROOM 178 sq. ft.

CLOSET

BATH 2 54 sq. ft.

LIN

2ND FLOOR OVERHANG

WASH DRY

REF

KITCHEN 88 sq. ft.

WH

SK

BEDROOM 3 136 sq. ft.

CLOSET

CLOSET

UP

LIVING ROOM 350 sq. ft.

ENTRY

FIRST FLOOR PLAN

MASTER BEDROOM 315 sq. ft.

BALCONY

SK   SK

BATH 1 46 sq. ft.

WALK–IN 46 sq. ft.

7' 6' 5'

DN

SK

STUDY 196 sq. ft.

OPEN TO BELOW

HALF–WALL OR RAIL

SECOND FLOOR PLAN

AMERICAN INGENUITY, Inc.

SPECIAL FEATURES:

▲ 3 Bedrooms, 2 Baths
▲ Cathedral ceiling in Living Room which adjoins Dining Room
▲ Convenient central Kitchen includes efficient design, breakfast bar, and laundry facilities
▲ Two Bedrooms share downstairs Bath
▲ Master Suite features its own Study, Bath, walk-in Closet, and balcony

---

▲ 34 ALPHA 11 ▲

LIVINGSPACE:

FIRST FLOOR	853 sq ft
SECOND FLOOR	402 sq ft

TOTAL: 1,255 sq ft

BEDROOM 3 114 sq. ft.

BEDROOM 2 114 sq. ft.

CLOSET

UTILITY 48 sq. ft.

W   D

WH

CLOSET

BATH 2 45 sq. ft.

2ND FLOOR OVERHANG

SK

KITCHEN 147 sq. ft.

REF

LIVING ROOM 228 sq. ft.

UP

FIRST FLOOR PLAN

WALK–IN 68 sq. ft.

SK

OPTIONAL CUPOLA

SK

MASTER BEDROOM 250 sq. ft.

BATH 1 84 sq. ft.

SK

7'

5'   6'   7'

6'

SK

OPEN TO BELOW

5'

SECOND FLOOR PLAN

AMERICAN INGENUITY, Inc.

SPECIAL FEATURES:

▲ 3 Bedrooms, 2 Baths
▲ Cathedral ceiling in Living Room
▲ Eat-in family Kitchen
▲ Spectacular upstairs Master Suite overlooking the Living Room

V-5

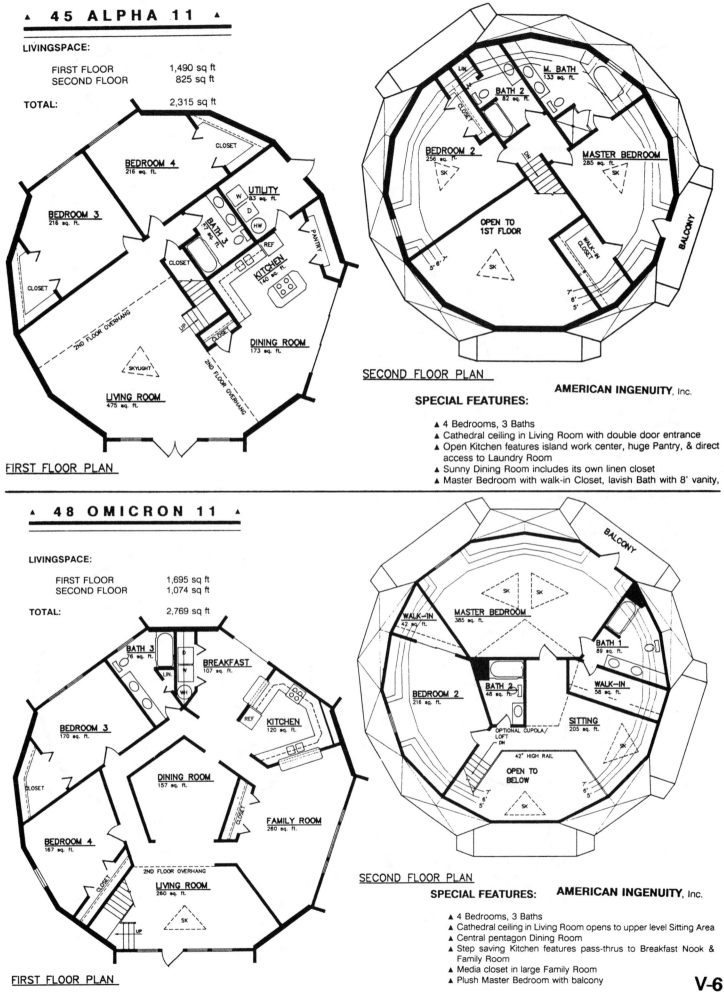

▲ 45 ALPHA 11 ▲

LIVINGSPACE:

FIRST FLOOR	1,490 sq ft
SECOND FLOOR	825 sq ft

TOTAL: 2,315 sq ft

BEDROOM 4 216 sq. ft.

BEDROOM 3 216 sq. ft.

CLOSET

CLOSET

UTILITY 83 sq. ft.
W D HW

BATH 3 67 sq. ft.

CLOSET

REF

KITCHEN 140 sq. ft.

PANTRY

CLOSET

UP

2ND FLOOR OVERHANG

2ND FLOOR OVERHANG

SKYLIGHT

DINING ROOM 173 sq. ft.

LIVING ROOM 475 sq. ft.

FIRST FLOOR PLAN

SECOND FLOOR PLAN

LIN.

M. BATH 133 sq. ft.

BATH 2 82 sq. ft.

CLOSET

BEDROOM 2 256 sq. ft.

SK

MASTER BEDROOM 285 sq. ft.

SK

DN

OPEN TO 1ST FLOOR

SK

WALK-IN CLOSET

BALCONY

5' 6' 7'

7'
6'
5'

AMERICAN INGENUITY, Inc.

SPECIAL FEATURES:

▲ 4 Bedrooms, 3 Baths
▲ Cathedral ceiling in Living Room with double door entrance
▲ Open Kitchen features island work center, huge Pantry, & direct access to Laundry Room
▲ Sunny Dining Room includes its own linen closet
▲ Master Bedroom with walk-in Closet, lavish Bath with 8' vanity,

▲ 48 OMICRON 11 ▲

LIVINGSPACE:

FIRST FLOOR	1,695 sq ft
SECOND FLOOR	1,074 sq ft

TOTAL: 2,769 sq ft

BATH 3 76 sq. ft.

D
LIN.
W
WH

BREAKFAST 107 sq. ft.

REF

KITCHEN 120 sq. ft.

BEDROOM 3 170 sq. ft.

CLOSET

DINING ROOM 157 sq. ft.

CLOSET

FAMILY ROOM 260 sq. ft.

BEDROOM 4 167 sq. ft.

CLOSET

2ND FLOOR OVERHANG

LIVING ROOM 260 sq. ft.

SK

UP

FIRST FLOOR PLAN

SECOND FLOOR PLAN

BALCONY

SK   SK

WALK-IN 42 sq. ft.

MASTER BEDROOM 385 sq. ft.

BATH 1 89 sq. ft.

BEDROOM 2 216 sq. ft.

BATH 2 48 sq. ft.

WALK-IN 58 sq. ft.

SITTING 205 sq. ft.

OPTIONAL CUPOLA/ LOFT DN

SK

42" HIGH RAIL

OPEN TO BELOW

7'
6'
5'

SK

SECOND FLOOR PLAN

SPECIAL FEATURES: **AMERICAN INGENUITY**, Inc.

▲ 4 Bedrooms, 3 Baths
▲ Cathedral ceiling in Living Room opens to upper level Sitting Area
▲ Central pentagon Dining Room
▲ Step saving Kitchen features pass-thrus to Breakfast Nook & Family Room
▲ Media closet in large Family Room
▲ Plush Master Bedroom with balcony

V-6

▲ 45 KAPPA 11 ▲

LIVINGSPACE:

FIRST FLOOR	1,490 sq ft
SECOND FLOOR	975 sq ft

TOTAL: 2,465 sq ft

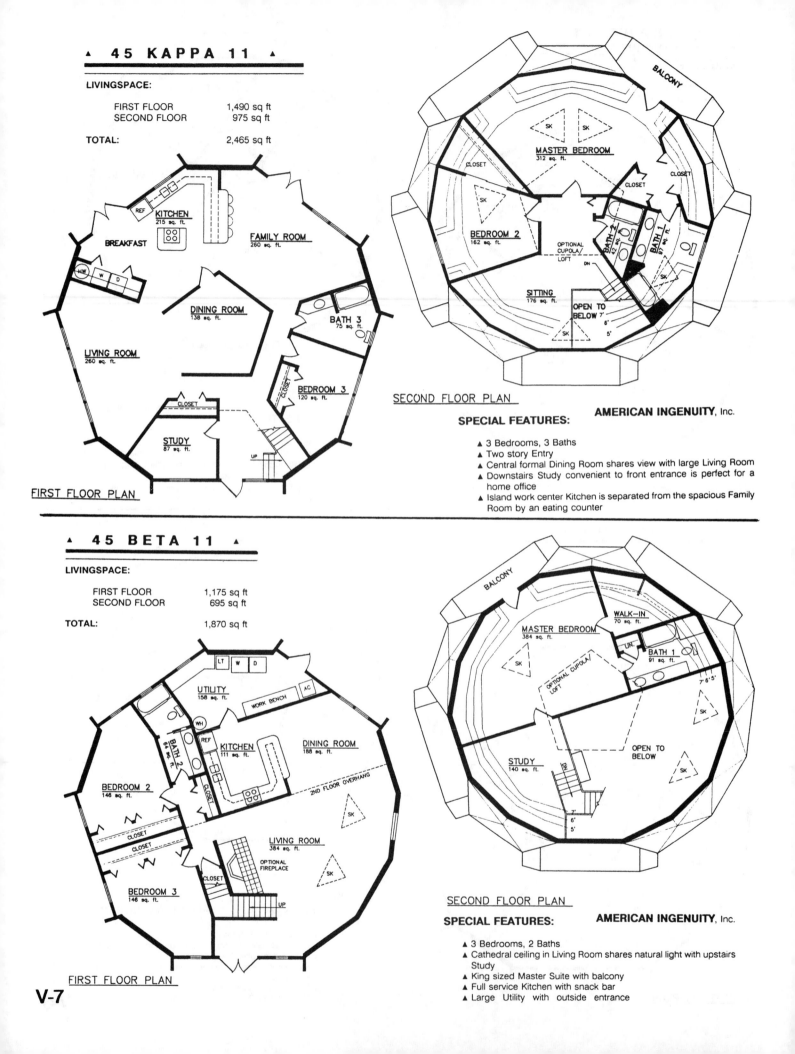

KITCHEN
215 sq. ft.

REF

BREAKFAST

FAMILY ROOM
260 sq. ft.

HW W D

DINING ROOM
138 sq. ft.

LIVING ROOM
260 sq. ft.

BATH 3
75 sq. ft.

CLOSET

BEDROOM 3
120 sq. ft.

CLOSET

STUDY
87 sq. ft.

UP

FIRST FLOOR PLAN

BALCONY

SK SK

MASTER BEDROOM
312 sq. ft.

CLOSET

SK

CLOSET

CLOSET

BEDROOM 2
162 sq. ft.

BATH 2
42 sq. ft.

BATH 1
87 sq. ft.

OPTIONAL CUPOLA/
LOFT

DN

SK

SITTING
176 sq. ft.

OPEN TO
BELOW 7'
6'
5'

SK

SECOND FLOOR PLAN

SPECIAL FEATURES:

AMERICAN INGENUITY, Inc.

- ▲ 3 Bedrooms, 3 Baths
- ▲ Two story Entry
- ▲ Central formal Dining Room shares view with large Living Room
- ▲ Downstairs Study convenient to front entrance is perfect for a home office
- ▲ Island work center Kitchen is separated from the spacious Family Room by an eating counter

▲ 45 BETA 11 ▲

LIVINGSPACE:

FIRST FLOOR	1,175 sq ft
SECOND FLOOR	695 sq ft

TOTAL: 1,870 sq ft

LT W D

UTILITY
158 sq. ft.

WORK BENCH

AC

WH

BATH 2
64 sq. ft.

REF

KITCHEN
111 sq. ft.

DINING ROOM
188 sq. ft.

BEDROOM 2
146 sq. ft.

CLOSET

2ND FLOOR OVERHANG

SK

CLOSET

CLOSET

LIVING ROOM
384 sq. ft.

OPTIONAL
FIREPLACE

CLOSET

SK

BEDROOM 3
146 sq. ft.

UP

FIRST FLOOR PLAN

BALCONY

WALK-IN
70 sq. ft.

MASTER BEDROOM
384 sq. ft.

LIN.

BATH 1
91 sq. ft.

SK

OPTIONAL CUPOLA/
LOFT

7' 6' 5'

SK

OPEN TO
BELOW

STUDY
140 sq. ft.

DN

7'
6'
5'

SK

SECOND FLOOR PLAN

SPECIAL FEATURES:

AMERICAN INGENUITY, Inc.

- ▲ 3 Bedrooms, 2 Baths
- ▲ Cathedral ceiling in Living Room shares natural light with upstairs Study
- ▲ King sized Master Suite with balcony
- ▲ Full service Kitchen with snack bar
- ▲ Large Utility with outside entrance

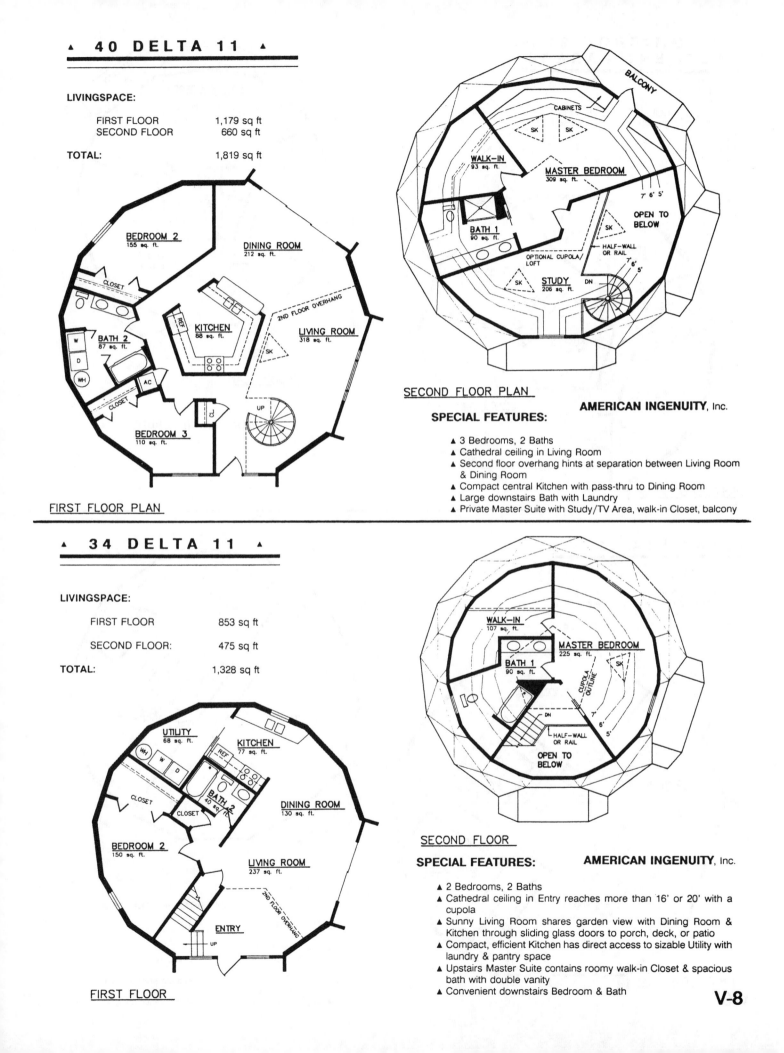

▲ 40 DELTA 11 ▲

LIVINGSPACE:

FIRST FLOOR	1,179 sq ft
SECOND FLOOR	660 sq ft
TOTAL:	1,819 sq ft

FIRST FLOOR PLAN

SECOND FLOOR PLAN

AMERICAN INGENUITY, Inc.

SPECIAL FEATURES:

- ▲ 3 Bedrooms, 2 Baths
- ▲ Cathedral ceiling in Living Room
- ▲ Second floor overhang hints at separation between Living Room & Dining Room
- ▲ Compact central Kitchen with pass-thru to Dining Room
- ▲ Large downstairs Bath with Laundry
- ▲ Private Master Suite with Study/TV Area, walk-in Closet, balcony

▲ 34 DELTA 11 ▲

LIVINGSPACE:

FIRST FLOOR	853 sq ft
SECOND FLOOR:	475 sq ft
TOTAL:	1,328 sq ft

FIRST FLOOR

SECOND FLOOR

SPECIAL FEATURES: **AMERICAN INGENUITY,** Inc.

- ▲ 2 Bedrooms, 2 Baths
- ▲ Cathedral ceiling in Entry reaches more than 16' or 20' with a cupola
- ▲ Sunny Living Room shares garden view with Dining Room & Kitchen through sliding glass doors to porch, deck, or patio
- ▲ Compact, efficient Kitchen has direct access to sizable Utility with laundry & pantry space
- ▲ Upstairs Master Suite contains roomy walk-in Closet & spacious bath with double vanity
- ▲ Convenient downstairs Bedroom & Bath

V-8

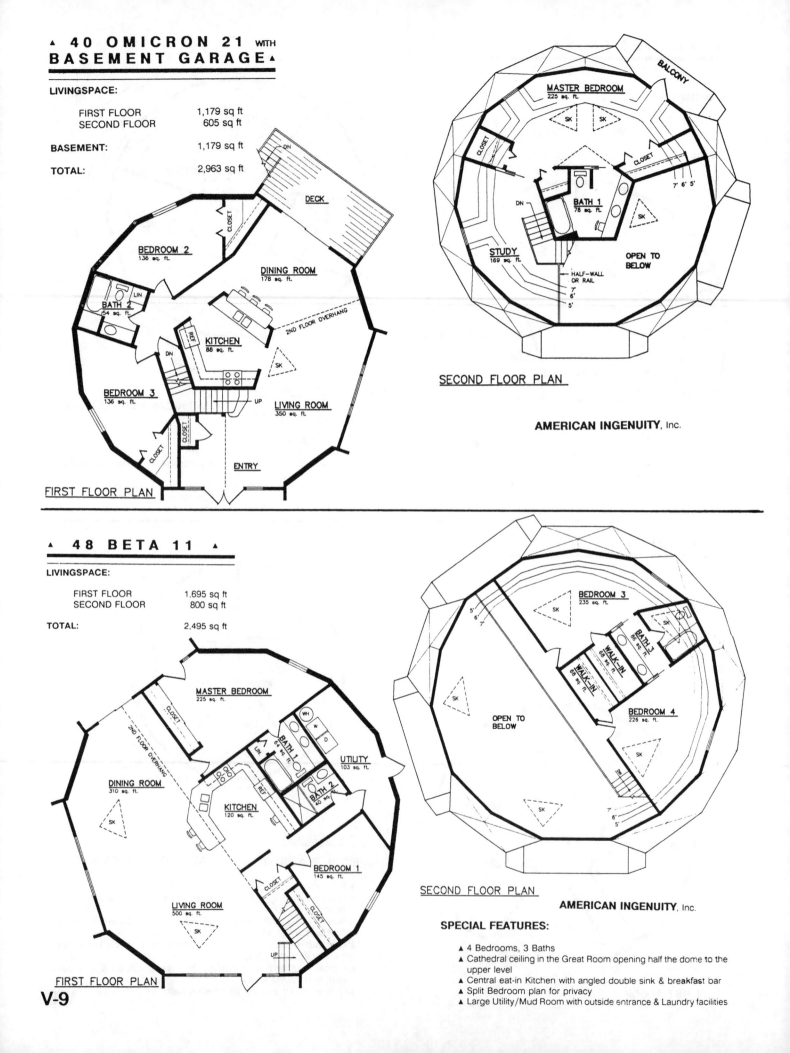

▲ 40 OMICRON 21 WITH
BASEMENT GARAGE ▲

LIVINGSPACE:

FIRST FLOOR	1,179 sq ft
SECOND FLOOR	605 sq ft
BASEMENT:	1,179 sq ft
TOTAL:	2,963 sq ft

FIRST FLOOR PLAN

SECOND FLOOR PLAN

AMERICAN INGENUITY, Inc.

▲ 48 BETA 11 ▲

LIVINGSPACE:

FIRST FLOOR	1,695 sq ft
SECOND FLOOR	800 sq ft
TOTAL:	2,495 sq ft

FIRST FLOOR PLAN

SECOND FLOOR PLAN

AMERICAN INGENUITY, Inc.

SPECIAL FEATURES:

▲ 4 Bedrooms, 3 Baths
▲ Cathedral ceiling in the Great Room opening half the dome to the
upper level
▲ Central eat-in Kitchen with angled double sink & breakfast bar
▲ Split Bedroom plan for privacy
▲ Large Utility/Mud Room with outside entrance & Laundry facilities

V-9

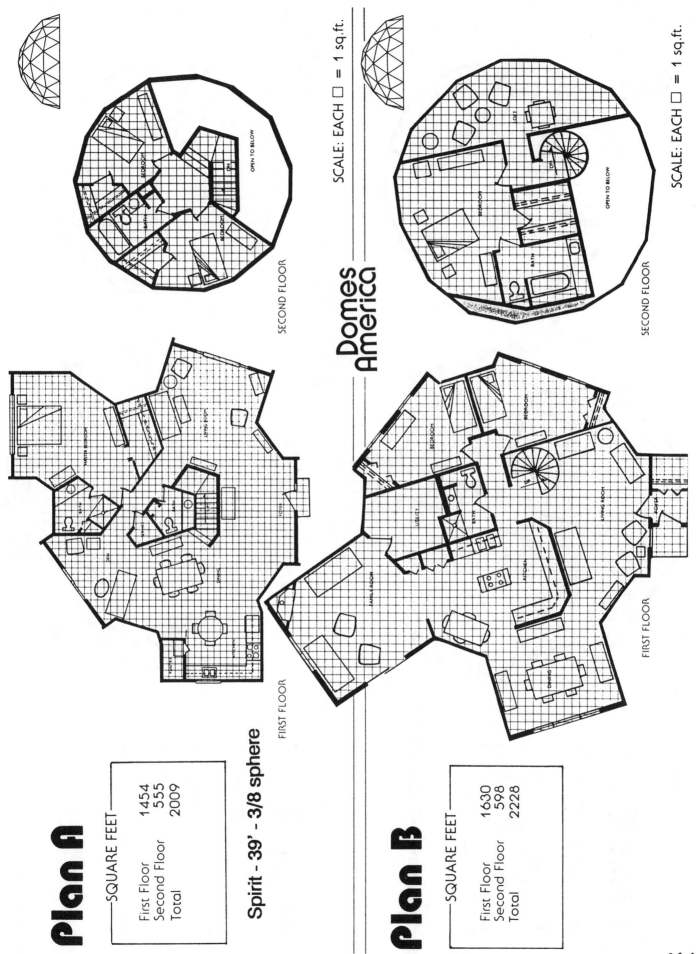

Plan A

SECOND FLOOR

FIRST FLOOR

SCALE: EACH □ = 1 sq.ft.

Domes America

SQUARE FEET

First Floor   1454
Second Floor   555
Total   2009

Spirit - 39' - 3/8 sphere

Plan B

SECOND FLOOR

FIRST FLOOR

SCALE: EACH □ = 1 sq.ft.

SQUARE FEET

First Floor   1630
Second Floor   598
Total   2228

V-10

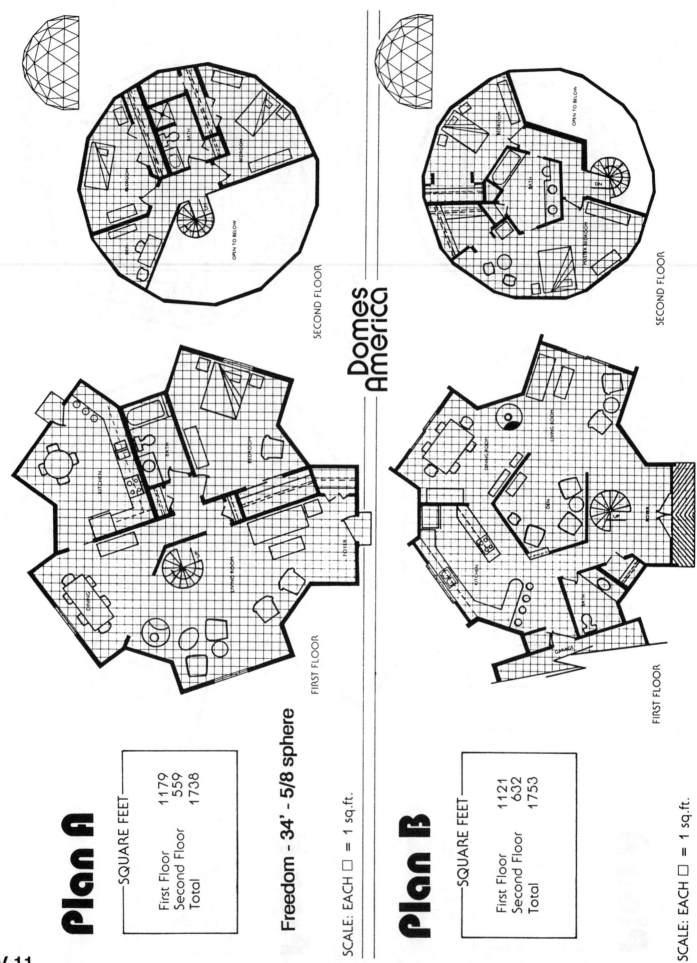

Plan A

SQUARE FEET

First Floor	1179
Second Floor	559
Total	1738

SECOND FLOOR

FIRST FLOOR

Freedom - 34' - 5/8 sphere

SCALE: EACH □ = 1 sq.ft.

Plan B

SQUARE FEET

First Floor	1121
Second Floor	632
Total	1753

SECOND FLOOR

FIRST FLOOR

SCALE: EACH □ = 1 sq.ft.

Domes America

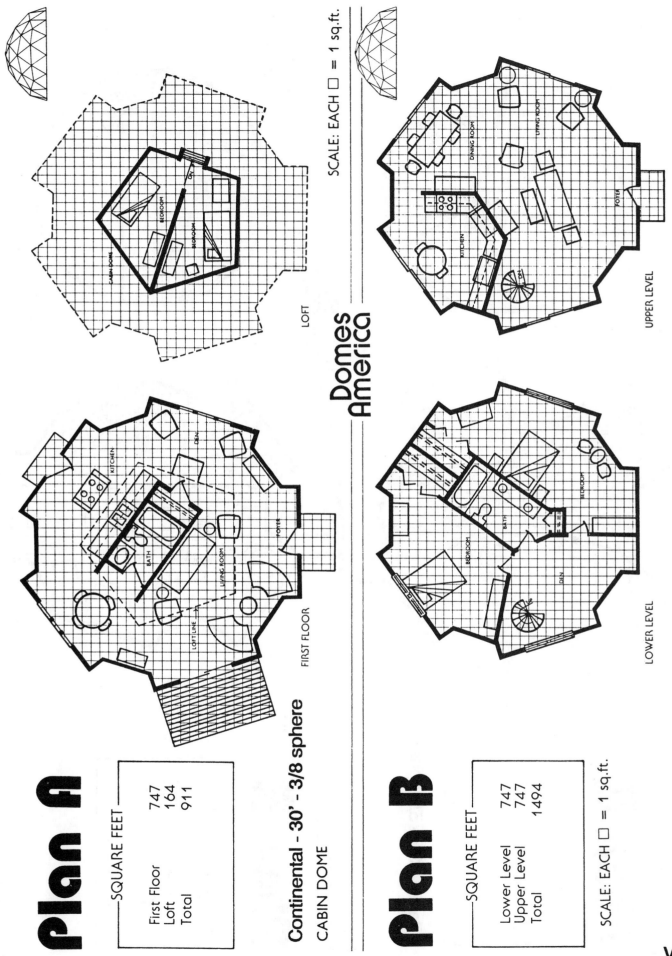

Plan A

SQUARE FEET

First Floor	747
Loft	164
Total	911

Continental - 30' - 3/8 sphere

CABIN DOME

FIRST FLOOR

LOFT

Domes
America

SCALE: EACH ☐ = 1 sq.ft.

UPPER LEVEL

Plan B

SQUARE FEET

Lower Level	747
Upper Level	747
Total	1494

SCALE: EACH ☐ = 1 sq.ft.

LOWER LEVEL

V-12

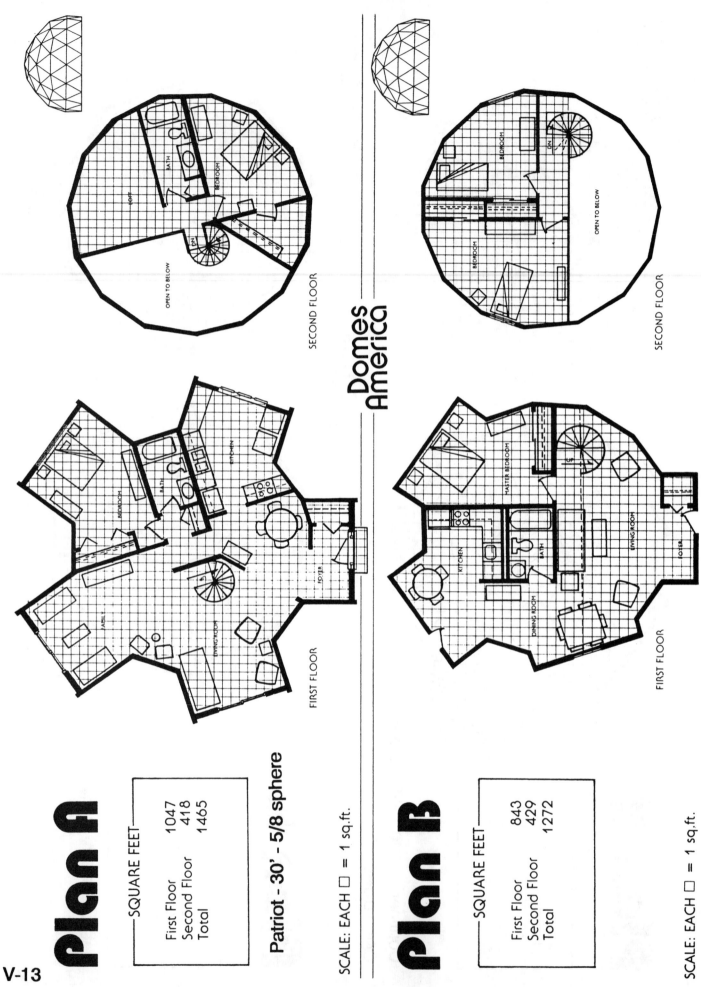

Plan A

SECOND FLOOR

OPEN TO BELOW

LOFT

BATH

BEDROOM

DN

FIRST FLOOR

BEDROOM

BATH

KITCHEN

FAMILY

LIVING ROOM

FOYER

SQUARE FEET

First Floor	1047
Second Floor	418
Total	1465

Patriot - 30' - 5/8 sphere

SCALE: EACH □ = 1 sq.ft.

Domes America

Plan B

SECOND FLOOR

BEDROOM

DN

OPEN TO BELOW

BEDROOM

FIRST FLOOR

MASTER BEDROOM

DN

LIVING ROOM

FOYER

KITCHEN

BATH

DINING ROOM

SQUARE FEET

First Floor	843
Second Floor	429
Total	1272

SCALE: EACH □ = 1 sq.ft.

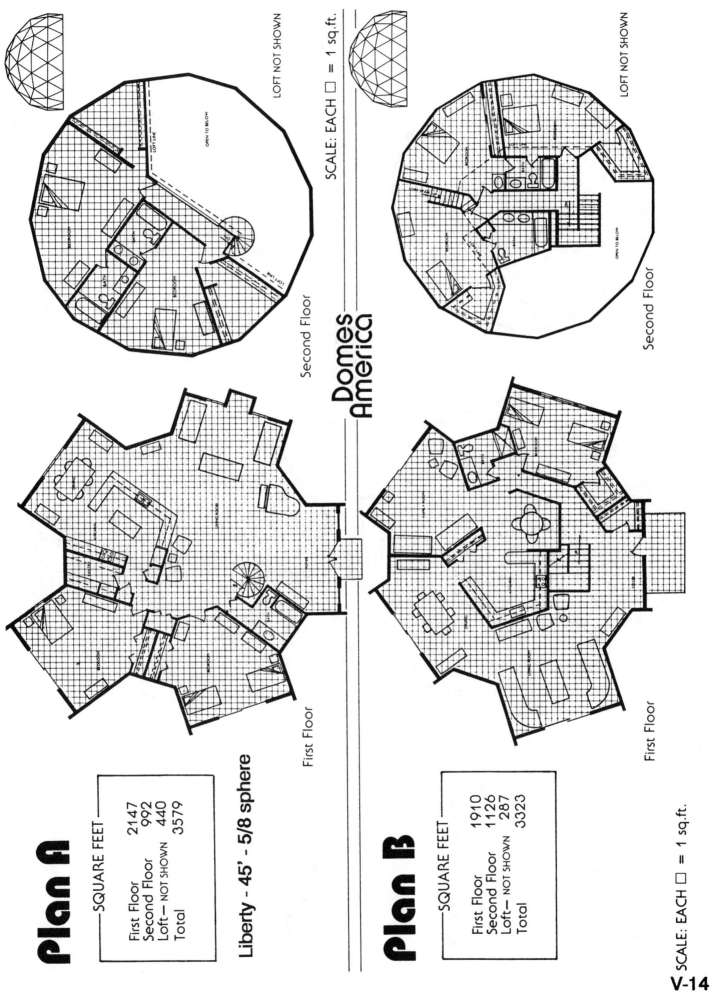

Plan A

SQUARE FEET

First Floor 2147
Second Floor 992
Loft— NOT SHOWN 440
Total 3579

Liberty - 45' - 5/8 sphere

First Floor

Second Floor

LOFT NOT SHOWN

SCALE: EACH ☐ = 1 sq.ft.

Domes America

Plan B

SQUARE FEET

First Floor 1910
Second Floor 1126
Loft— NOT SHOWN 287
Total 3323

First Floor

Second Floor

LOFT NOT SHOWN

SCALE: EACH ☐ = 1 sq.ft.

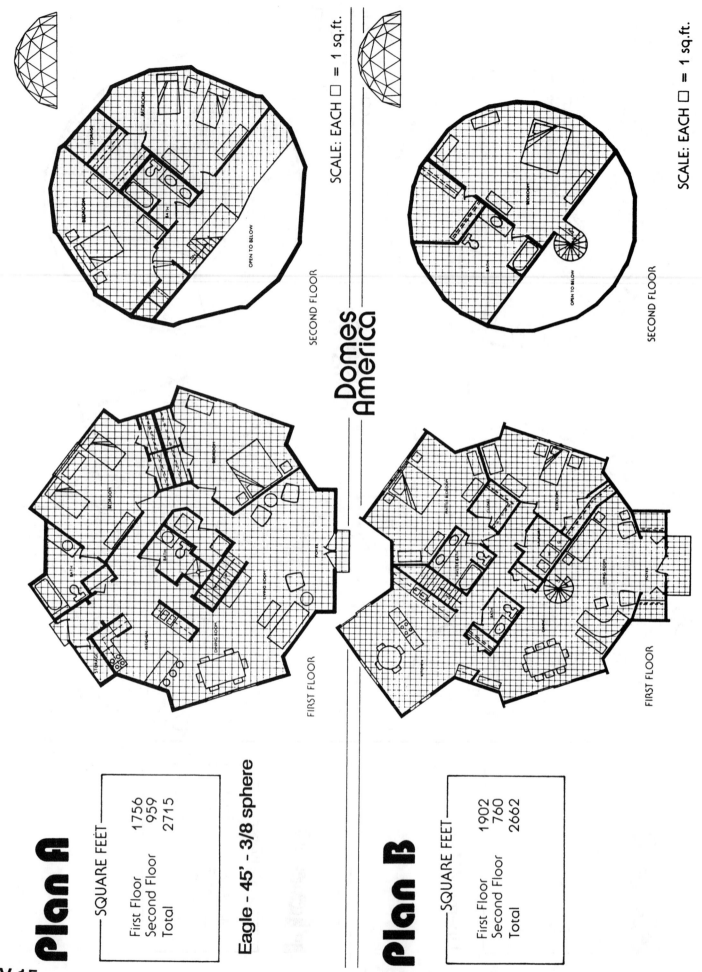

Plan A

SQUARE FEET

First Floor   1756
Second Floor   959
Total   2715

Eagle - 45' - 3/8 sphere

Plan B

SQUARE FEET

First Floor   1902
Second Floor   760
Total   2662

SCALE: EACH ☐ = 1 sq.ft.

SCALE: EACH ☐ = 1 sq.ft.

SECOND FLOOR

SECOND FLOOR

FIRST FLOOR

FIRST FLOOR

OPEN TO BELOW

OPEN TO BELOW

Domes
America

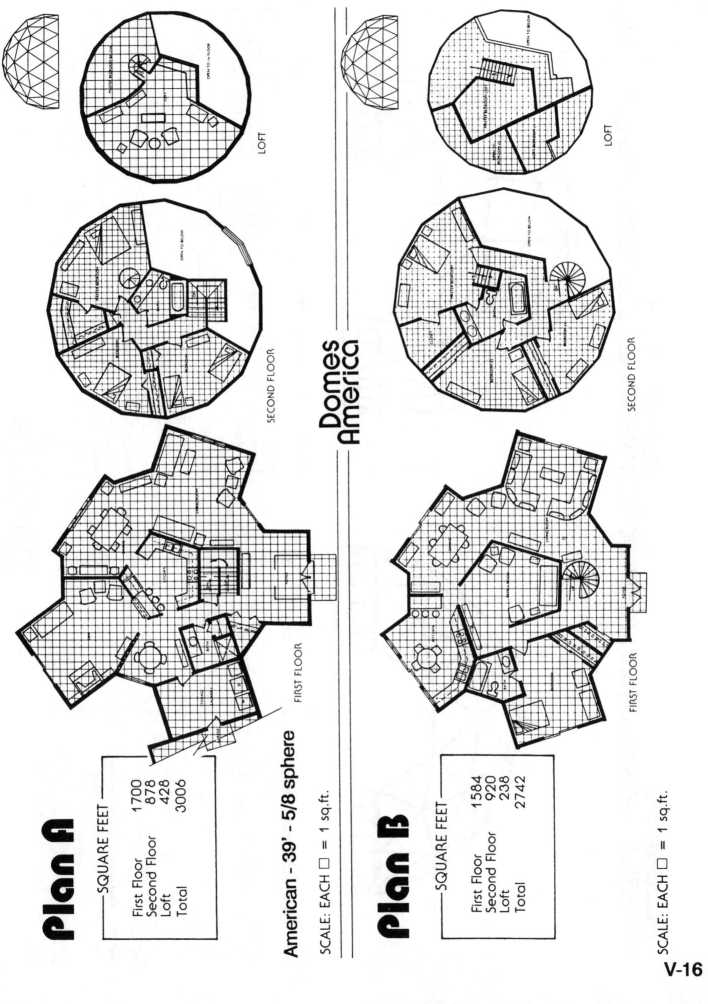

Plan A

SQUARE FEET

First Floor	1700
Second Floor	878
Loft	428
Total	3006

LOFT

SECOND FLOOR

FIRST FLOOR

Domes America

American - 39' - 5/8 sphere

SCALE: EACH ☐ = 1 sq.ft.

Plan B

SQUARE FEET

First Floor	1584
Second Floor	920
Loft	238
Total	2742

LOFT

SECOND FLOOR

FIRST FLOOR

SCALE: EACH ☐ = 1 sq.ft.

Specifications
TIMBERLINE GEODESICS 5/8 SPHERE DOME

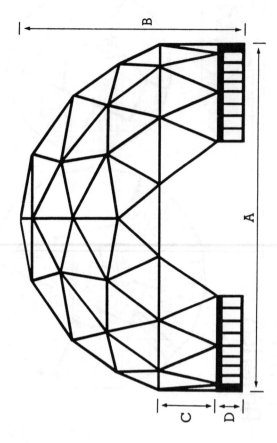

Diameter at Hemisphere

	24'	30'	35'
Base Diameter at A	23' 7"	29' 5½"	34' 4½"
Floorspace without loft or second floor	424 sq ft	662 sq ft	902 sq ft
Roof Area	1040 sq ft	1625 sq ft	2212 sq ft
Volume	4625 cu ft	9034 cu ft	14346 cu ft
Height at B	17' 9"	20' 2"	22' 3"
Height at C	4' 10"	5' 11"	6' 10"
Height of Riser Wall D	3' 2"	2' 1"	1' 2"
Height of Door Opening	8' 0"	8' 0"	8' 0"
Snow and Wind Loads	150 psf/125 mph	110 psf/125 mph	80 psf/125 mph

Specifications for Do-It-Yourselfers*

	24'	30'	35'
Board feet of struts, T-blocking & studs	1964'	2411'	2966'
Number of 4' × 8' plywood sheets needed	45	84	99

*Includes all materials needed for a dome with two door openings and no windows or skylights. The finished design of your dome may require less materials.

Every 5/8 sphere dome includes 61 connectors, 165 struts, and 105 triangular panels.

Specifications
TIMBERLINE GEODESICS 3/8 SPHERE DOME

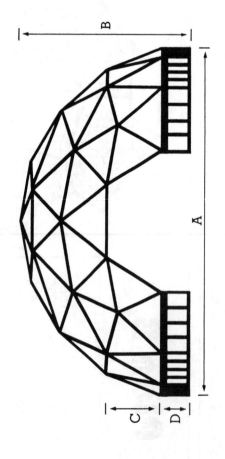

Diameter at Hemisphere

	24'	30'	35'
Base Diameter at A	23' 7"	29' 5½"	34' 4½"
Floorspace without loft or second floor	424 sq ft	662 sq ft	902 sq ft
Roof Area	770 sq ft	1203 sq ft	1637 sq ft
Volume	2613 cu ft	5103 cu ft	8104 cu ft
Height at B	13' 9"	15' 2"	16' 4"
Height at C	4' 5"	5' 5"	6' 3"
Height of Riser Wall D	3' 7"	2' 7"	1' 9"
Height of Door Opening	8' 0"	8' 0"	8' 0"
Snow and Wind Loads	150 psf/125 mph	110 psf/125 mph	80 psf/125 mph

Specifications for Do-It-Yourselfers*

	24'	30'	35'
Board feet of struts, T-blocking & studs	1457'	1796'	2150'
Number of 4' × 8' plywood sheets needed	30	54	69

*Includes all materials needed for a dome with two door openings and no windows or skylights. The finished design of your dome may require less materials.

Every 3/8 sphere dome includes 46 connectors, 120 struts, and 75 triangular panels.

TIMBERLINE
GEODESICS.

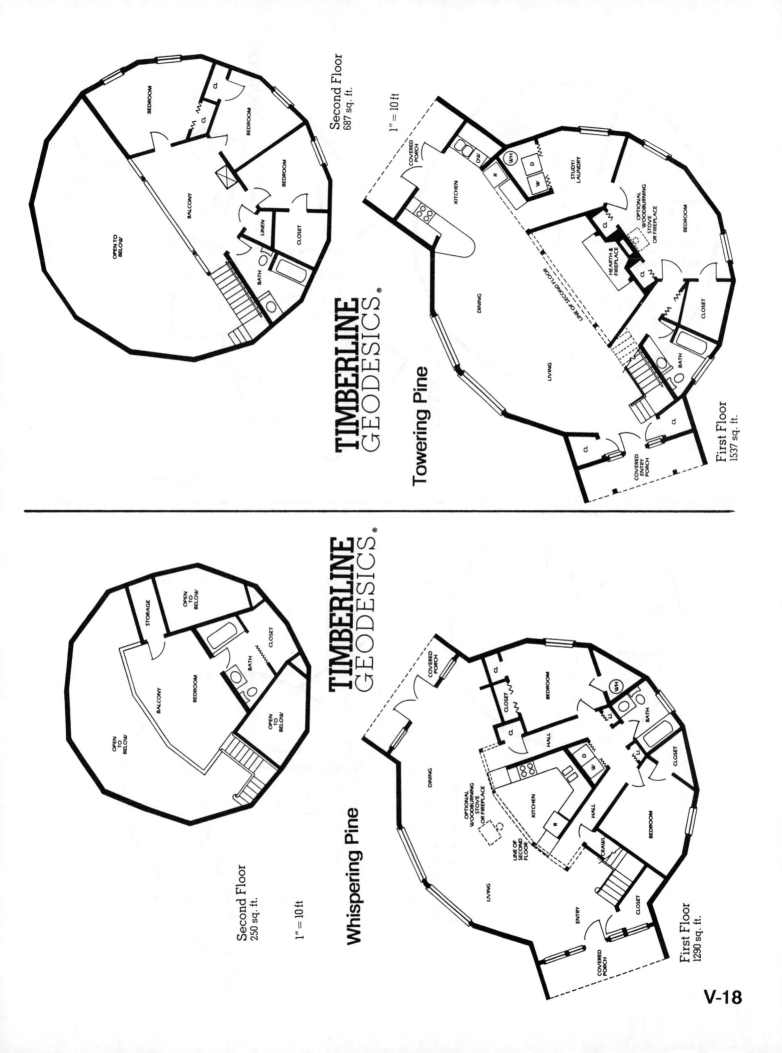

TIMBERLINE
GEODESICS®

Towering Pine

Second Floor
687 sq. ft.

1" = 10 ft

BEDROOM

CL

BEDROOM

BALCONY

OPEN TO BELOW

BEDROOM

LINEN

CLOSET

BATH

COVERED PORCH

KITCHEN

R

W/H

DW

D

W

STUDY/ LAUNDRY

DINING

HEARTH & FIREPLACE

OPTIONAL WOODBURNING STOVE OR FIREPLACE

CL

BEDROOM

LINE OF SECOND FLOOR

LIVING

BATH

CLOSET

CL

CL

COVERED ENTRY PORCH

First Floor
1537 sq. ft.

1" = 10 ft

TIMBERLINE
GEODESICS®

Whispering Pine

Second Floor
250 sq. ft.

1" = 10 ft

STORAGE

OPEN TO BELOW

OPEN TO BELOW

BALCONY

BEDROOM

BATH

CLOSET

OPEN TO BELOW

COVERED PORCH

DINING

CL

CLOSET

BEDROOM

W/H

HALL

BATH

OPTIONAL WOODBURNING STOVE OR FIREPLACE

KITCHEN

R

W

D

HALL

CLOSET

LINE OF SECOND FLOOR

CRAWL

BEDROOM

LIVING

ENTRY

CLOSET

COVERED PORCH

First Floor
1290 sq. ft.

V-18

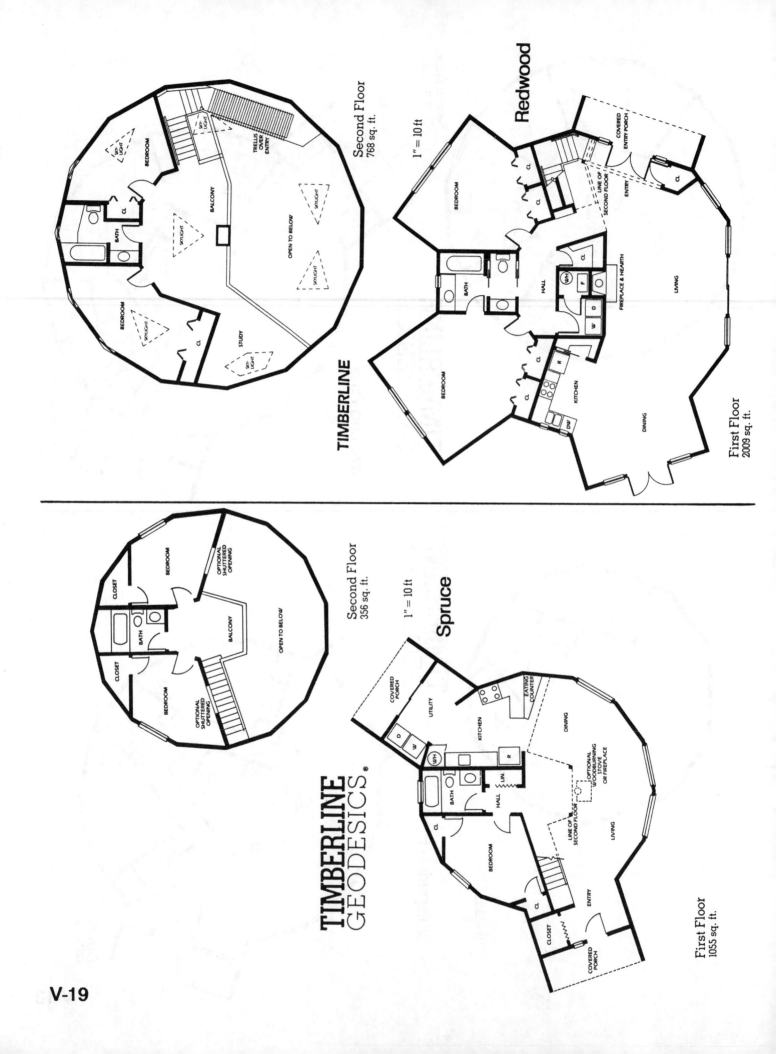

Redwood

Second Floor
768 sq. ft.

1" = 10 ft

TIMBERLINE

First Floor
2009 sq. ft.

SKY-LIGHT

BEDROOM

CL

BATH

BALCONY

SKYLIGHT

OPEN TO BELOW

SKYLIGHT

SKYLIGHT

TRELLIS OVER ENTRY

BEDROOM

SKYLIGHT

CL

STUDY

SKY-LIGHT

COVERED ENTRY PORCH

BEDROOM

CL

CL

LINE OF SECOND FLOOR

ENTRY

CL

BATH

HALL

WH

F

D

W

FIREPLACE & HEARTH

LIVING

BEDROOM

CL

CL

R

KITCHEN

DW

DINING

Spruce

Second Floor
356 sq. ft.

1" = 10 ft

CLOSET

BEDROOM

BATH

CLOSET

BALCONY

OPTIONAL SHUTTERED OPENING

OPEN TO BELOW

BEDROOM

OPTIONAL SHUTTERED OPENING

TIMBERLINE
GEODESICS.®

COVERED PORCH

UTILITY

D

W

WH

BATH

LIN.

HALL

KITCHEN

EATING COUNTER

DINING

R

OPTIONAL WOODBURNING STOVE OR FIREPLACE

LINE OF SECOND FLOOR

LIVING

CL

BEDROOM

CL

ENTRY

CLOSET

COVERED PORCH

First Floor
1055 sq. ft.

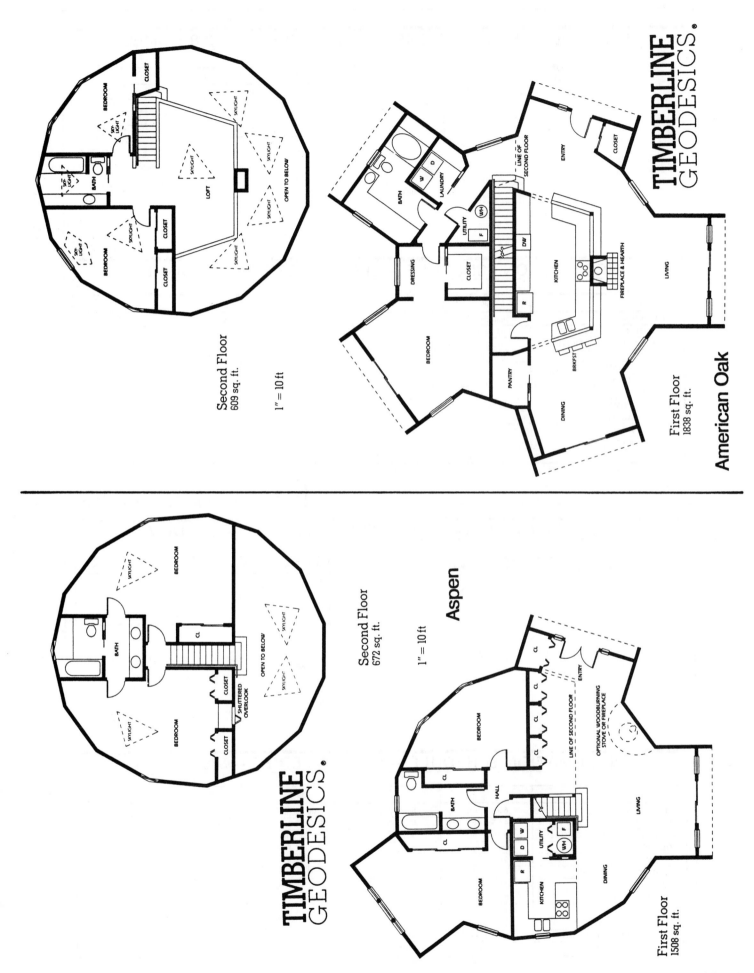

TIMBERLINE GEODESICS®

Second Floor
609 sq. ft.

1" = 10 ft

BEDROOM
CLOSET
SKY-LIGHT
SKYLIGHT
SKYLIGHT
SKYLIGHT
BATH
SKY-LIGHT
LOFT
SKYLIGHT
SKYLIGHT
OPEN TO BELOW
BEDROOM
CLOSET
CLOSET
SKY-LIGHT
SKYLIGHT

BATH
W
D
LAUNDRY
VH
UTILITY
F
LINE OF SECOND FLOOR
ENTRY
CLOSET
DRESSING
CLOSET
DW
R
KITCHEN
FIREPLACE & HEARTH
LIVING
BEDROOM
PANTRY
BRKFST
DINING

First Floor
1838 sq. ft.

American Oak

Second Floor
672 sq. ft.

1" = 10 ft

Aspen

BEDROOM
BATH
CL
OPEN TO BELOW
SKYLIGHT
SKYLIGHT
SKYLIGHT
CLOSET
SHUTTERED OVERLOOK
BEDROOM
CLOSET
SKYLIGHT

TIMBERLINE GEODESICS®

CL
CL
CL
CL
CL
ENTRY
BEDROOM
LINE OF SECOND FLOOR
OPTIONAL WOODBURNING STOVE OR FIREPLACE
HALL
BATH
CL
W
D
UTILITY
F
VH
R
KITCHEN
LIVING
BEDROOM
DINING

First Floor
1508 sq. ft.

V-20

SCHEDULE OF ELEVATIONS — SIERRA SERIES — 3/8 DOMES

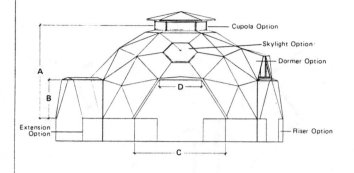

DIAMETER	30'	35'	39'	45'	50'
A	12' 10''	15'	16' 8''	19'	21' 1''
B	5' 5''	6' 5''	7' 3''	8' 3''	9' 1''
C	12' 4''	14' 4''	15' 11''	18' 5''	20' 5''
D	5' 10''	6' 9''	7' 7''	8' 11''	9' 11''

FEATURES:

1. Sixty pre-assembled, pre-drilled, pre-sheathed *Monoface — Wedge* ™ panels.
2. All necessary zinc coated hardware and hurricane straps.
3. 5' Riser Wall for 30' and 35' diameter models.
4. Five sets of rain shedding canopies.
5. Insulating Sill Sealer.
6. Detailed Prints and Assembly Manual.
7. Use of *Geopole* ™ for Assembly.

INFORMATION SCHEDULE — SIERRA SERIES — 3/8 DOMES

DIAMETER	30'	35'	39'	45'	50'
1ST FLOOR AREA	650 Sq. Ft.	885 Sq. Ft.	1100 Sq. Ft.	1500 Sq. Ft.	1800 Sq. Ft.
AREA PER 4' OF EXTENSION	49 Sq. Ft.	57 Sq. Ft.	64 Sq. Ft.	74 Sq. Ft.	81 Sq. Ft.
AREA—2ND FLOOR POTENTIAL*	325 Sq. Ft.	442 Sq. Ft.	660 Sq. Ft.	750 Sq. Ft.	900 Sq. Ft.
VOLUME	8092 C.F.	12136 C.F.	10500 C.F.	16000 C.F.	22000 C.F.
CIRCUMFERENCE	91'	107'	120'	138'	173'
SHINGLES (DOME ONLY)	17 Sq.	22 Sq.	26 Sq.	33 Sq.	38 Sq.
4'' SLAB	7.5 C.Y.	10.5 C.Y.	14 C.Y.	18.5 C.Y.	25 C.Y.
ASSEMBLY TIME**	2 Days	2 Days	2 Days	3 Days	3 Days
SEATING (AUDITORIUM)***	X	X	X	100-200	150-200
SURFACE AREA (DOME ONLY)	1200 Sq. Ft.	1430 Sq. Ft.	1600 Sq. Ft.	2200 Sq. Ft.	2700 Sq. Ft.
SURFACE AREA (5 OPENINGS)	230 Sq. Ft.	310 Sq. Ft.	400 Sq. Ft.	535 Sq. Ft.	644 Sq. Ft.
INSULATION (CAVITY)	1008 Sq. Ft.	1202 Sq. Ft.	1344 Sq. Ft.	1848 Sq. Ft.	2268 Sq. Ft.

*Assumes riser wall and 1/3 vaulted ceiling.   **Assumes 3-6 people.   ***Larger number assumes extensions.

Geodesic Domes, Inc.

SCHEDULE OF ELEVATIONS — SIERRA SERIES — 5/8 DOMES

DIAMETER	30'	35'	39'	45'	50'
A	18' 4''	21' 4''	23'	27' 3''	30' 7''
B	6' 1''	7' 1''	7' 2''	8' 3''	9' 3''
C	12' 4''	14' 4''	15' 11''	18' 5''	20' 5''
D	5' 10''	6' 9''	7' 7''	8' 11''	9' 11''

FEATURES:

1. Ninety pre-assembled, pre-drilled, pre-sheathed *Monoface — Wedge* ™ panels.
2. All necessary zinc coated hardware and hurricane straps.
3. 5' Riser Wall for 30' and 35' diameter models.
4. Five sets of rain shedding canopies.
5. Insulating Sill Sealer.
6. Detailed Prints and Assembly Manual.
7. Use of *Geopole* ™ for Assembly.

INFORMATION SCHEDULE — SIERRA SERIES — 5/8 DOMES

DIAMETER	30'	35'	39'	45'	50'
1ST FLOOR AREA	650 Sq. Ft.	885 Sq. Ft.	1100 Sq. Ft.	1500 Sq. Ft.	1800 Sq. Ft.
AREA PER 4' OF EXTENSION	49 Sq. Ft.	57 Sq. Ft.	64 Sq. Ft.	74 Sq. Ft.	81 Sq. Ft.
AREA—2ND FLOOR POTENTIAL*	390 Sq. Ft.	531 Sq. Ft.	760 Sq. Ft.	900 Sq. Ft.	1100 Sq. Ft.
VOLUME	9992 C.F.	14657 C.F.	17600 C.F.	27000 C.F.	37000 C.F.
CIRCUMFERENCE	91'	107'	120'	138'	173'
SHINGLES (DOME ONLY)	22 Sq.	26 Sq.	34 Sq.	46 Sq.	52 Sq.
4'' SLAB	7.5 C.Y.	10.5 C.Y.	14 C.Y.	18.5 C.Y.	25 C.Y.
ASSEMBLY TIME**	2 Days	2 Days	3 Days	3 Days	3 Days
SEATING (AUDITORIUM)***	X	X	X	100-200	150-200
SURFACE AREA (DOME ONLY)	1700 Sq. Ft.	2100 Sq. Ft.	2400 Sq. Ft.	3800 Sq. Ft.	4100 Sq. Ft.
SURFACE AREA (5 OPENINGS)	230 Sq. Ft.	310 Sq. Ft.	400 Sq. Ft.	535 Sq. Ft.	644 Sq. Ft.
INSULATION (CAVITY)	1428 Sq. Ft.	1764 Sq. Ft.	2016 Sq. Ft.	3192 Sq. Ft.	3444 Sq. Ft.

*Assumes riser wall and 1/3 vaulted ceiling.   **Assumes 3-6 people.   ***Larger number assumes extensions.

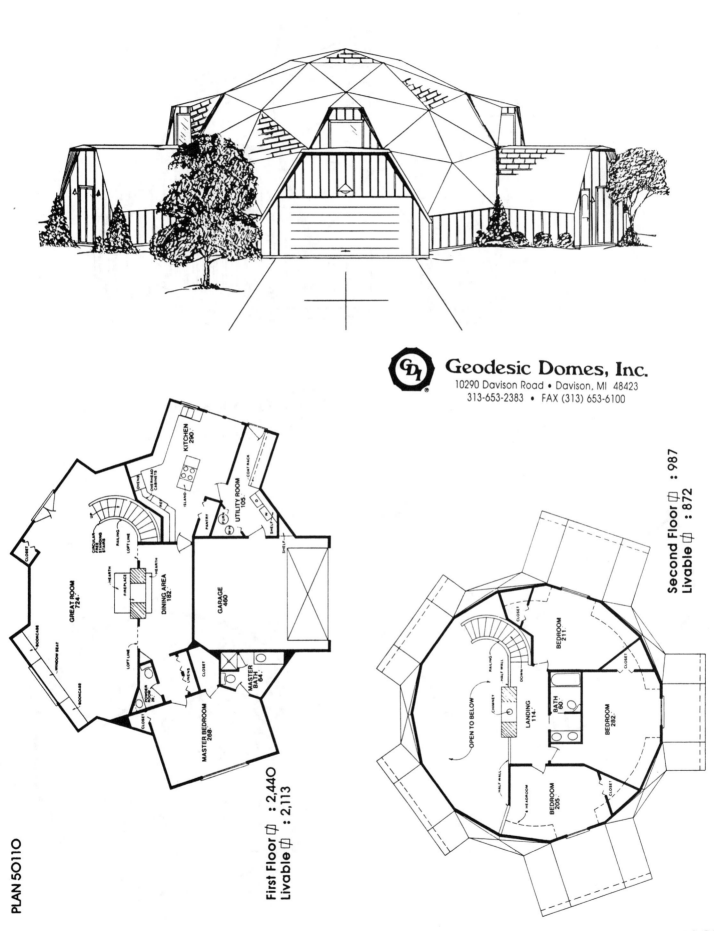

Geodesic Domes, Inc.
10290 Davison Road • Davison, MI 48423
313-653-2383 • FAX (313) 653-6100

PLAN 50110

KITCHEN
290.

OVERHEAD CABINETS

ISLAND

UTILITY ROOM
105.

PANTRY

COAT RACK

FURN.

SHELF

CIRCULAR FREE STANDING STAIRS

RAILING

LOFT LINE

UP

CLOSET

GREAT ROOM
724.

HEARTH

FIREPLACE

HEARTH

DINING AREA
182.

GARAGE
460

WINDOW SEAT

BOOKCASE

BOOKCASE

LOFT LINE

POWDER ROOM 20.

LINENS

CLOSET

CLOSET

MASTER BATH 64.

MASTER BEDROOM 268.

First Floor ⊡ : 2,440
Livable ⊡ : 2,113

Second Floor ⊡ : 987
Livable ⊡ : 872

CLOSET

BEDROOM
211.

RAILING

HALF WALL

DOWN

CLOSET

OPEN TO BELOW

CHIMNEY

LANDING
114.

BATH
60.

BEDROOM
282.

HALF WALL

HEADROOM

BEDROOM
205.

CLOSET

V-22

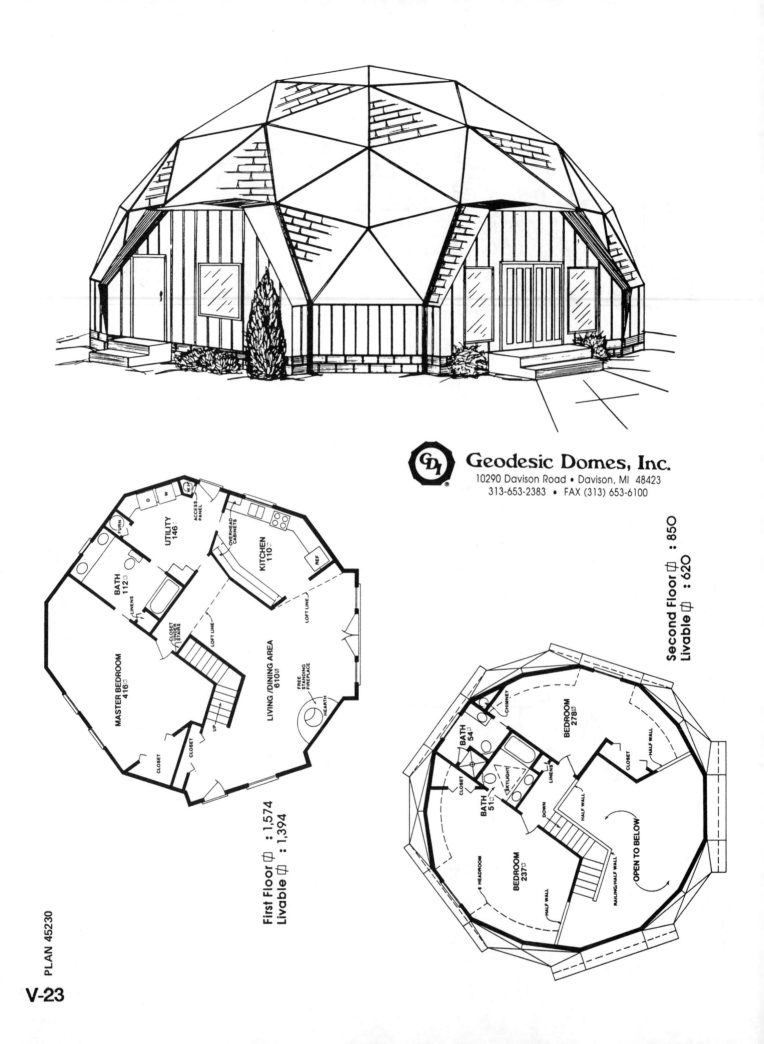

Geodesic Domes, Inc.
10290 Davison Road • Davison, MI 48423
313-653-2383 • FAX (313) 653-6100

Second Floor ▱ : 850
Livable ▱ : 620

First Floor ▱ : 1,574
Livable ▱ : 1,394

MASTER BEDROOM 416▱

UTILITY 146▱

BATH 112▱

KITCHEN 110▱

LIVING/DINING AREA 610▱

FURN

D   W

ACCESS PANEL

OVERHEAD CABINETS

REF

LINENS

CLOSET UNDER STAIRS

LOFT LINE

LOFT LINE

FREE STANDING FIREPLACE

HEARTH

CLOSET

CLOSET

UP

BEDROOM 278▱

BATH 54▱

BATH 51▱

BEDROOM 237▱

CHIMNEY

CLOSET

SKYLIGHT

LINENS

DOWN

CLOSET

HALF WALL

HALF WALL

HALF WALL

RAILING/HALF WALL

HALF WALL

6' HEADROOM

OPEN TO BELOW

PLAN 45230

V-23

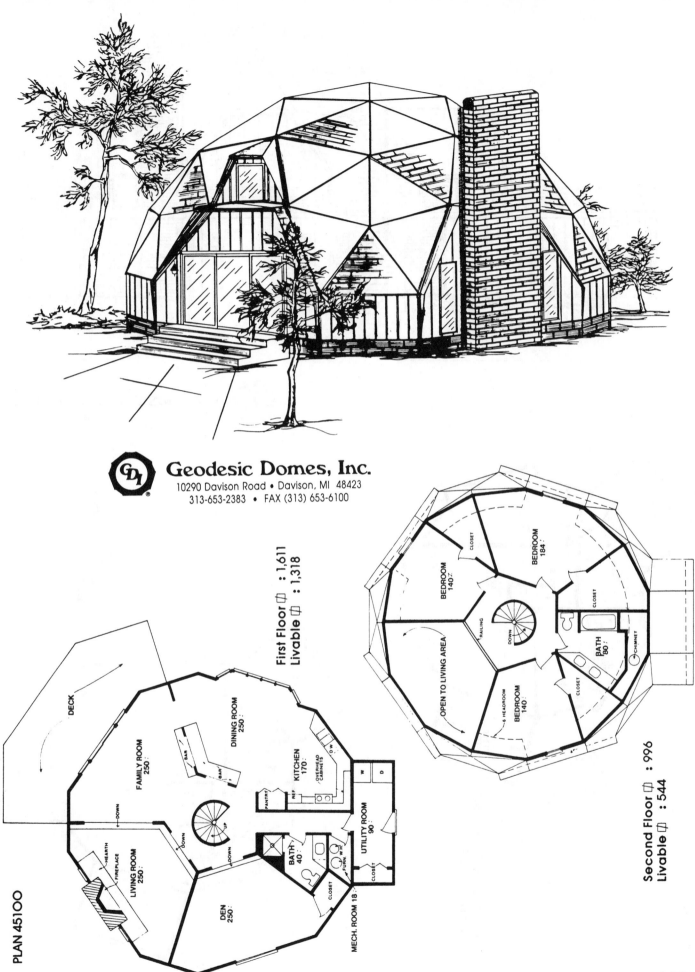

Geodesic Domes, Inc.

10290 Davison Road • Davison, MI 48423

313-653-2383 • FAX (313) 653-6100

First Floor ⬚ : 1,611
Livable ⬚ : 1,318

Second Floor ⬚ : 996
Livable ⬚ : 544

PLAN 45100

DECK

FAMILY ROOM
250

DINING ROOM
250

BAR

KITCHEN
170

OVERHEAD CABINETS

REF.

D W

PANTRY

W

D

UTILITY ROOM
90

DOWN

DOWN

UP

DOWN

LIVING ROOM
250

HEARTH

FIREPLACE

BATH
40

FURN.

WH

CLOSET

CLOSET

MECH. ROOM 18

DEN
250

BEDROOM
140z

CLOSET

BEDROOM
184

OPEN TO LIVING AREA

RAILING

DOWN

CLOSET

BATH
80

CHIMNEY

6 HEADROOM

BEDROOM
140

CLOSET

V-24

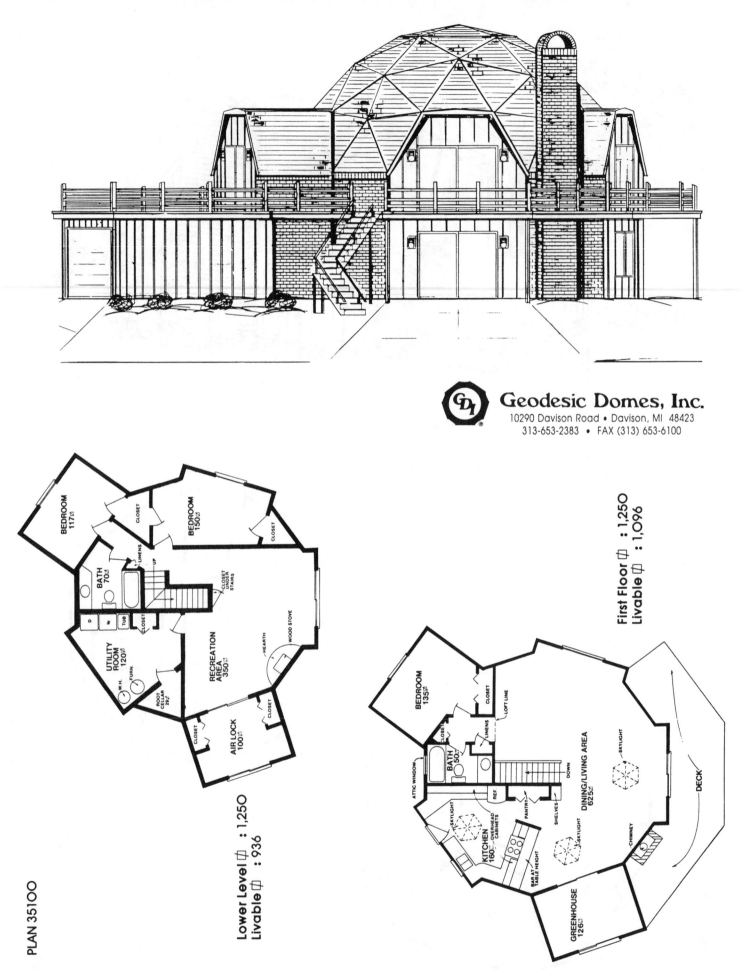

Geodesic Domes, Inc.
10290 Davison Road • Davison, MI 48423
313-653-2383 • FAX (313) 653-6100

PLAN 35100

V-25

First Floor ⌀ : 1,250
Livable ⌀ : 1,096

Lower Level ⌀ : 1,250
Livable ⌀ : 936

BEDROOM 117⌀

CLOSET

BEDROOM 150⌀

CLOSET

LINENS

UP

CLOSET UNDER STAIRS

BATH 70⌀

W D

W

TUB

CLOSET

UTILITY ROOM 120⌀

FURN.

W.H.

ROOT CELLAR 25⌀

RECREATION AREA 350⌀

HEARTH

WOOD STOVE

CLOSET

AIR LOCK 100⌀

CLOSET

BEDROOM 135⌀

CLOSET

LOFT LINE

LINENS

CLOSET

BATH 50⌀

ATTIC WINDOW

REF.

DOWN

PANTRY

SHELVES

OVERHEAD CABINETS

KITCHEN 160⌀

SKYLIGHT

BAR AT TABLE HEIGHT

SKYLIGHT

DINING/LIVING AREA 625⌀

SKYLIGHT

SKYLIGHT

CHIMNEY

DECK

GREENHOUSE 126⌀

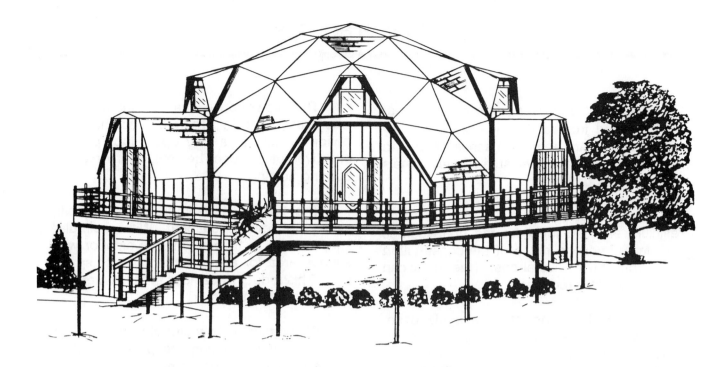

Geodesic Domes, Inc.
10290 Davison Road • Davison, MI 48423
313-653-2383 • FAX (313) 653-6100

PLAN 39215

Lower Level ☐ : 1,676
Livable ☐ : 1,615

MECH. ROOM 64☐
BY FURN.
PLAYROOM 230☐
SHOP 633☐
GARAGE 445☐
STORAGE 108☐
FRUIT CELLAR 72☐
STORAGE 63☐
UP

First Floor ☐ : 1,676
Livable ☐ : 1,349

CHIMNEY
SEWING TABLE
UTILITY ROOM 160☐
STORAGE
DUMB WAITER
W D
AIRLOCK 24☐
CLOSET
BATH 70☐
LINEN
KITCHEN 172☐
DESK
OVERHEAD CABINETS
GRILL
REF
PANTRY
PASS THRU
DN
UP
LIVING ROOM 389☐
LOFT LINE
COUNTER
BEDROOM 190☐
CLOSET
DINING ROOM 180☐
GREENHOUSE 160☐

Second Floor ☐ : 650
Livable ☐ : 500

BEDROOM 155☐
6' HEADROOM
DUMB WAITER
HALF WALL
SITTING ROOM 105☐
DN
SKYLIGHT
RAILING
OPEN TO BELOW
CLOSET
UNDER COUNTER REF
CABINETS
BENCH
BATH 85☐
LINEN
CLOSET
BEDROOM 155☐
HALF WALL

V-26

Most of the houses you see that appear to be round from a distance are not really round. They are actually a series of four- to eight-foot long, heavily-insulated wall panels connected together.

These types of houses are extremely energy efficient and are ideal for the do-it-yourself builder. If you do much of the construction work yourself, the overall cost of the house can be substantially reduced.

One basic design sets on a regular basement, crawl space, slab foundation. The other design is supported on a 14-foot diameter concrete pedestal under the center of the house. This pedestal locates the house about 10 feet above the ground. With the pedestal design, a smaller foundation is needed. Also, the floor is made of trusses, similar to a roof, and it is well insulated for high efficiency.

The wall panels can be custom-made to your plans and delivered to your site. The most common insulation package includes fiberglass batts covered with insulated sheathing for an insulating value of R-19. You can order the panels with high-efficiency windows and doors already assembled in them.

The roof is made of insulated panels. The standard roof panels contain 5-1/2 inches of fiberglass insulation with a 6 mil plastic vapor barrier. The exterior is covered with shingles for a total insulating R-value of R-22. You can also upgrade to R-30 or R-40 roof panels. The panels are mounted directly over roof trusses.

What is particularly unique about these houses is that the roof is self-supporting. It is supported by a special truss system design, so there are no interior supporting walls required. The pedestal design uses one steel center support column from the pedestal to the roof. The roof trusses are attached to this support column at a steel collar.

This allows you to locate the interior walls wherever you desire. Therefore, you have the option of making a very open floor plan to effectively utilize space heaters, solar, or wood-burning heating.

The circular shape improves energy efficiency for several reasons. With a circular shape, there is 15 percent less exterior wall surface area for a given interior floor space size. This reduces heat loss in the winter and heat gain in the summer.

Winds tend to flow smoothly around the circular shape reducing the pressure differences on the sides of the house. That minimizes air leakage into it and indoor drafts. The circular shape provides wall space for large windows in each room for effective passive solar heating.

Some of basic floor plans are designed primarily for passive solar heating. In these houses, the bedroom are located in the lower level and the living on the upper level. Since heat rises, the upper living areas stay naturally warmer and the bedrooms stay naturally cooler. This type of layout is also safer. In case of fires, it is much easier to escape from the first story bedroom than from a typical second story bedroom.

You can order a basic house plan kit or have one designed for your floor plans. The sizes for standard kits range from 500 square feet to more than 4,000 square feet. For additional space and unique designs, you can add rectangular rooms to the sides or combine several circular sections.

With the circular shape and no tight corners on outside walls, you get more actual usable floor space than with a rectangular house. Therefore, you may be able to get by with less floor area than you had thought you would need. This reduces your building costs and further reduces your utility bills.

MANUFACTURERS OF CIRCULAR/OCTAGONAL HOUSES

DELTEC HOMES, 604 College St., Asheville, NC 28801
(800) 642-2508 (704) 253-0483
size range - 517 sq. ft. to 4,140 sq. ft.
panel width - 8 ft.   insulation levels - floor: R-13, wall: R-19, roof: R-30

EAGLE'S NEST HOMES, 205 Eagle's Nest Dr., Canton, GA 30114
(404) 479-9700
size range - 752 sq. ft. to 4,090 sq. ft.
panel width - 8 ft.   insulation levels - floor: R-13, wall: R-19, roof: R-19 or R-30

HELIKON DESIGN CORP., P.O. Box 48, Cavetown, MD 21720
(800) 323-7863 (301) 824-2254
size range - 1,000 sq. ft. and 2,000 sq. ft.
panel width - 4 feet   insulation levels - floor: R-23, wall: R-24, roof: R-33

OCTA-STRUCTURE OF FL., 2516 W. 23th St., Panama City, FL 32405
(904) 763-6553
size range - 725 sq. ft. to 1,980 sq. ft.
panel width - widths vary   insulation levels - wall: R-13, roof: R-19

TOPSIDER HOMES, P.O. Box 1490, Clemmons, NC 27012
(910) 766-9300
size range - 475 sq. ft. to 2,250 sq. ft.
panel width - widths vary   insulation levels - floor: R-13, wall: R-11, roof: R-22

Deltec has specialized in Poly-rama circular homes for over 18 years. With its unique flexibility, the Deltec home can fulfill a variety of building needs. Basic units of 500 to 2000 square feet can be stacked up to three stories high or linked in virtually any configuration for home, office, restaurant, office complex, retail park, multi-unit resort project or condominium development. In addition, this circular structure fits well on beach, lakefront, mountainside, or commercial property, and adapts easily to extremely difficult building sites. Windows can be oriented to the natural view or 360° around the building. Patios or decks can be added for total integration of indoor and outdoor living and entertaining.

Deltec circular homes are manufactured for and marketed to developers, contractors and individual home builders. The Deltec package includes everything to finish the "shell" of the home, including shingles, felt, nails, caulking, and insulation. The plumbing, heating, electrical wiring, cabinets, and interior finish are left to the customer.

EXTERIOR WALL SYSTEMS

The Deltec basic "shell" package for slab construction includes all exterior walls with factory applied siding and installed windows. All glass is insulated and window options are maintenance-free aluminum thermal break or vinyl clad wood casements. Walls can be factory insulated. Exterior siding is "clear" grade Douglas Fir of the highest quality available. Exterior walls are rough framed for field installation of entry doors, which are steel clad with rigid foam cores (R-14.5) and refrigerator-type magnetic weatherstripping. Door locksets are shipped separately.

FLOOR SYSTEMS

The Deltec basic "shell" package includes all components for slab construction. If there is need for the house to be placed on a basement, pier or pile system, then Deltec offers a separate wood floor. The wood floor system is a sturdy, insulated sandwich panel with plywood glued and nailed on the top and nailed on the bottom. Triple 2 x 10 Southern Yellow Pine beams support this rigid structure. Steel center posts are included for 2nd and 3rd levels.

ROOF SYSTEMS

The heart of the Poly-Rama structural system is the unique radial roof system. Half scissor trusses made of Southern Yellow Pine bear against a center steel compression ring. Double 2 x 10 headers of Southern Yellow Pine are built into all exterior wall panels resulting in a roof loading capacity of over 50 lbs. per square foot. The Deltec Basic "Shell" Package provides all roof framing materials including trusses, roof decking, felt, nails, truss anchor straps, panel jointing plates, roof hardware, and shingles. Shingle tabs for ridge lines are pre-cut. Facia, subfacia, and soffits with factory applied vents are also furnished. Ceiling insulation is shipped in bundles. Deltec roof/ceiling assembly options have an energy rating of R-19 or R-30.

OTHER AVAILABLE OPTIONS

1) Decks, Pressure Treated Lumber

2) Deluxe Energy Package R-19/R-30

3) Deluxe Overhang Energy Saving Package

4) Western Red Cedar RB and B, or Cedar Lap Siding over CDX Plywood

5) Interior Sprial Stairs (60" diameter)

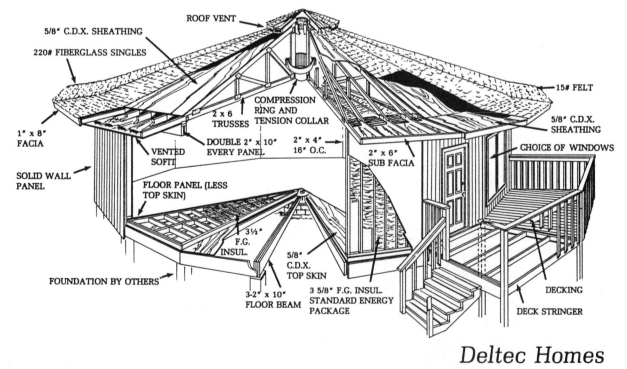

Deltec Homes

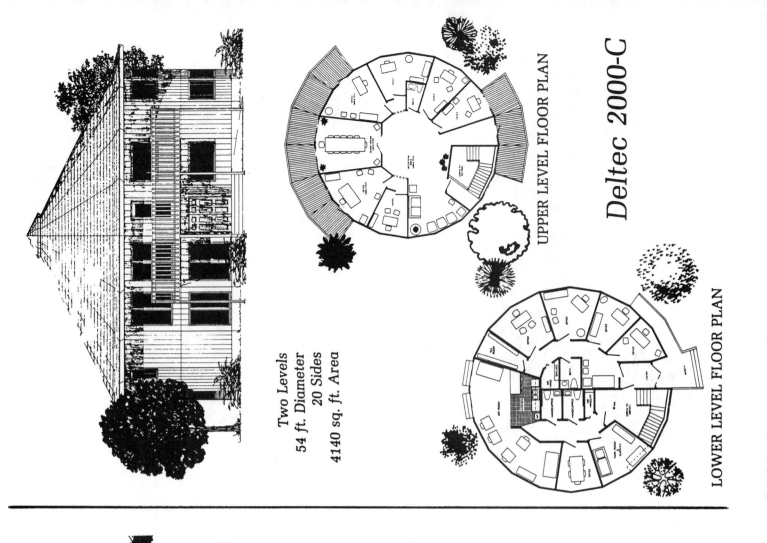

Deltec 2000-C

UPPER LEVEL FLOOR PLAN

LOWER LEVEL FLOOR PLAN

Two Levels
54 ft. Diameter
20 Sides
4140 sq. ft. Area

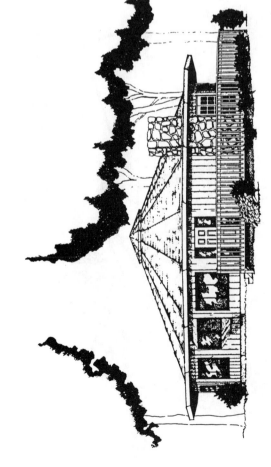

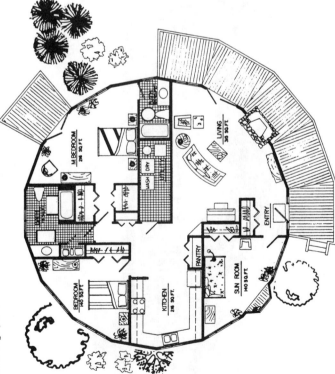

Deltec 1600-A

One Level
45 ft. Diameter
18 Sides
1680 sq. ft. Area

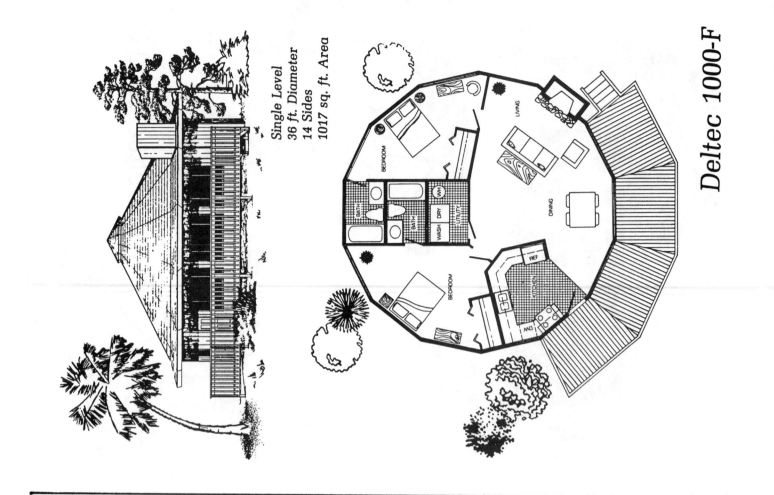

Deltec 1000-F

Single Level
36 ft. Diameter
14 Sides
1017 sq. ft. Area

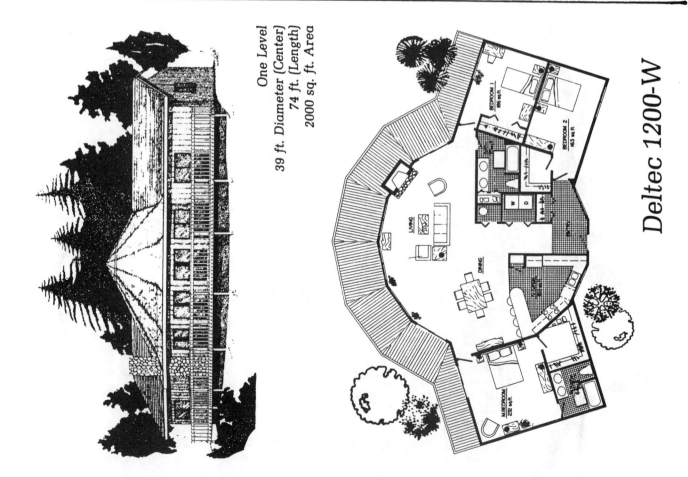

Deltec 1200-W

One Level
39 ft. Diameter (Center)
74 ft. (Length)
2000 sq. ft. Area

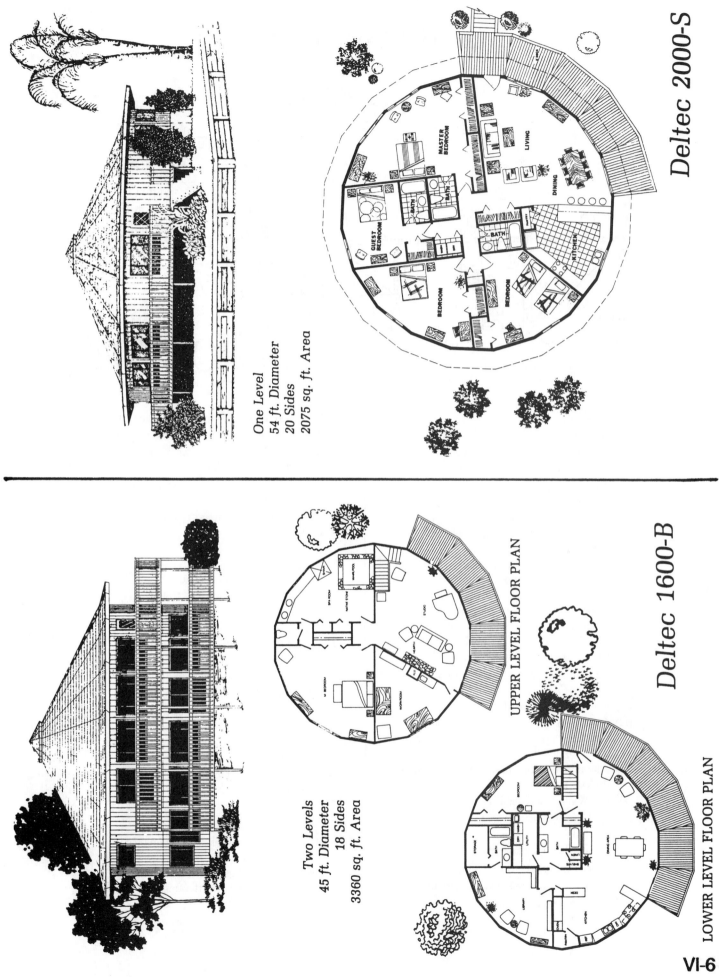

Deltec 2000-S

One Level
54 ft. Diameter
20 Sides
2075 sq. ft. Area

MASTER BEDROOM

LIVING

DINING

BATH

GUEST BEDROOM

BATH

KITCHEN

BEDROOM

BEDROOM

Deltec 1600-B

Two Levels
45 ft. Diameter
18 Sides
3360 sq. ft. Area

UPPER LEVEL FLOOR PLAN

LOWER LEVEL FLOOR PLAN

VI-6

Material Specifications

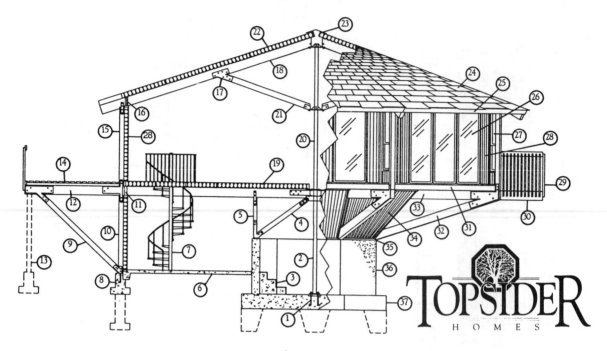

1. 18" Base plate anchor bolts.
2. Floor truss support column (lower column).
3. Stairs to pedestal floor (by owner/builder).
4. 6 x 6 Diagonal floor truss member.
5. 4 x 6 Vertical floor truss member (diagonal for some models).
6. 4" Turn-down concrete slab floor (typical for one-story and two-story non-pedestal model floors).
7. 4'6" Steel spiral stairway (standard for two-story and pedestal models with ground level enclosures).
8. Concrete pier (footing) for floor truss exterior wood column (to frost line by owner/builder).
9. 6 x 6 Treated lumber diagonal drop post for 9'6" width deck (with optional deck).
10. 6 x 6 Treated lumber floor truss exterior column.
11. Lower level wall header.
12. 6 x 10 or 6 x 12 Laminated treated lumber extended floor truss member for 9'6" width decks (optional).
13. Alternative vertical positions for 9'6" width deck drop post.
14. 9'6" Width treated lumber deck package (optional).
15. 6 x 6 Treated lumber roof truss exterior column.
16. Double 2 x 8 roof truss spacer.
17. Typical 1/4" plate steel coupling.
18. 2 x 8 or 2 x 10 Laminated roof truss member.
19. 2 x 6 Insulated floor panel.

20. Roof truss support column (upper column).
21. 2 x 8 or 2 x 10 Laminated roof truss support member (knee brace).
22. 2 x 6 Insulated roof panels.
23. 12" x 12" Copper or aluminum roof cap (by owner/builder).
24. Shingles above two layers of roofing felt (by owner/builder).
25. 2 x 8 Roof fascia.
26. Typical 39" x 87" fixed double pane, insulating safety glass window.
27. Corner panel with 18" x 72" double hung, double pane obscure glass window.
28. Insulated exterior solid wall panel.
29. Typical 2" x 2" x 42" treated lumber deck picket (with optional deck).
30. 6 x 10 or 6 x 12 Laminated treated lumber extended floor truss member for 4'6" width decks (optional).
31. 2 x 6 Floor fascia.
32. 6 x 8 Laminated diagonal floor truss members.
33. 6 x 10 or 6 x 12 Laminated horizontal floor truss member.
34. Insulated basement panels.
35. Basement panel mounting plate.
36. 10" Thick poured-in-place steel reinforced concrete pedestal walls (by owner/builder).
37. 18" Thick poured-in-place steel reinforced concrete slab foundation (footings to frost line by owner/builder).

The above illustration is for general description purposes only. It depicts most major house components for a Topsider Homes 02 structural type. Some materials shown are optional, or provided locally.

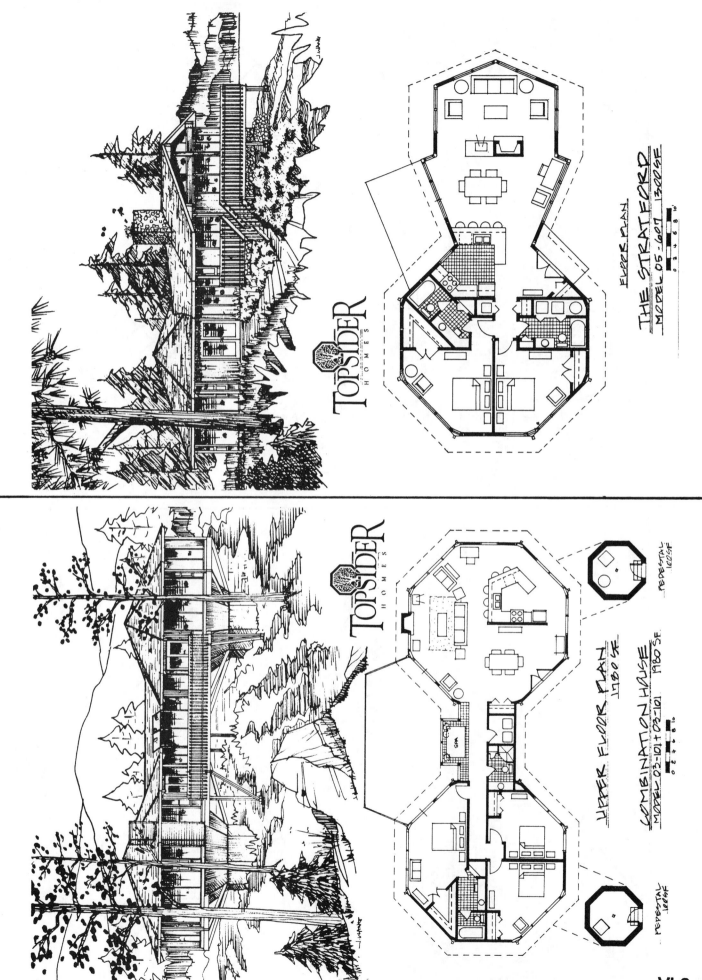

TOPSIDER
H O M E S

FLOOR PLAN

THE STRATFORD
MODEL 05-607 13,005F

TOPSIDER
H O M E S

UPPER FLOOR PLAN 1,130 SF

COMBINATION HOUSE
MODEL 02-101 + 02-101 1,980 SF

PEDESTAL 1,005F

PEDESTAL 1,005F

VI-8

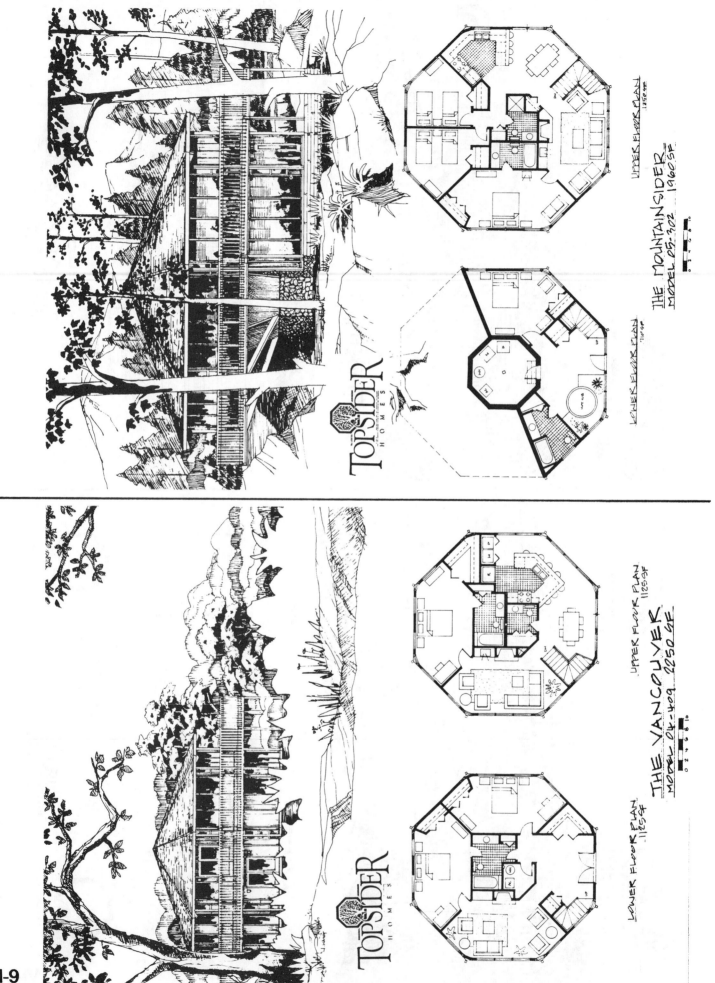

TOPSIDER
HOMES

LOWER FLOOR PLAN 1160SF

UPPER FLOOR PLAN 1160SF

THE MOUNTAINSIDER
MODEL 05-302 ....1960 SF

TOPSIDER
HOMES

LOWER FLOOR PLAN 1125SF

UPPER FLOOR PLAN 1125SF

THE VANCOUVER
MODEL 04-409 ....2250 SF

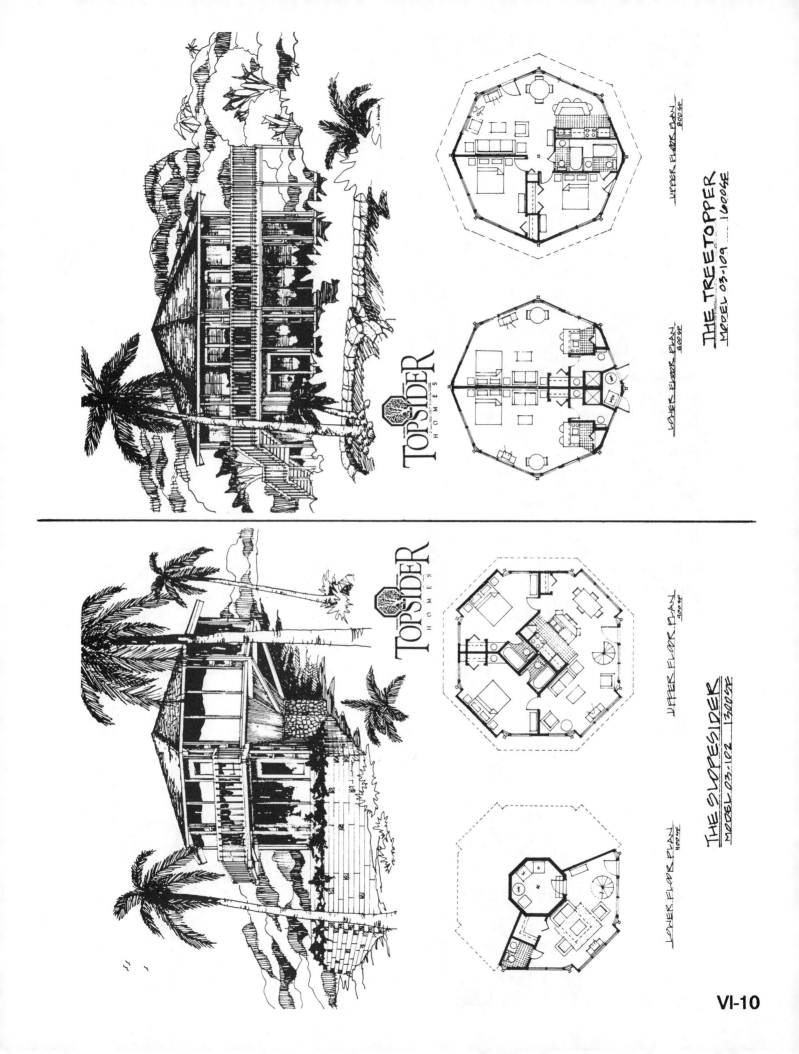

TOPSIDER
HOMES

UPPER FLOOR PLAN 800 SF

LOWER FLOOR PLAN 800 SF

THE TREETOPPER
MODEL 03-109 1600 SF

TOPSIDER
HOMES

UPPER FLOOR PLAN 900 SF

LOWER FLOOR PLAN 400 SF

THE SLOPESIDER
MODEL 03-102 1300 SF

VI-10

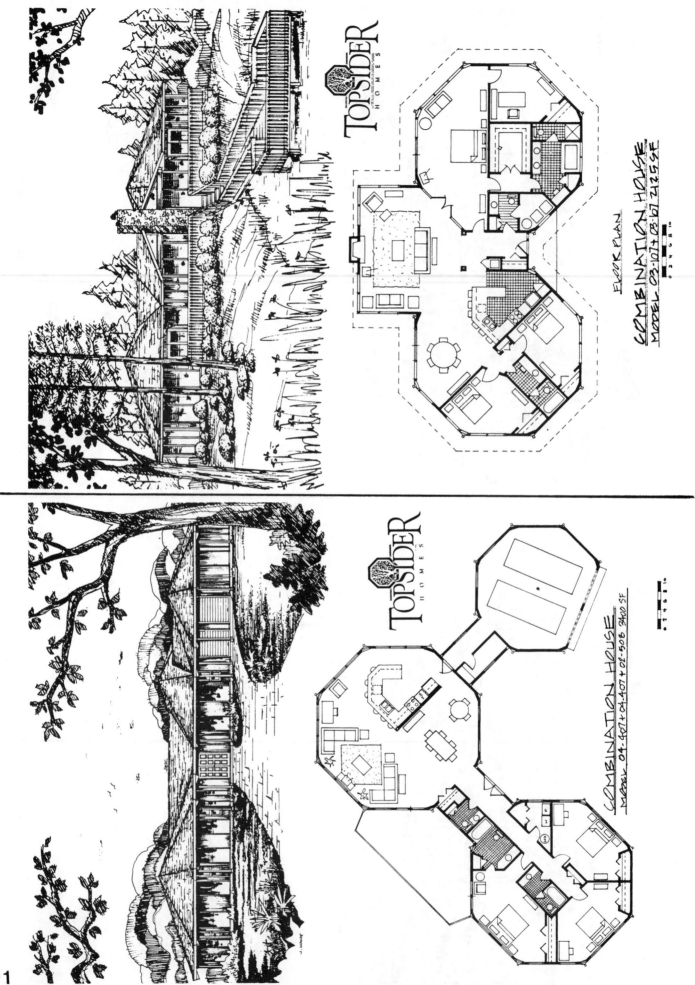

TOPSIDER
HOMES

FLOOR PLAN

COMBINATION HOUSE
MODEL 03-101 + 03-107 2155 SF

TOPSIDER
HOMES

COMBINATION HOUSE
MODEL 04-407 + 04-407 + 02-506 3400 SF

VI-11

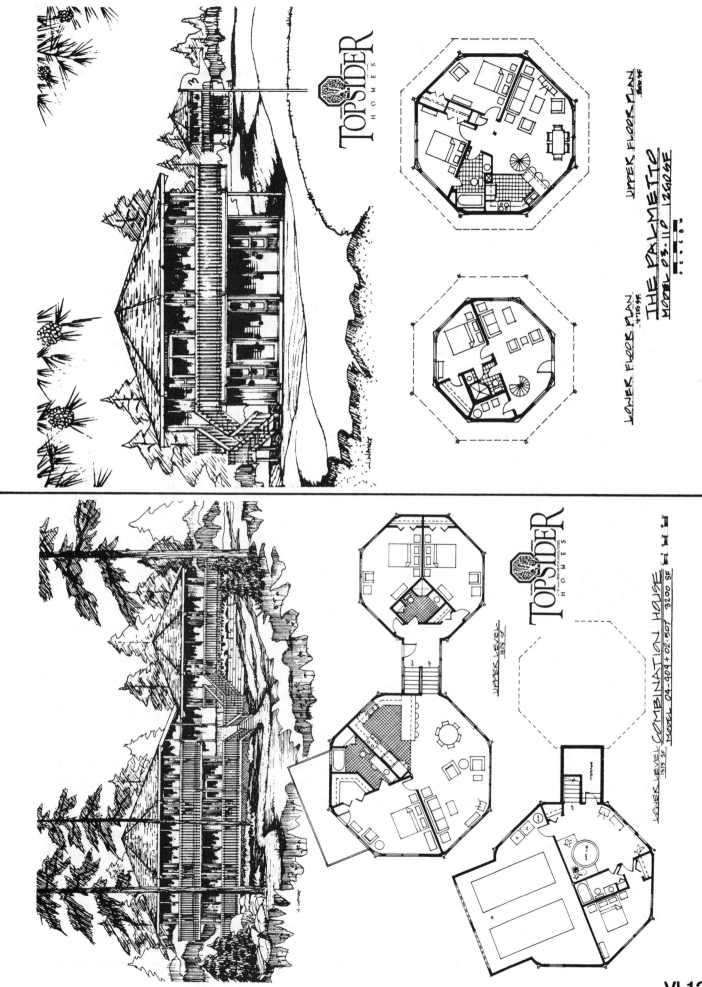

TOPSIDER
HOMES

LOWER FLOOR PLAN

UPPER FLOOR PLAN

THE PALMETTO
MODEL 03-110   2604SF

TOPSIDER
HOMES

UPPER LEVEL
1825 SF

LOWER LEVEL
1375 SF   COMBINATION HOUSE
MODEL 04-909 + 02-507   3200 SF

VI-12

PANELIZED HOUSES

Foam core and pre-built studded panels are some of the most energy efficient and cost-effective building methods available today. With super-high insulation levels and airtightness, a panelized house should have extremely low heating and cooling costs. A reduction of 50% on utility bills as compared to a typically-constructed house is reasonable.

Some companies just make the panels to your architectural drawings. Others also offer complete house packages. The large panels are delivered to your building site. You can also select from many standard house design packages to reduce the overall costs. Elegant custom panelized houses costing over one million dollars have been designed and built.

This construction method is simple and you should be able to do much of the work yourself. Most panel manufacturers will rent you any necessary tools for construction. Once the foundation or basement is poured, it should only take a few days to close in a house (walls and roof).

A structural stress-skin panel is made of thick rigid foam insulation. A 7/16-inch thick sheet of exterior-grade plywood or waferboard is bonded to each side of the insulation forming the panel. Some manufacturers squirt foam insulation in between the skins so it adheres completely to the skins. You can attach siding, stucco, brick, etc. to the outdoor surface and drywall or paneling to the indoor surface.

These panels are called "structural" because no supporting wall framing is needed. The strength of the interior and exterior panel skins is great enough to form a very rigid structure. A typical stress-skin panel is 4-1/2 inches thick with an insulating R-value of R-26. Thicker panels are also available up to R-40. Standard foam core panels do not have as strong an exterior skin. These foam core panels are supported by a post and beam or timber-framed structure.

You can purchase the panels with the window and door openings already cut and framed. Just slip them in. If you want to add a window later, you just saw a rectangular hole through the wall. Then rout out a little foam, frame the opening, and set in the window.

The foam insulation is routed out to accept standard lumber at the top and bottom. Once your foundation is complete and the sill lumber is in place, tilt up the freestanding panels and the routed-out bottom fits and seals over the sill. Nail the panels to the sill. Each panel is joined vertically and sealed along the joints with 2x4 or insulated splines.

To build the house, you work your way around the foundation until all of the walls are up and properly positioned. The corners are nailed together through studs that are in the routed-out ends of the special corner panels. This forms an extremely strong and rigid house.

Electrical wiring chases are provided in the insulation behind the indoor waferskin. To install the electrical conduit boxes, you just rout a shallow hole in the interior waferskin. Let the conduit box extend out the thickness of the drywall or wood paneling. It makes wiring easy with no air leaks or insulation voids as with studded-wall construction.

With the plywood or waferboard interior skin, it is very easy to finish the interior walls of a panelized house. The drywall or wood paneling can either be nailed or glued directly to the interior skin. Kitchen and bathroom cabinets can also be screwed directly into the skin. There is no need to search for studs as with a conventional framed wall.

Since a stress-skin panel house is so efficient and airtight, you should install an air-to-air heat exchanger ventilation system. This gives you complete control over the ventilation in your house. Outdoor noise, dust, pollens, etc. are almost totally eliminated.

MANUFACTURERS OF PANELS AND COMPLETE PANELIZED HOUSES

ALH BUILDING SYSTEMS, P.O. Box 288, Markle, IN 46770
(219) 758-2141

ACTIVE HOMES CORP., 7938 S. Van Dyke, Marlette, MI 48453
(517) 635-3532

AMOS WINTER HOMES, RR5 Box 168B, Brattleboro, VT 05301
(802) 254-3435

ARMSTRONG LUMBER, 2709 Auburn Way N., Auburn, WA 98002
(206) 833-5878

BARDEN & ROBESON, P.O. Box 210, Homer, NY 13077
(607) 749-2641

BLUE RIDGE TRUSS, 1099 Orkney Grade, Bayse, VA 22810
(540) 856-2191

CAROLINA MODEL HOME, P.O. Box 53278, Fayetteville, NC 28305
(910) 323-5000

CEDAR FOREST PRODUCTS, 107 W. Colden St., Polo, IL 61064
(815) 946-3994

ENERCEPT INC., 3100 9th Ave. S.E., Watertown, SD 57201
(800) 658-3303 (605) 882-2222

ENDURE-A-LIFETIME PROD., 7500 N.W. 72 nd Ave., Miami, FL 33166
(305) 885-9901

FISCHER CORP., 1843 N. Western Pky., Louisville, KY 40203
(502) 778-5577

FOREST HOME SYSTEMS, RD #1, Box 131K, Selinsgrove, PA 17870
(800) 872-1492 (717) 374-0131

FOAM PRODUCTS CORP., 2525 Adie Road, Maryland Hts., MO 63043
(800) 824-2211 (314) 739-8100

FUTUREBILT INTERN'L., A104 Plaza del Sol, Wimberly, TX 78676
(512) 847-5721

GENTRY HOMES, P.O. Box 295, Honolulu, HI 96809
(808) 671-6411

HARVEST HOMES, 185 Railroad Ave., Delanson, NY 12053
(518) 895-2341

EPT INSULSPAN, P.O. Box 121823, Nashville, TN 37212
(800) 726-3510 (615) 826-1281

J DECK BLGD. SYS., 2587 Harriosn Rd., Columbus, OH 43204
(614) 274-7755

KORWALL INDUSTRIES, 326 N. Bowen Rd., Arlington, TX 76012
(817) 277-6741

LAMIT INDUSTRIES, INC., P.O. Box 07928, Columbus, OH 43207
(614) 444-0110

MANUFACTURERS OF PANELS AND COMPLETE PANELIZED HOUSES - contd.

MURUS, PO Box 220, Dept. F, Rt. 549, Mansfield, PA 16933
(717) 549-2100

NEW ENGLAND HOMES, 270 Ocean Rd., Greenland, NH 03840
(603) 436-8830

NORTHERN COUNTIES HOMES, P.O. Box 97, Upperville, VA 22176
(540) 592-3232

NORTHERN DESIGN & BLDG. ASSOC., P.O. Box 47, Hudson Falls, NY 12839
(518) 747-2200

NORTHERN HOMES, 51 Glenwood Ave., Queensbury, NY 12804
(518) 798-6007

PERMA-R-PRODUCTS, P.O. Box 5235 EKS, Johnson City, TN 37603
(800) 251-7532 (423) 929-8007

SHELTER SYSTEMS CORP., P.O. Box 830, Westminster, MD 21157
(410) 876-3900

STRUCTURAL PANELS, 350 Burbank Rd., Oldsmar, FL 34677
(813) 855-2627

THERMASTRUCTURE LTD., 609 Rock Rd., Radford, VA 24141
(540) 633-5000

TIMBER TRUSS HOUSING, 525 McClelland St., Salem, VAS 24153
(703) 387-0273

U.S. HOUSING COMPONENTS, 5890 Sawmill Rd., Dublin, OH 43017
(614) 766-5501

UNIFIED CORP., 4844 Shannon Hill Rd., Columbia, VA 23038
(804) 457-3622

UNIHOME CORP., Iron Horse Park, N. Billerica, MA 01862
(508) 663-6511

VERMONT STRESS SKIN PANELS, RR 2, Box 2794, Cambridge, VT 05444
(800) 644-8885

WAUSAU HOMES, P.O. Box 8005, Wausau, WI 54402
(715) 359-7272

WESTERN BLDG. COMPONENTS, 1601 N. Townsend Ave., Montrose, CO 81401
(303) 249-8999

WINTER PANEL CORP., RR 5, Box 168B, Brattleboro, VT 05301
(802) 254-3435

YANKEE BARN HOMES, HCR 63, Box 2, Grantham, NH 03753
(800) 258-9786 (603) 863-4545

ITEM	STANDARD MATERIALS	POPULAR OPTIONS
Foundation		
Conventional poured or block foundation or slab.	Not included.	
First Floor Subfloor		
Conventional girders, joists, lally columns and plywood.	Not included.	
Frame		
Post and beam structural frame, cut to length, notched, and prestained.	Rough sawn antique timbers	Planed antique timbers, prestained in a choice of colors, or New, planed Douglas Fir timbers, prestained in a choice of colors.
Interior trim for windows and exterior doors.	Flat 1x4 Pine trim with sills.	Decorative beams, to be cut to length on site.
Interior partitions.	Not included.	Posts and beams to outline interior partitions.
Walls		
Factory-built exterior wall panels complete with insulation, interior and exterior finish, and most windows installed.	1) Factory applied 1/2″ drywall inside finish. 2) 2x4 studs 24″ o.c. with 3-1/4″ foil faced rigid Thermax® insulation (R-26)* covered by 1/2″ plywood outside skin. 3) Prestained, kiln dried 1x8 White Pine shiplap siding factory applied over housewrap.	5/8″ Roughtex Douglas Fir paneling, or 1x8 White Pine or Cedar boards, kiln dried and prestained. Prestained 1/2″x6″ Red Cedar clapboards, site applied, or Prestained 1x8 Red Cedar shiplap, factory applied, or Unstained White Cedar shingles, site applied.
Windows		
Andersen Perma-Shield® windows with high performance insulating glass, pre-installed in panels whenever possible.	Casement windows with screens. Fixed glass in Flexiframes with high performance glass.	Double-hung windows with screens. Custom sized Flexiframes in a variety of shapes ready for site installation of fixed glass (glass not included). Removable wood grids.
Exterior Doors		
Exterior doors.	Custom made entry door. Andersen Perma-Shield® sliding patio door with high performance insulating glass.	Prehung Morgan solid wood door. Morgan wood terrace and french patio doors. Andersen Frenchwood sliding or hinged patio doors. Removable wood grids.
Exterior Trim		
Exterior trim.	Prestained 2″ thick kiln dried Pine.	Prestained 5/4 Red Cedar (unstained with shingle siding).
Roof		
Factory-built stressed-skin roof panels with plywood skins glued and stapled to 2x4 ribs, 16″ o.c.	5/8″ Roughtex Douglas Fir paneling on interior and 1/2″ CDX plywood exterior with 3-1/4″ foil faced rigid Thermax® insulation between (R-26)*.	1/2″ drywall on interior, or 1x6 pine boards Extra 1″ Thermax blanket (R-34 total)* with 1/2″ CDX plywood roof sheathing.
Roof shingles.	Not included.	
Skylights	Not included.	
Second Floor		
Factory-built stressed-skin panels with plywood skins glued and stapled to 2x4 ribs, 16″ o.c.	5/8″ plywood subfloor with 5/8″ Roughtex Douglas Fir paneling finish for ceiling below.	1/2″ CDX plywood ceiling (for on site application of drywall). 3-1/2″ Fiberglass batt insulation for extra sound deadening. Plank floor of nominal 3x6 and 3x8 laminated tongue and groove Southern Yellow Pine structural planking.
Attic Floor		
Prairie Barn: structural planking	Plank floor of nominal 3x6 and 3x8 laminated tongue and groove Southern Yellow Pine structural planking.	
Hampton Series: factory-built stressed-skin panels	5/8″ plywood subfloor with 1/2″ CDX plywood ceiling (for site application of drywall finish for ceiling below).	
Stairs		
Main and attic stair sets.	Kiln dried Southern Yellow Pine including posts and handrail.	Antique material, including posts and handrail.
Fastenings		
Fastenings and flashing.	Wrought head decorative nails, galvanized common nails, construction adhesive, aluminum flashing, expandable foam gaskets, insulating foam spray.	

YANKEE BARN HOMES

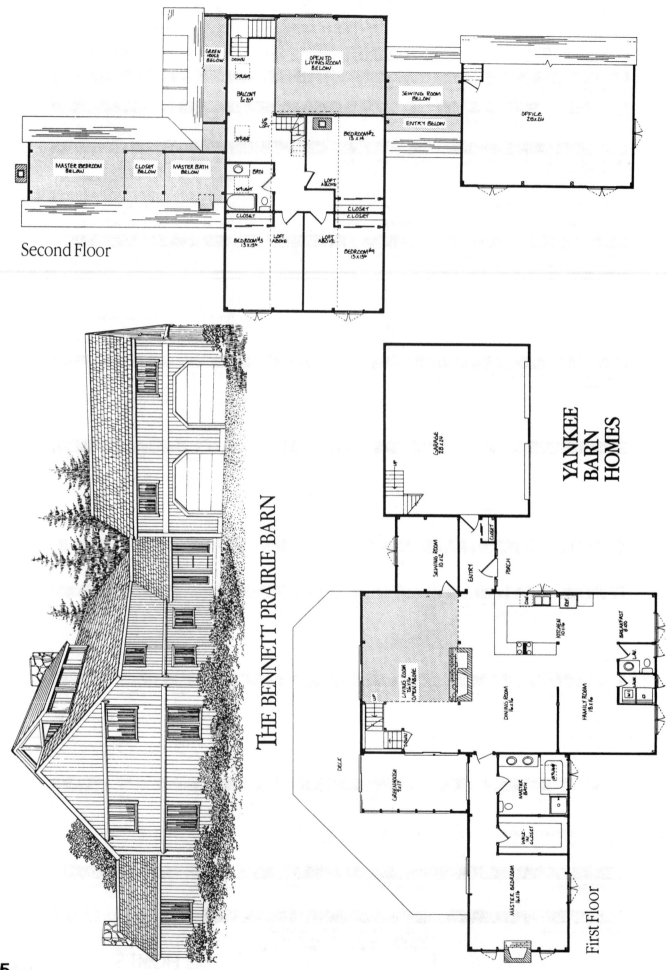

Second Floor

THE BENNETT PRAIRIE BARN

YANKEE
BARN
HOMES

First Floor

VII-5

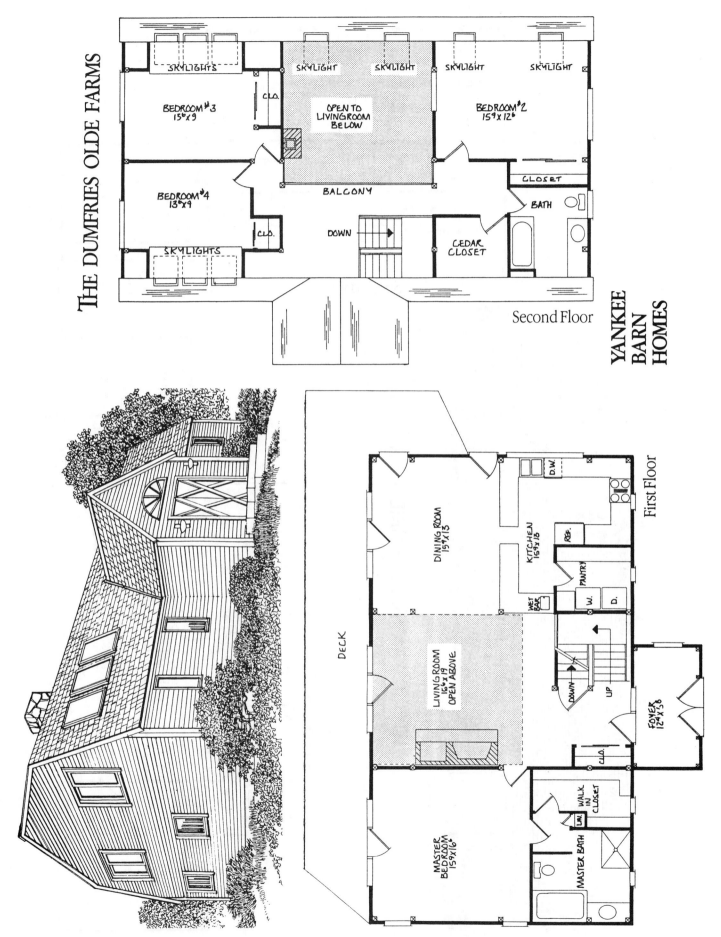

THE DUMFRIES OLDE FARMS

SKYLIGHTS

SKYLIGHT   SKYLIGHT   SKYLIGHT   SKYLIGHT

CLO.

BEDROOM #3
15⁶×9

OPEN TO
LIVING ROOM
BELOW

BEDROOM #2
15⁹×12⁶

CLOSET

BEDROOM #4
13⁶×9

BALCONY

BATH

CLO.

DOWN

CEDAR
CLOSET

SKYLIGHTS

Second Floor

YANKEE
BARN
HOMES

DECK

DINING ROOM
15⁹×13

D.W.

KITCHEN
15⁹×18

REF.

WET
BAR

PANTRY

W.   D.

LIVING ROOM
16⁶×19
OPEN ABOVE

DOWN   UP

CLO.

FOYER
12⁴×3⁸

MASTER
BEDROOM
15⁹×16⁶

WALK
IN
CLOSET

LIN.

MASTER BATH

First Floor

VII-6

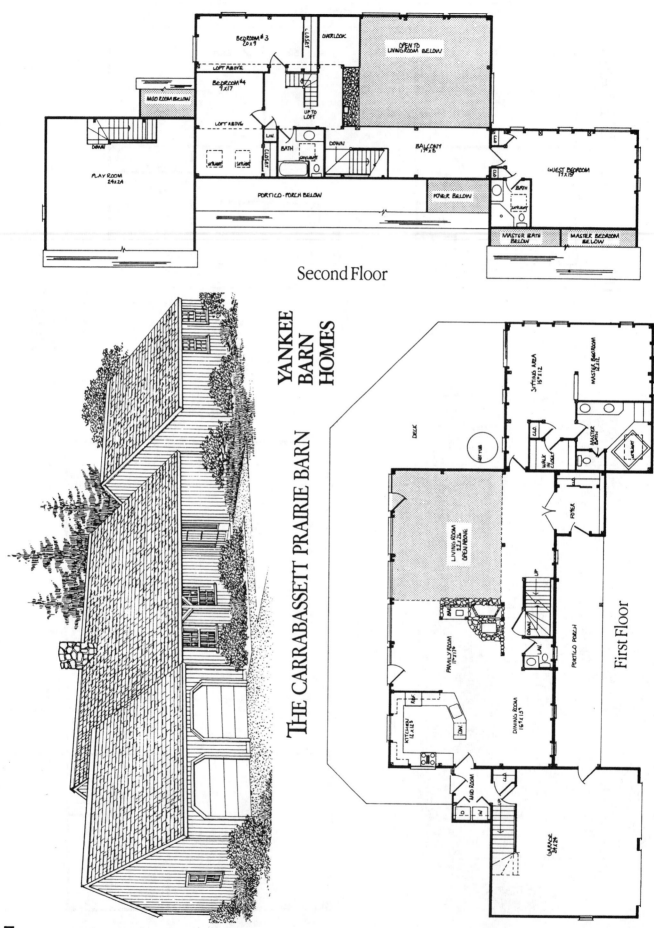

Second Floor

BEDROOM #3
20 x 9

OVERLOOK

OPEN TO
LIVINGROOM BELOW

CLOSET

LOFT ABOVE

BEDROOM #4
9 x 17

MUD ROOM BELOW

DOWN

LOFT ABOVE

UP TO
LOFT

PLAY ROOM
24 x 2A

DOWN

CLOSET

LIN.

BATH

SKYLIGHT

BALCONY
17 x 8

GUEST BEDROOM
17 x 19

SKYLIGHT

SKYLIGHT

PORTICO - PORCH BELOW

FOYER BELOW

BATH

MASTER BATH
BELOW

MASTER BEDROOM
BELOW

SKYLIGHT

YANKEE BARN HOMES

The CARRABASSETT PRAIRIE BARN

DECK

HOT TUB

SITTING AREA
15 x 12

MASTER BEDROOM
13 x 12

CLO.

MASTER
BATH

WALK CLOSET

SKYLIGHT

FOYER

LIVING ROOM
22 x 26
OPEN ABOVE

UP

BAR

FAMILY ROOM
19 x 17

DOWN

LAV.

PORTICO PORCH

SKYLIGHT

KITCHEN
12 x 12.5

DINING ROOM
16 x 13.5

MUD ROOM

CLO.

GARAGE
24 x 24

First Floor

VII-7

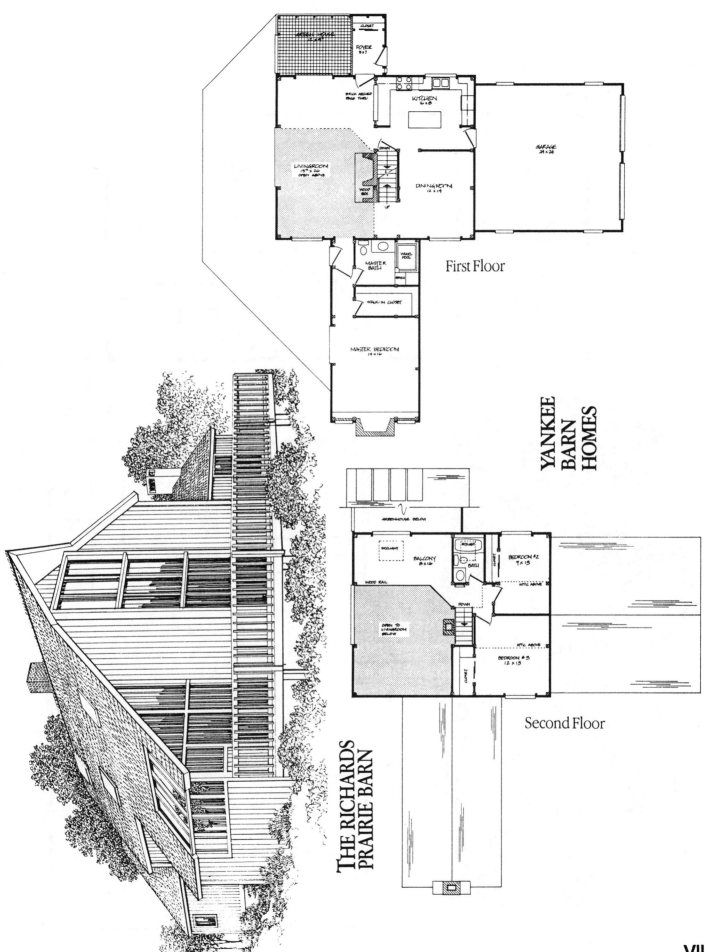

First Floor

GREENHOUSE
8 x 24

CLOSET

FOYER
5 x 7

BRICK ARCHED
PASS THRU

KITCHEN
16 x 8

GARAGE
24 x 24

LIVINGROOM
15' x 26'
OPEN ABOVE

DOWN

WOOD BOX

UP

DINING ROOM
12 x 14

MASTER
BATH

WHIRL
POOL

SHELF

WALK-IN CLOSET

MASTER BEDROOM
14 x 16

YANKEE
BARN
HOMES

GREENHOUSE BELOW

SKYLIGHT

BALCONY
8 x 16

SKYLIGHT

BATH

CLOSET

BEDROOM #2
9 x 13

ATTIC ABOVE

WOOD RAIL

OPEN TO
LIVINGROOM
BELOW

DOWN

ATTIC ABOVE

CLOSET

BEDROOM #3
12 x 13

Second Floor

THE RICHARDS
PRAIRIE BARN

VII-8

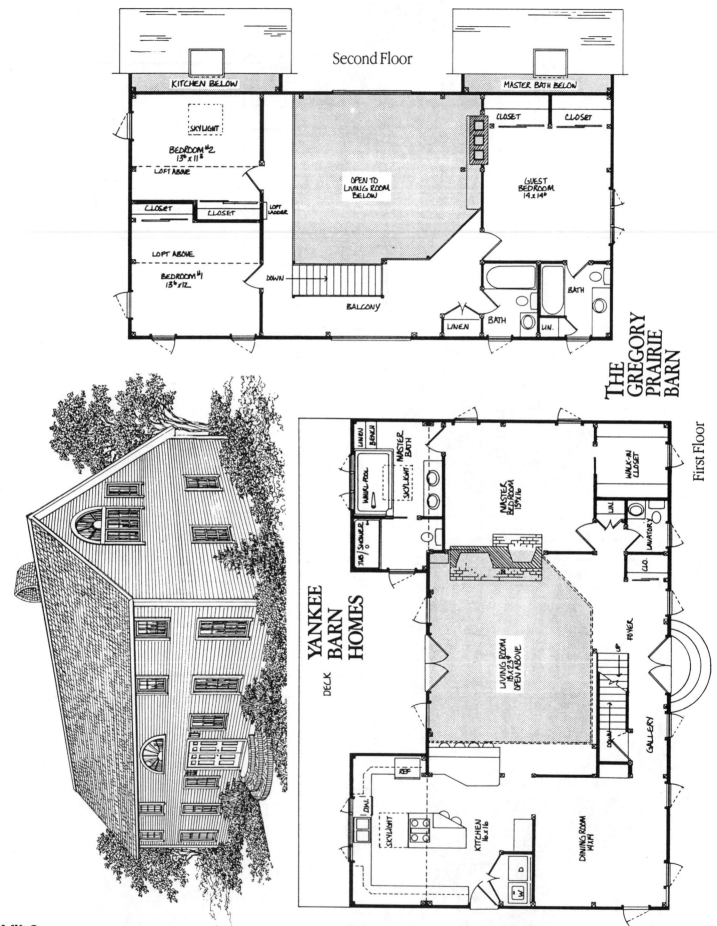

Second Floor

KITCHEN BELOW

MASTER BATH BELOW

SKYLIGHT

BEDROOM #2
13⁶ x 11⁸

LOFT ABOVE

CLOSET   CLOSET

CLOSET
CLOSET

LOFT LADDER

OPEN TO LIVING ROOM BELOW

GUEST BEDROOM
14 x 14⁶

LOFT ABOVE

DOWN

BEDROOM #1
13⁶ x 12

BALCONY

LINEN   BATH

BATH

LIN.

BATH

THE GREGORY PRAIRIE BARN

YANKEE BARN HOMES

DECK

First Floor

LINEN   BENCH

MASTER BATH

WHIRL-POOL

SKYLIGHT

TUB/SHOWER

MASTER BEDROOM
15⁹ x 16

WALK-IN CLOSET

LIN.

CLO.   LAVATORY

LIVING ROOM
16 x 23⁹
OPEN ABOVE

FOYER

UP

DOWN

GALLERY

REF

DW.

SKYLIGHT

KITCHEN
16 x 16

DINING ROOM
14 x 14

D

W

VII-9

Second Floor

MASTER BEDROOM
28 x 19

SKYLIGHT   SKYLIGHT

LOW STORAGE

CLOSET

DRESSING   BATH   SKYLIGHT

OPEN TO KITCHEN BELOW   OPEN BELOW

SKYLIGHT   BALCONY
12 x 10

OPEN TO
LIVING ROOM
BELOW

BALCONY

DOWN   CLO

BEDROOM #3
18 x 19

CLO   BATH

BEDROOM #2
18 x 14

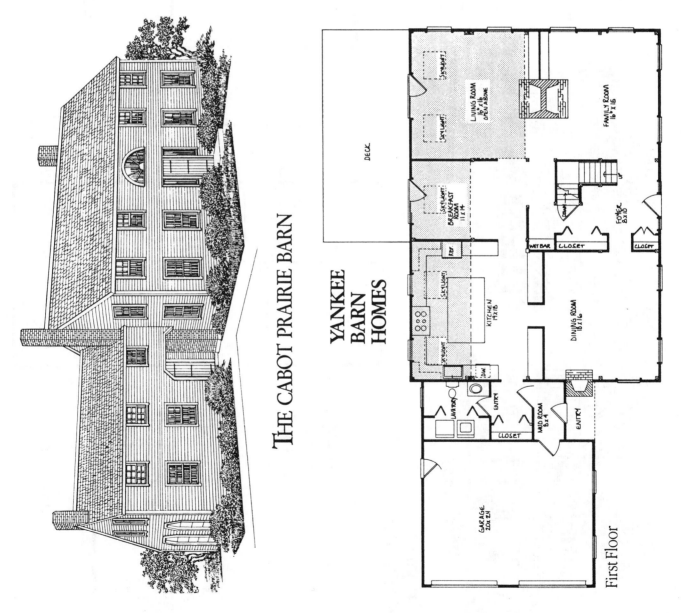

THE CABOT PRAIRIE BARN

YANKEE
BARN
HOMES

DECK

SKYLIGHT

SKYLIGHT

LIVING ROOM
16 x 16
OPEN ABOVE

SKYLIGHT
BREAKFAST
ROOM
11 x 14

FAMILY ROOM
16 x 16

REF

SKYLIGHT

WET BAR   CLOSET

FOYER
8 x 10   CLOSET

UP

DOWN

KITCHEN
19 x 16

SKYLIGHT

DINING ROOM
18 x 16

DW

LAVATORY   ENTRY

MUD ROOM
8 x 4   ENTRY

CLOSET

GARAGE
20 x 24

First Floor

VII-10

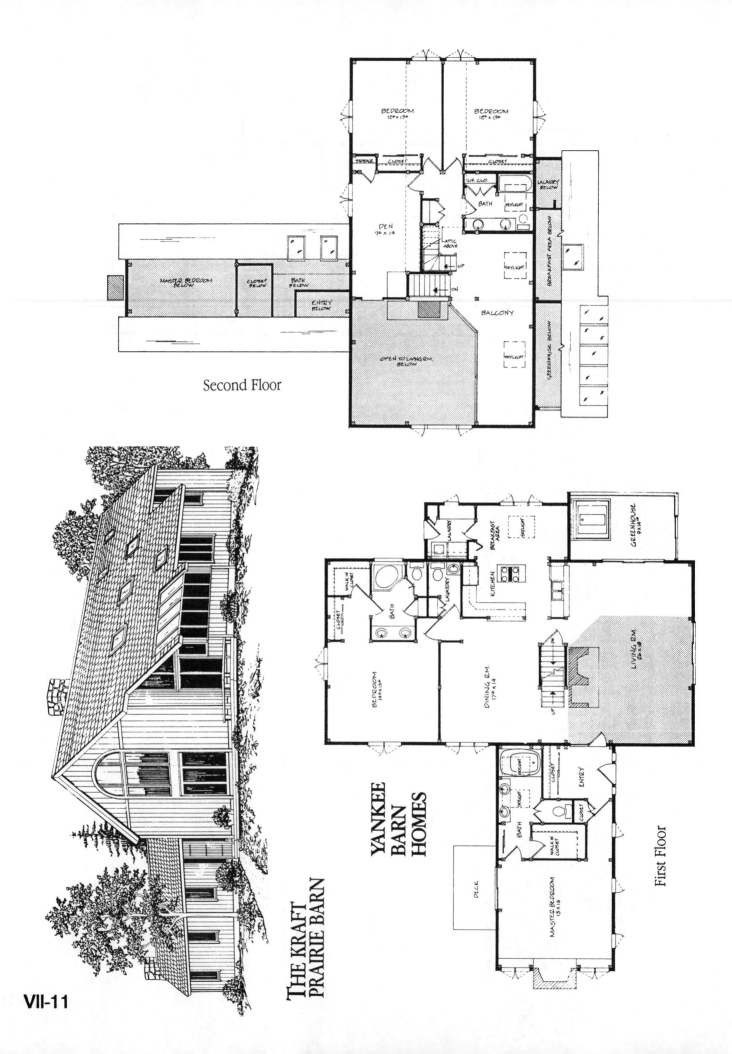

Second Floor

THE KRAFT
PRAIRIE BARN

YANKEE
BARN
HOMES

First Floor

VII-11

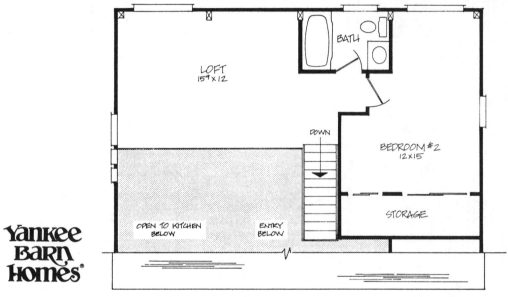

LOFT
15⁹x12

BATH

DOWN

BEDROOM #2
12x15

STORAGE

OPEN TO KITCHEN
BELOW

ENTRY
BELOW

Second Floor

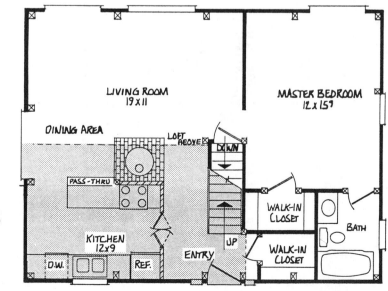

LIVING ROOM
19x11

MASTER BEDROOM
12 x 15⁹

DINING AREA

LOFT
ABOVE

DOWN

PASS-THRU

WALK-IN
CLOSET

BATH

THE CONNORS
STUDIO
SALTBOX

KITCHEN
12x9

UP

WALK-IN
CLOSET

D.W.

REF.

ENTRY

First Floor

VII-12

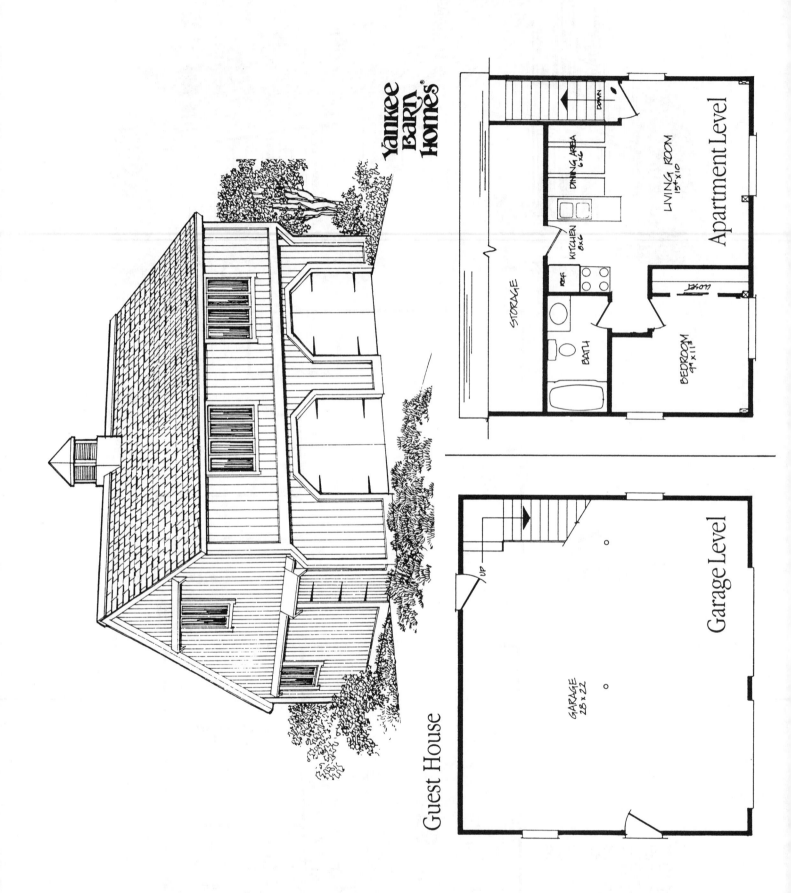

Yankee Barn Homes®

Guest House

Apartment Level

LIVING ROOM
15' x 10'

DINING AREA
6 x 6

KITCHEN
8 x 6

REF

STORAGE

BATH

BEDROOM
9' x 11'

CLOSET

DOWN

Garage Level

GARAGE
28 x 22

UP

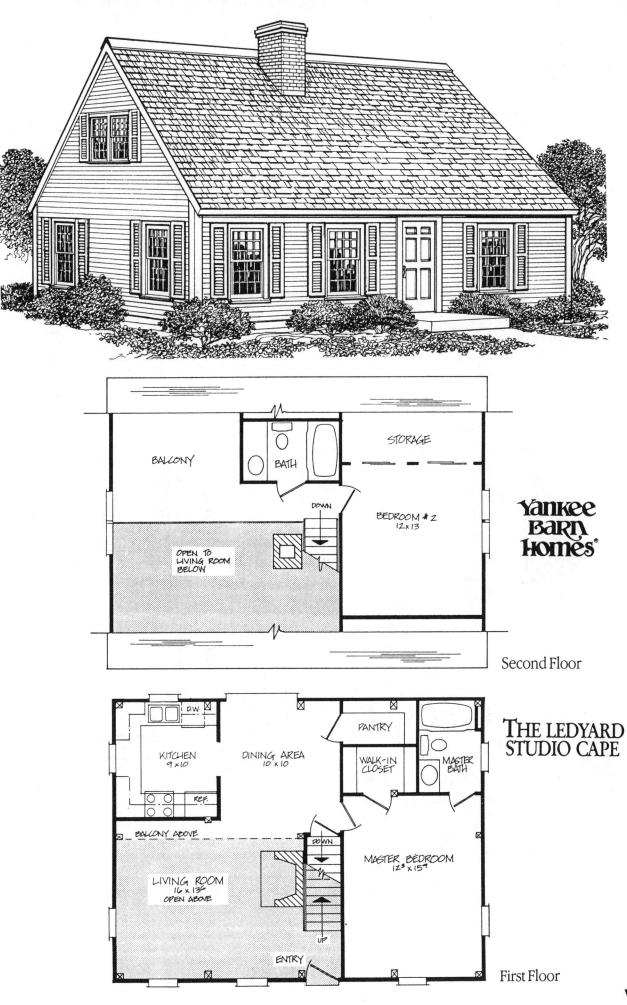

BALCONY

BATH

STORAGE

DOWN

OPEN TO
LIVING ROOM
BELOW

BEDROOM #2
12 x 13

Yankee Barn Homes®

Second Floor

D.W.

PANTRY

KITCHEN
9 x 10

DINING AREA
10 x 10

WALK-IN
CLOSET

MASTER
BATH

REF.

BALCONY ABOVE

DOWN

LIVING ROOM
16 x 13⁶
OPEN ABOVE

MASTER BEDROOM
12³ x 15⁷

UP

ENTRY

**THE LEDYARD
STUDIO CAPE**

First Floor

VII-14

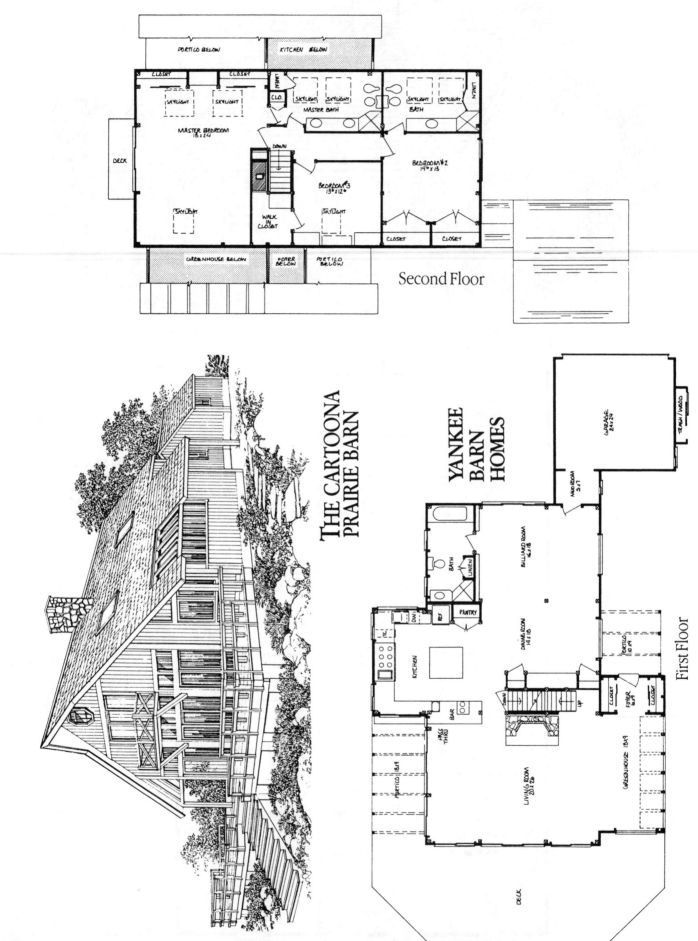

Second Floor

PORTICO BELOW

KITCHEN BELOW

CLOSET CLOSET

SKYLIGHT SKYLIGHT

MASTER BEDROOM
18 x 24

DECK

SKYLIGHT

WALK IN CLOSET

DOWN

CLO.

LINEN

SKYLIGHT SKYLIGHT

MASTER BATH

SKYLIGHT SKYLIGHT

BATH

LINEN

BEDROOM #2
14'6" x 13

BEDROOM #3
13'6" x 12'6"

SKYLIGHT

CLOSET CLOSET

GREENHOUSE BELOW

FOYER BELOW

PORTICO BELOW

THE CARTOONA PRAIRIE BARN

YANKEE BARN HOMES

First Floor

GARAGE
24 x 24

TRASH / WOOD

MUD ROOM
5 x 7

BATH

LINEN

PANTRY

DW

REF

KITCHEN

BAR

PASS THRU

PORTICO
18 x 9

BILLIARD ROOM
16 x 18

DINING ROOM
14 x 16

UP

DOWN

CLOSET

FOYER
16 x 9

CLOSET

PORTICO
10 x 9

LIVING ROOM
20 x 26

GREENHOUSE 18 x 9

DECK

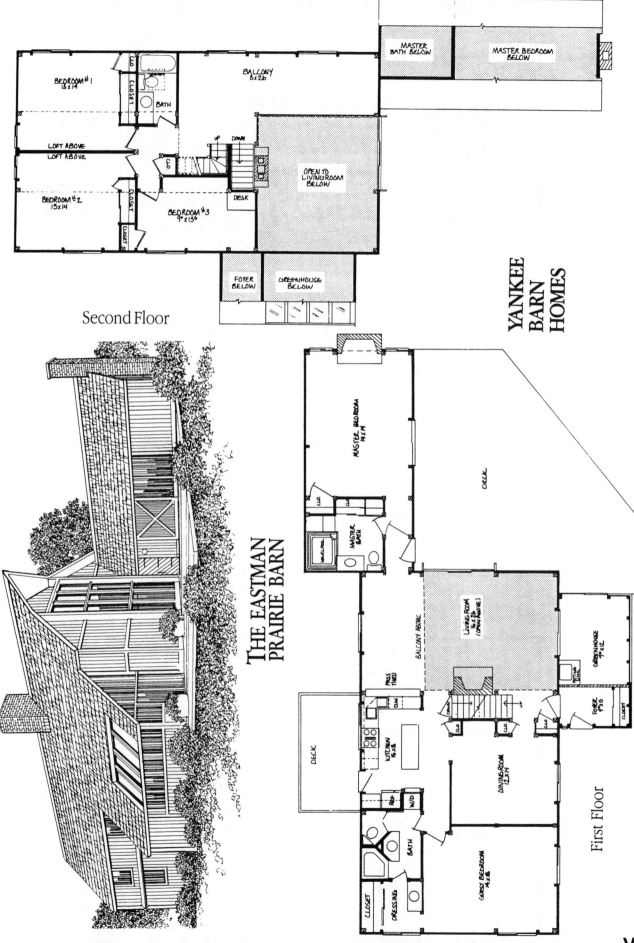

Second Floor

BEDROOM #1
13 x 14

CLOSET

BATH

LOFT ABOVE
LOFT ABOVE

BEDROOM #2
13 x 14

CLOSET

UP   DOWN

BEDROOM #3
9 x 13.6

DESK

BALCONY
5 x 26

OPEN TO
LIVING ROOM
BELOW

MASTER
BATH BELOW

MASTER BEDROOM
BELOW

FOYER
BELOW

GREENHOUSE
BELOW

YANKEE BARN HOMES

THE EASTMAN PRAIRIE BARN

First Floor

MASTER BEDROOM
14 x 14

CLO.   CLO.

MASTER
BATH

DECK

BALCONY ABOVE

LIVING ROOM
16 x 26
(OPEN ABOVE)

PASS THRU

KITCHEN
16 x 18

REF.   W/D

DECK

CLO.   CLO.

DINING ROOM
12 x 14

CLO.

GREENHOUSE
7 x 12

FOYER
9 x 6

CLOSET

BATH

CLOSET

DRESSING

GUEST BEDROOM
14 x 16

VII-16

The Thomas Paine

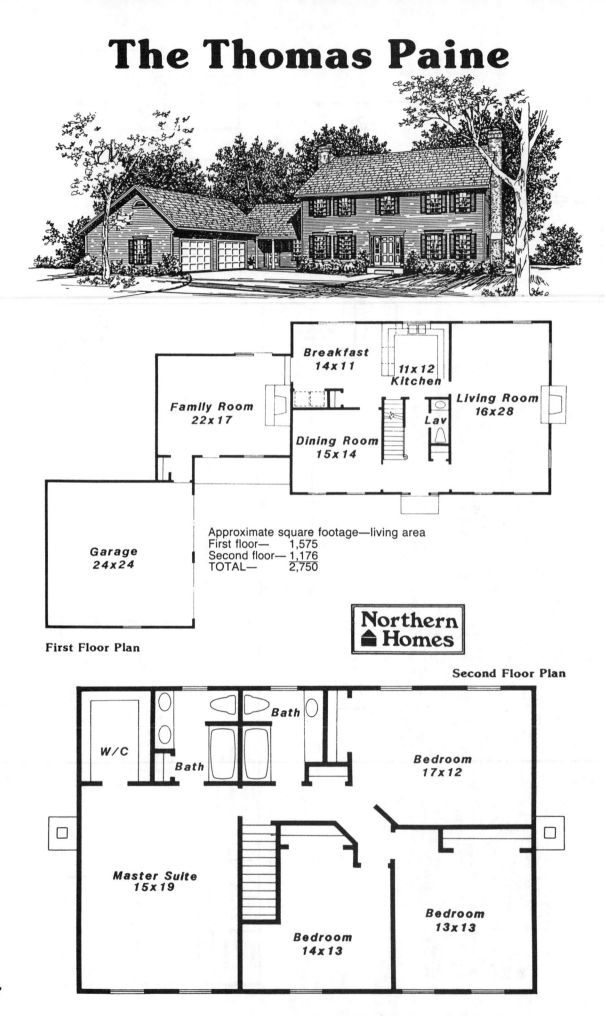

Breakfast
14x11

11x12
Kitchen

Living Room
16x28

Family Room
22x17

Lav

Dining Room
15x14

Approximate square footage—living area
First floor— 1,575
Second floor— 1,176
TOTAL— 2,750

Garage
24x24

Northern Homes

First Floor Plan

Second Floor Plan

W/C

Bath

Bath

Bath

Bedroom
17x12

Master Suite
15x19

Bedroom
14x13

Bedroom
13x13

The Daniel Webster

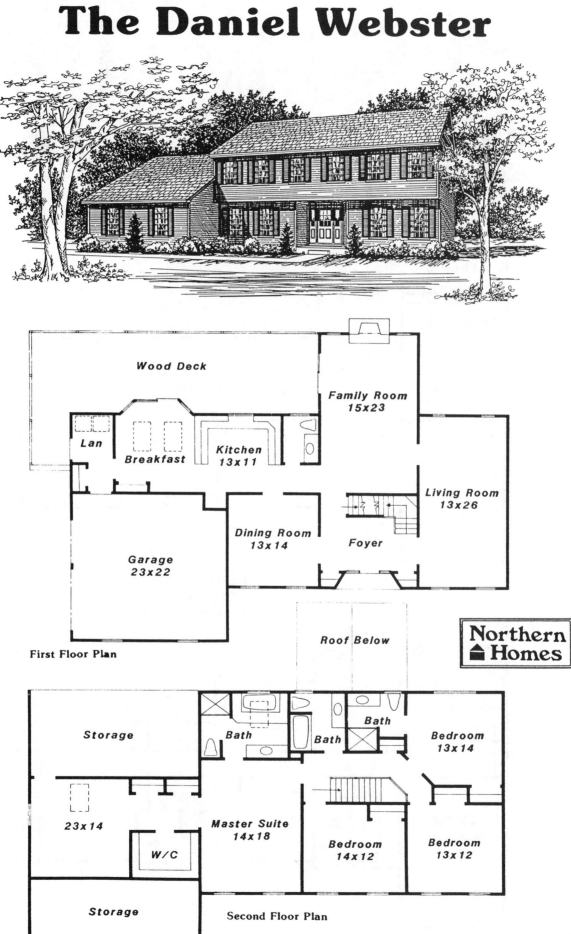

Wood Deck

Family Room
15x23

Lan

Breakfast

Kitchen
13x11

Living Room
13x26

Dining Room
13x14

Foyer

Garage
23x22

First Floor Plan

Roof Below

Northern ▲ Homes

Storage

Bath

Bath

Bath

Bedroom
13x14

23x14

Master Suite
14x18

W/C

Bedroom
14x12

Bedroom
13x12

Storage

Second Floor Plan

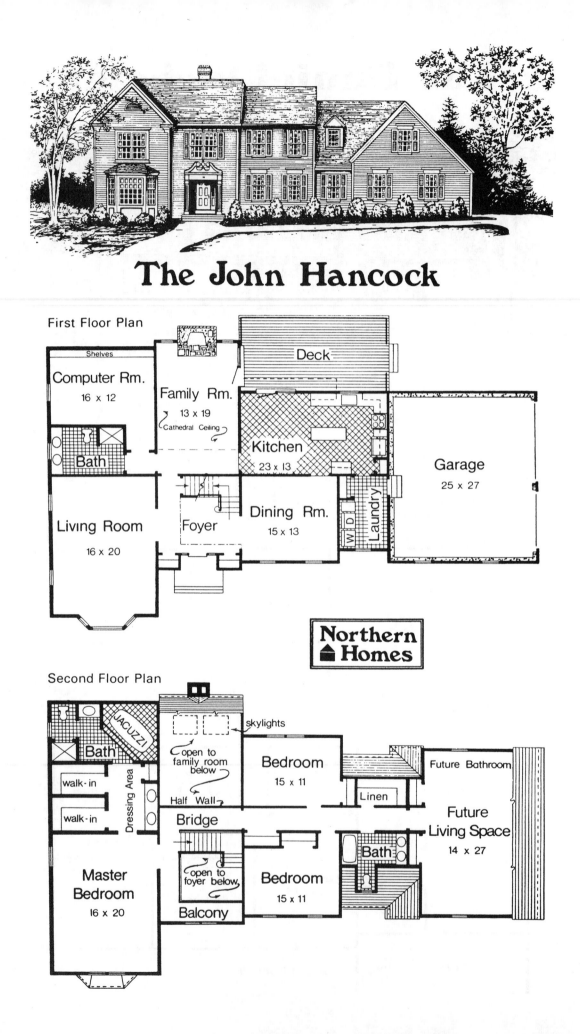

The John Hancock

First Floor Plan

Shelves

Computer Rm.
16 x 12

Family Rm.

Deck

13 x 19
Cathedral Ceiling

Bath

Kitchen
23 x 13

Garage
25 x 27

Living Room
16 x 20

Foyer

Dining Rm.
15 x 13

W D

Laundry

Northern Homes

Second Floor Plan

JACUZZI

Bath

skylights

walk-in

open to
family room
below

Bedroom
15 x 11

Future Bathroom

walk-in

Dressing Area

Half Wall

Linen

Future
Living Space
14 x 27

Bridge

open to
foyer below

Bedroom
15 x 11

Bath

Master
Bedroom
16 x 20

Balcony

The Joseph Warren

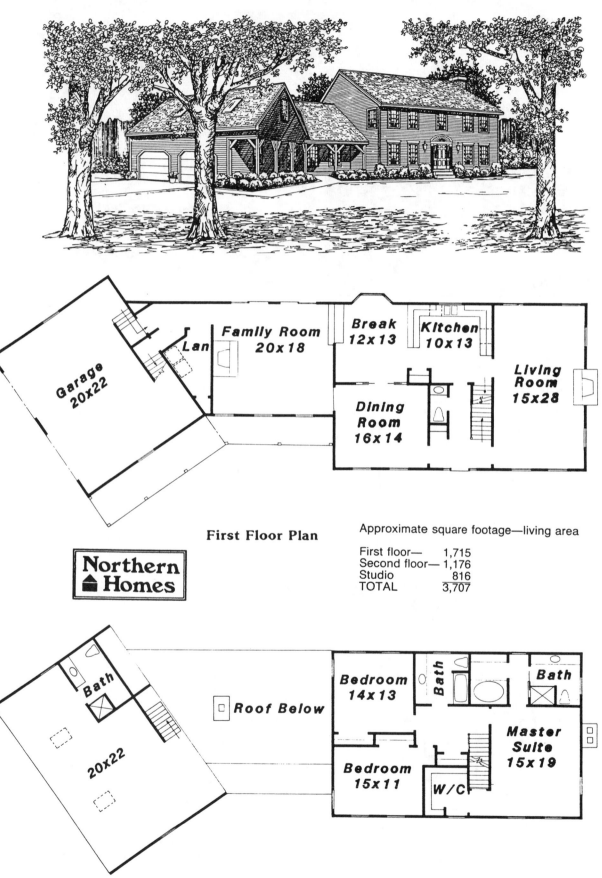

First Floor Plan

Northern Homes

Approximate square footage—living area

First floor—	1,715
Second floor—	1,176
Studio	816
TOTAL	3,707

Garage 20x22

Lan

Family Room 20x18

Break 12x13

Kitchen 10x13

Living Room 15x28

Dining Room 16x14

Bath

20x22

Roof Below

Bedroom 14x13

Bath

Bath

Master Suite 15x19

Bedroom 15x11

W/C

Second Floor Plan

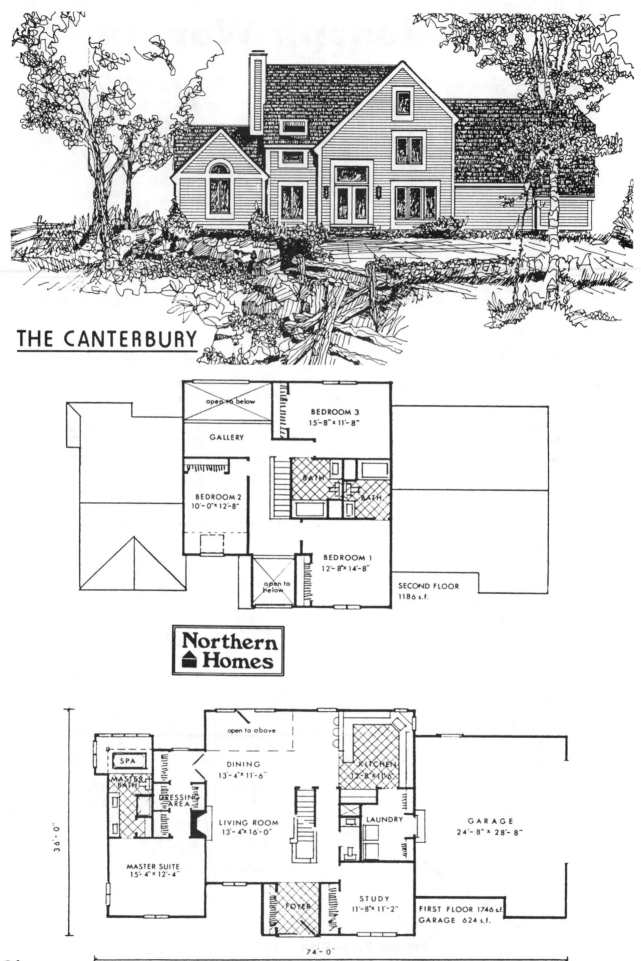

THE CANTERBURY

BEDROOM 3
15'-8" x 11'-8"

GALLERY

open to below

BEDROOM 2
10'-0" x 12'-8"

BATH

BATH

BEDROOM 1
12'-8" x 14'-8"

open to below

SECOND FLOOR
1186 s.f.

Northern Homes

open to above

SPA

MASTER BATH

DINING
13'-4" x 11'-6"

KITCHEN
12'-8" x 11'-6"

DRESSING AREA

LIVING ROOM
13'-4" x 16'-0"

LAUNDRY

GARAGE
24'-8" x 28'-8"

MASTER SUITE
15'-4" x 12'-4"

36'-0"

FOYER

STUDY
11'-8" x 11'-2"

FIRST FLOOR 1746 s.f.
GARAGE 624 s.f.

74'-0"

The Margate Bay

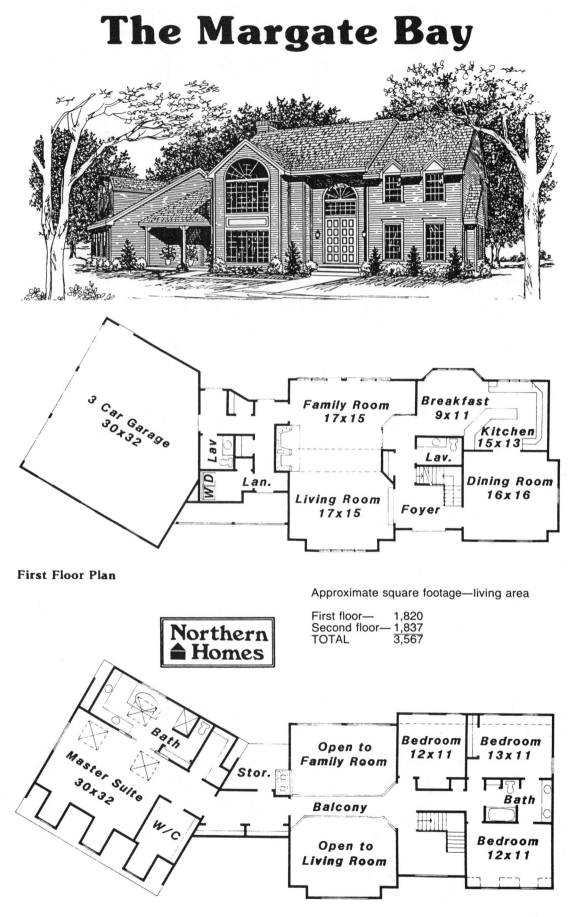

First Floor Plan

Approximate square footage—living area

First floor— 1,820
Second floor— 1,837
TOTAL 3,567

Northern
Homes

Second Floor Plan

WINTER PANEL CORP.

STRUCTUREWALL™
TECHNICAL INFORMATION

Product Data	No. S-1.2

General Description

Structurewall™, manufactured by Winter Panel Corporation, is a structural-grade stresskin panel for use in panelized home construction. The panel provides more than three times the strength of a standard 2x4 wall system. It achieves this remarkable strength through its laminated construction, with two skins of 7/16" oriented strand board or random waferboard (a structural grade of waferboard) surrounding a core of high-density isocyanurate insulation.

Structurewall™ is manufactured in a continuous lamination process in which the foam directly bonds to the skins, providing the highest strength bond possible. The high-density isocyanurate insulation (an advanced formulation of urethane) provides very high insulation levels (R-26 for the 4-9/16"-thick panel) and excellent fire safety characteristics. Structurewall™ panels insulate as well as 9" of fiberglass or 6" of 1-lb density expanded polystyrene (EPS), yet at an overall thickness of only 5" for the entire wall system.

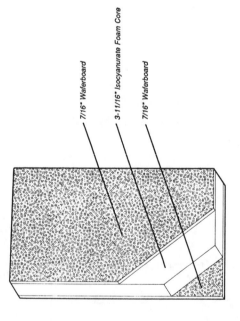

7/16" Waferboard

3-11/16" Isocyanurate Foam Core

7/16" Waferboard

Applications

Structurewall™ panels provide an alternative to conventional studwall and rafter framing systems in residential and light commercial buildings, offering superior strength, thermal performance, and ease of installation. Four foot wide panels, joined by inset "splines," produce an extremely strong wall or roof system. Upper floor walls are stabilized by truss-joist floor deck systems. Roof loads are carried by ridge and purlin laminated beams and the intersecting wall plate or floor platform. 2x4 splines are

typically used for wall joints, sill or floor deck attachment and corner intersections. Dual 5/8 x 3" splines are recommended for panel joints in roofs.

Structurewall™ panels may also be used for enclosing timber-frame houses where extra strength, greater spans between framing members, or a cabinet nail base is required. These panels are frequently used in kitchens and bathrooms, while Curtainwall panels (with drywall on the interior) are used in enclosing the rest of the timber frame.

DIMENSIONS AND PHYSICAL PROPERTIES

OUTER SKIN 7/16" Oriented strand board (OSB) or random waferboard, a high-quality, exterior-rated, wood composite board.

INNER SKIN (identical to outer skin).

INSULATION CORE 3-11/16" polyisocyanurate, a 2-lb/ft³ density, Class I, closed-cell foam. The foam insulation contains no formaldehyde or formaldehyde-related chemicals.

ADHESION An extremely strong and durable bond between foam and skins is provided by the continuous lamination manufacturing process with injected foam expanding against the two skins under pressure.

DIMENSIONS AND WEIGHT:

Overall Thickness	4-9/16"
Thickness Tolerance	+/- 1/16"
Width	48"
Width Tolerance	+0 -1/8"
Standard Lengths (ft)	8, 9, 10, 12, 14, 16, 20, 24, 28
Length Tolerance	+0 -1/4"
Weight	3.75 lb/ft²

STRUCTURAL PROPERTIES OF FOAM:

Compressive Strength	23.7 psi	(ASTM C-365)[1]
Shear Strength	11.9 psi	(ASTM C-273)[1]
Tensile Adhesion	16 psi	(ASTM C-297)[1]
Flexural Modulus	760 psi	(ASTM C-393)[2]
Shear Modulus	750 psi	(ASTM C-273)[2]

1. Source: Pittsburgh Testing Laboratory
2. Source: Mobay Chemical Corp.

STRUCTURAL DESIGN GUIDELINES (PANELS):

ROOF SPAN TABLE (FT/IN) - HORIZONTAL SPAN

DEFLECTION LIMITS	UNIFORM LOAD (LIVE LOAD PLUS DEAD LOAD)						
	20 psf	30 psf	40 psf	50 psf	60 psf	70 psf	80 psf
L/180	12'4"	10'3"	9'0"	8'0"	7'3"	6'7"	6'1"
L/240	11'0"	9'2"	7'10"	6'10"	6'3"	5'7"	5'2"
L/360	9'0"	7'4"	6'3"	5'4"	4'9"	4'3"	
L/480	7'9"	6'2"	5'2"	4'5"			

WALL LOAD TABLE (ALLOWABLE AXIAL LOADS (plf))

WALL HEIGHT	WIND LOAD				
	13 psf	16 psf	20 psf	23 psf	25 psf
4'	7800	7700	7600	7525	7475
5'	7525	7400	7225	7100	7025
6'	7150	6975	6725	6575	6475
7'	6675	6450	6150	5575*	5150*
8'	6150	5500*	4525*	3800*	3325*
9'	4875*	4050*	2950*	2125*	1575*
10'	3600*	2675*	1450*	550*	
11'	2425*	1400*	75*		
12'	1325*	225*			
13'	325*				
14'					

* Loads limited by L/240 deflection.
Other loads limited by combined stress analysis.

Roof Load

Horizontal Span

Axial Load lbs/linear foot

Wall Panel

Wind Load lbs/ft²

Wall Height

THERMAL PERFORMANCE:

Conductivity of Foam (k value) (aged 6 months)	.13 - .15	[Btu-in/rt/hr-F]
Minimum R-Value of Panel (aged 6 months)	26	[F/hr-F/Btu]

WATER VAPOR PERMEABILITY:
less than 1 perm.

WATER ABSORPTION:
2.4% (ASTM C-209)

FIRE SAFETY:

Finish Rating	1/2" drywall facing required to meet standard 15-minute finish rating.
Foam Fire Rating	Class I
Smoke Developed	300 (ASTM E-84)
Flame Spread	23 (ASTM E-84)
Structural Integrity in Fire Conditions	Isocyanurate foam is a "thermoset" plastic. It retains its structural integrity until completely consumed by fire. Melting does not occur.
Toxicity of Combustion Products	Dangerous gases may be given off in a fire. Combustion products are similar to those produced by burning wood.

Flexural

Tensile Adhesion

Compression   Shear

WARRANTY AND CODE COMPLIANCE:

Winter Panel Structurewall™ Panels come with a full ten-year warranty covering defects in materials and workmanship. For complete warranty information, contact the company. Structurewall™ panels have been thoroughly tested for structural properties, R-value, fire safety and durability by independent testing laboratories. Test results are available upon request.

Code Compliance:

Meets Massachusetts Building Code Requirements
Rhode Island Building Code Standards Committee (see Report #83-150)

FOR MORE INFORMATION

For additional information on Winter Panel stresskin products and applications, contact the company:

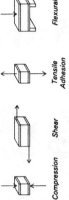

WINTER PANEL CORP.

Winter Panel Corp.
RR 5, Box 168 B
Brattleboro, VT 05301
(802) 254-3435

I. IMPORTANT INFORMATION

Keep Panels Off the Ground and Dry

Panels should be kept at least 6" off the ground with blocking and protected from rain until use. Space the blocking no more than 4' on center (o.c.) and make sure the ground is flat (so panels will not twist). Some exposure to rain will not cause damage, but extended exposure will cause edges to swell — requiring sanding for a smooth finish later. If the panels will remain at the site for more than a week or two before installation, they should be stacked in a barn or shed under cover.

Make Sure the Foundation is Square and Level

Panel construction depends on the foundation being square and level to within very tight tolerances. If the foundation is out of square or not level, panel installation will be much more difficult. Refer to Section II for foundation tolerances. The foundation is the responsibility of the customer. Supplied drawings of the foundation are intended to show size and bearing points for the supplied house shell kit. Local codes and soil conditions may require additional engineering for compliance.

Follow Load and Span Limits Carefully

Load and span limits for Structurewall™ panels and other building components, such as engineered joists and laminated beams are given in the manufacturer's literature for those products. An Amos Winter Home will be fully engineered to satisfy all structural limits, but if you customize any part of a house design, without consulting with Amos Winter Home designers, it is your responsibility to ensure that the building is properly engineered.

Splines are Required on All Panel Joints

Two 5/8 x 3" or single 2x4 splines are required at all joints between panels. In some cases, heavier duty splines such as 4x4s are used as described later in this guide. Panel joists must be sealed with foam sealant during installation. Failure to install splines or improper installation of splines will violate the structural continuity of the building shell.

Panels for Amos Winter Homes are shipped pre-routed for splines. If on-site modifications are made, or if panels are found to be improperly routed, you will need to rout the panels with the proper power or hand tools as described in Appendix I. Inspect all panels as they are installed and make sure they are properly routed.

Follow Nail/Screw Specifications Carefully

Using the proper fasteners and spacings is very important with Amos Winter Homes. The following table provides a quick reference for nail and screw specifications with the most common applications. More complete information is provided throughout this guide.

Amos Winter Homes, Inc.

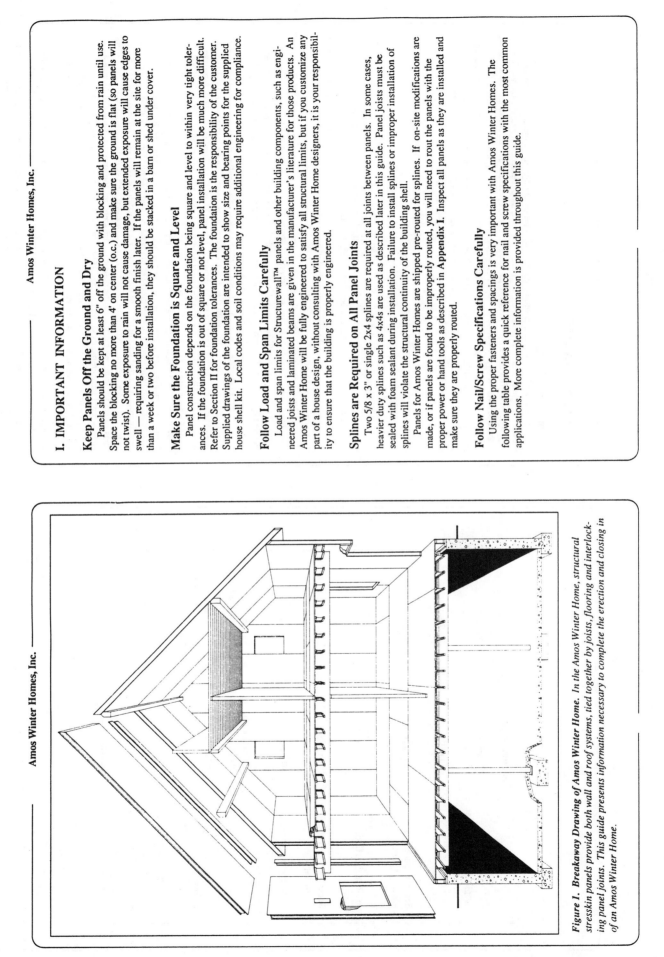

Figure 1. Breakaway Drawing of Amos Winter Home. In the Amos Winter Home, structural stresskin panels provide both wall and roof systems, tied together by joists, flooring and interlocking panel joints. This guide presents information necessary to complete the erection and closing in of an Amos Winter Home.

II. GETTING STARTED

1. Foundation Design

The outside of the foundation should be flush with the outer edge of the installed panels as shown in **Figures 2 and 3** (the siding, to be installed later, should extend out past the foundation slightly). With full basement and crawlspace applications, a pressure-treated sill should be anchored to the frost wall with foundation tie straps as indicated in the plans (typically 6' o.c. and 2' from all corners). The outer edge of the sill should be flush with the outside of the foundation if the foundation matches the building dimensions. If the foundation varies from the building dimensions, if corners are not square, or if the top of frost wall is not level enough, you will need to correct for this when setting the sill plates. **It is extremely important that you provide an accurate, level and square platform on which to set the pre-cut structure.**

Interior insulation is generally recommended on frost walls. The insulation should either extend up to the sill, as shown in **Figure 2a**, or overlap the sill, extending to the bottom of the joists. The insulation can be installed before or after erection of the building shell.

If using exterior foundation insulation, the top edge should be beveled at 45° to the top of the sill as shown in **Figure 2b**. Nail the top edge of the insulation into the sill, protect insulation with stucco or other material as per insulation manufacturer's recommendations, and cover the joint with a pressure-treated skirt board, also beveled at 45°. Install drip cap flashing above the skirt board and install siding over it, leaving a 1/8" - 1/4" space between the bottom of the siding and the flashing to prevent rot. As shown in the illustration, the full width of the wall panels should be supported on the concrete frost wall.

With slab-on-grade foundations, there are several alternatives. A pressure-treated 2x6 sill can be embedded in the concrete, with the top of it flush with the top surface of the slab, as shown in **Figure 3a**. The sill should be secured to the foundation with mud sill anchors, such as those manufactured by Simpson Co., which are set into the wet concrete and provide a seat for the embedded sill.

A second alternative is to rip a 2x6 to 4-1/2" (the width of a panel) and secure it to the top of the slab, as shown in **Figure 3b**. With this detail, conventional foundation tie straps or mud sill anchors should be used. The inset to **Figure 3b** shows a Simpson Mudsill Anchor Singleside, which can also be used. Which detail is to be used must be established in advance of panel design, as it establishes panel height.

With slabs, insulation is generally installed on the inside of the frost wall as shown in **Figure 3**. If using exterior insulation, bevel it as shown in full basement application (see **Figure 2b**).

Use accepted foundation design practices in laying out and building the foundation. It is extremely important that the sill plate of the house exactly match the out-to-out dimensions of the house and that all corners be square. Foundation width and length shall be within 1/4" of the dimensions called for in the plans. Check the diagonal measurements for square as shown in **Figure 4**. The diagonal measurements shall be within 1/2". The top level of the frost wall or slab shall not vary by more than 1/4" in 10' along the wall. Slight variations in foundation dimensions can be dealt with when setting the sill, but variations outside of these tolerances will make panel installation significantly more difficult.

Slight inaccuracies in the foundation dimensions can be corrected when setting the sill. If the foundation is supposed to be 36' long, for example, but measures 36' 1/2", the sills can be held in 1/4" from the outside of the foundation on each end, providing the exact dimension of 36' 0", out-to-out. If the diagonals do not match exactly, some adjustment can be made when setting the sills. If

Table 1.
Fastener Specifications

Application	Fastener Type	On-Center Spacing
Securing panels to 2x4 splines	8d nails or 2-1/2" screws	8" - from both sides
Securing panels to 5/8 x 3" splines	6d nails or 2" screws	8" - from both sides
Securing bottom splines to top splines to sill and/or floor system	16d nails or 3" screws	6" in two offset rows
Securing corner spline to edge spline	16d nails	8"
Securing joist hangers to top splines or laminated beams	16d nails	into edge of top plate
	1-1/2" joist hanger nails	into top of top wall plate
Securing joist to joist hanger	6d nail each side	in pre-drilled holes for bottom flange
T&G floor decking to joists and top splines at perimeter	8d ring-shank nails or 2" screws	6" along edge 12" on intermediate joists

In areas where termite and ant damage is common, install a termite shield between the sill and foundation in accordance with locally accepted practices. Insect protection can also be provided by a layer of tar between the panel and the sill. As an added precaution, the ground around the house can be treated with insecticide by a licensed exterminator. Ask your local building official for information on accepted practices to protect against insect damage.

To seal against air infiltration under the sill, use a closed-cell foam sill sealer, and apply caulk between the termite shield (if used) and the sill.

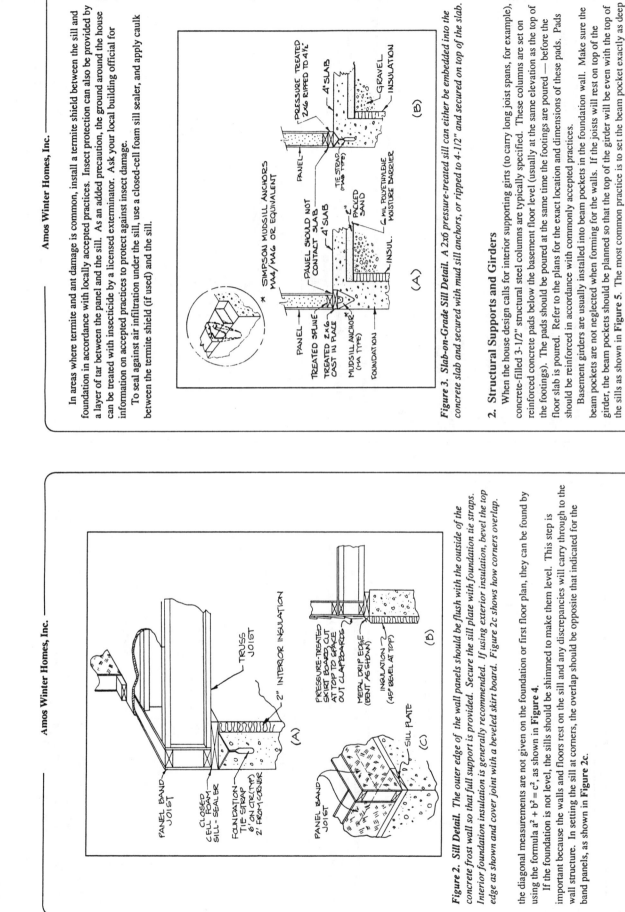

Figure 3. Slab-on-Grade Sill Detail. *A 2x6 pressure-treated sill can either be embedded into the concrete slab and secured with mud sill anchors, or ripped to 4-1/2" and secured on top of the slab.*

2. Structural Supports and Girders

When the house design calls for interior supporting girts (to carry long joist spans, for example), concrete-filled 3-1/2" structural steel columns are typically specified. These columns are set on reinforced concrete pads below the basement floor level (usually at the same elevation as the top of the footings). The pads should be poured at the same time the footings are poured — before the floor slab is poured. Refer to the plans for the exact location and dimensions of these pads. Pads should be reinforced in accordance with commonly accepted practices.

Basement girders are usually installed into beam pockets in the foundation wall. Make sure the beam pockets are not neglected when forming for the walls. If the joists will rest on top of the girder, the beam pockets should be planned so that the top of the girder will be even with the top of the sills as shown in **Figure 5.** The most common practice is to set the beam pocket exactly as deep as the girder and install a short section of pressure-treated two-by lumber in the bottom of the beam

---

Figure 2. Sill Detail. *The outer edge of the wall panels should be flush with the outside of the concrete frost wall so that full support is provided. Secure the sill plate with foundation tie straps. Interior foundation insulation is generally recommended. If using exterior insulation, bevel the top edge as shown and cover joint with a beveled skirt board. Figure 2c shows how corners overlap.*

the diagonal measurements are not given on the foundation or first floor plan, they can be found by using the formula $a^2 + b^2 = c^2$, as shown in **Figure 4.**

If the foundation is not level, the sills should be shimmed to make them level. This step is important because the walls and floors rest on the sill and any discrepancies will carry through to the wall structure. In setting the sill at corners, the overlap should be opposite that indicated for the band panels, as shown in **Figure 2c.**

Amos Winter Homes, Inc.

When installing the beam, allow 1/2" at each end for air circulation. Set the beam in place, then run a string along the side of the beam at the bottom to determine the length needed for any supporting columns. By measuring from the string, any sagging of the beam will not throw off the floor level. Cut the steel column slightly long (about 1/8") to account for settling. Also, check to make sure the basement girder is straight. If not, straighten it and brace it in place. The braces will help to hold it in place until joists are installed.

III. FIRST FLOOR DECK

The first floor deck is laid on joists (usually engineered "truss" joists), which span from sill to sill or to basement girder. Special "band panels" are used to tie the joists together rather than conventional band joists. The band panels provide the same insulation value as the wall system. Band panels are installed around the whole sill perimeter. Spanning joists should be nailed into the sill with two 16d nails at each end (one on each side of web).

1. Install Band Panels

Band panels are sections of Structurewall™ panel that are the same depth as the joists used for the first floor deck (9-1/2", 11-7/8", etc.). Assuming the sill plate is level and square, and it matches the outside dimensions of the building, the band panels can be set directly in line with the outer edge of the treated sill plate. Use the framing plan to properly position the band panels. Usually band panels are installed before the joists, but in some situations, joists will be installed first. In that case, you will need to allow space for the thickness of the band panels when setting the joists. When installing the band panel, it is necessary to seal butt joints with expanding foam sealant and reinforce any overlapping corner joints with adhesive (see **Figure 6**).

Figure 6. Band panels. Band panels are set on the outside edge of the sill around the whole perimeter of the building. Overlap band panels on sills as called for in plans.

pocket (this is the same thickness as the sill and will bring the top of the girder up to be even with the top of the sill). The beam pocket should be sized 1/2" larger on each side and at the end to prevent direct contact of the girder to the foundation.

Figure 4. Checking Foundation Square. With rectangular foundations, the diagonal measurements should be identical. To determine if a corner is square, use the formula $a^2 + b^2 = c^2$. Be sure to carefully measure and inspect the foundation before beginning to erect the house.

$$(a^2 + b^2 = c^2)$$

Figure 5. Beam Pocket in Foundation Wall. Basement girders are set into beam pockets in the foundation wall. Allow 1/2" on each side of the girder and at the end. Size the pocket the exact depth of the girder and install a short section of pressure-treated two-by lumber in the bottom of the pocket. This will protect the bottom of the beam and bring the top level up even with the top of the sill.

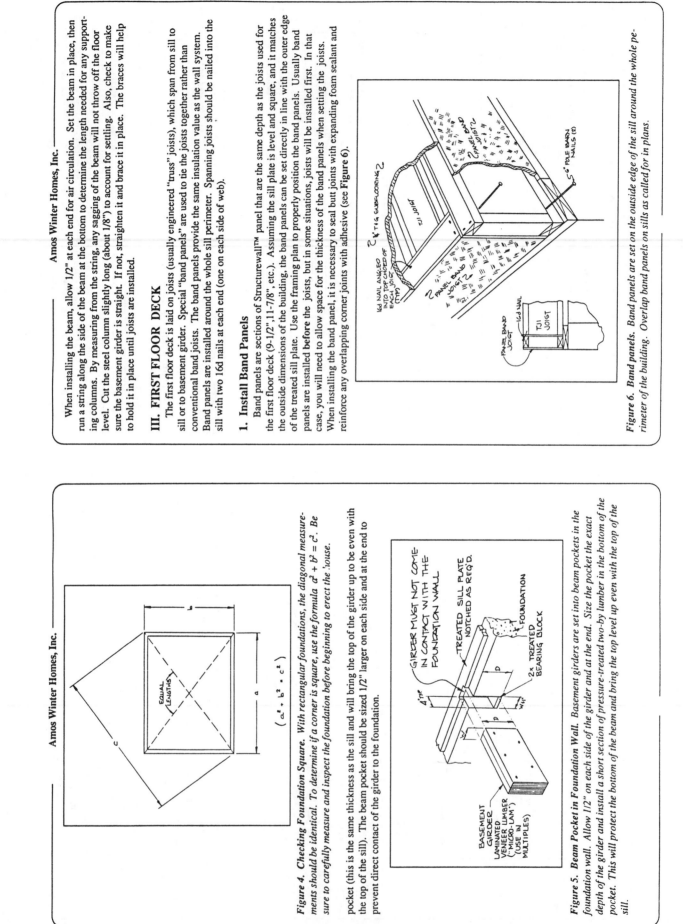

2. Set Spanning Joists

All joists should arrive at the building site pre-cut to the exact dimension required. Check the dimensions, and, if they are not already cut to the right length as shown in the cutting list (this may be a fraction of an inch less than lengths shown on the framing plan drawings), do so with a circular saw. Laminated joists and beams will expand with moisture, so try to keep them dry. Lay out joists as specified in the plans. Take note of where measurements for on-center spacing of joists should start. Nail through the band panels into the spanning joist top chord with 16d nails as shown in **Figure 6**. Each spanning joist should be nailed into the sill with two 16d nails at each end (one on each side of web).

Joists also need to be nailed into any spanning girder they rest on. Before nailing joists into a basement girder, check to make sure that the girder is straight and level. Straighten and brace it as necessary. Nail joists into girders with two 16d nails (one on each side of web). Install joist blocking above girders if specified in the plans. With engineered joists, follow specifications from the manufacturer relative to bracing requirements. When using hangers off a basement girder, be sure that all top hanger nail holes are used (special Simpson nails should penetrate vertically through the hanger top straps and 16d common nails should be used for securing the top of the hanger into the girder face). Use two 6d nails to connect the joist hanger into the bottom flange of the joist (one on each side). The joist hanger must be pushed up against the girder before installing these nails.

Double or triple joists are used at stairway penetrations or as joist headers when the joists change direction. Multiple joists should be glued and nailed together 12" o.c. at both top and bottom using 16d nails (with engineered joists, follow manufacturer's recommendations). Typical floor framing is shown in **Figure 7**.

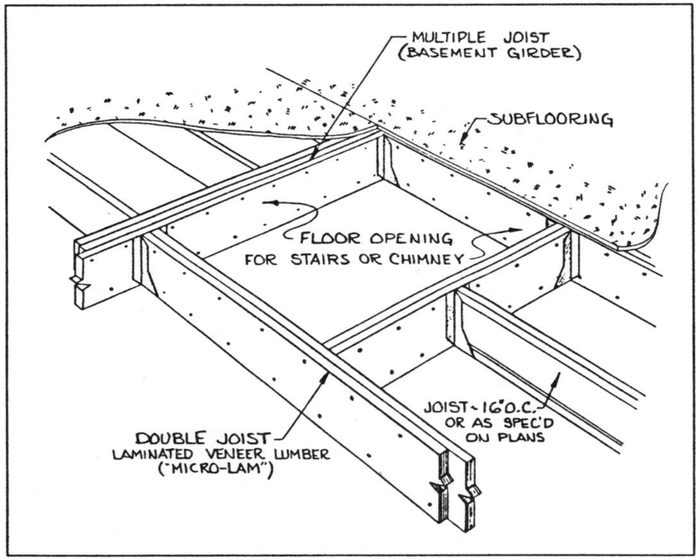

Figure 7. Floor Framing with Engineered Joists. Follow plans carefully relative to joist spacing. Double and triple joists should be glued and nailed together as per specifications.

Use a great deal of care when working with engineered joist products. While they have considerable strength when loaded from the top, they have very little lateral strength. Do not stand or walk on engineered joists until they have been adequately braced or sheathed with subflooring. Also use care when picking up long engineered joists; if they are not on edge when picked up, they can break.

3. Lay Subfloor

Lay a 3/4" tongue-and-groove subfloor on top of the joists. The subfloor should extend out to the edge of the panel band joist. Run 4 x 8' sheets perpendicular to the joists, as shown in **Figure 8**, starting from the point indicated on the subfloor layout plan. Apply a bead of construction adhesive on each joist, and nail the subflooring on with 8d nails or 2" screws 6" o.c. along edges and 12" o.c. along intermediate joists. The two rows of fasteners at butt joints over a single joist must be staggered (see **Figure 8**). It is important that the subfloor be nailed down before the adhesive starts to set up (follow manufacturer's recommendations).

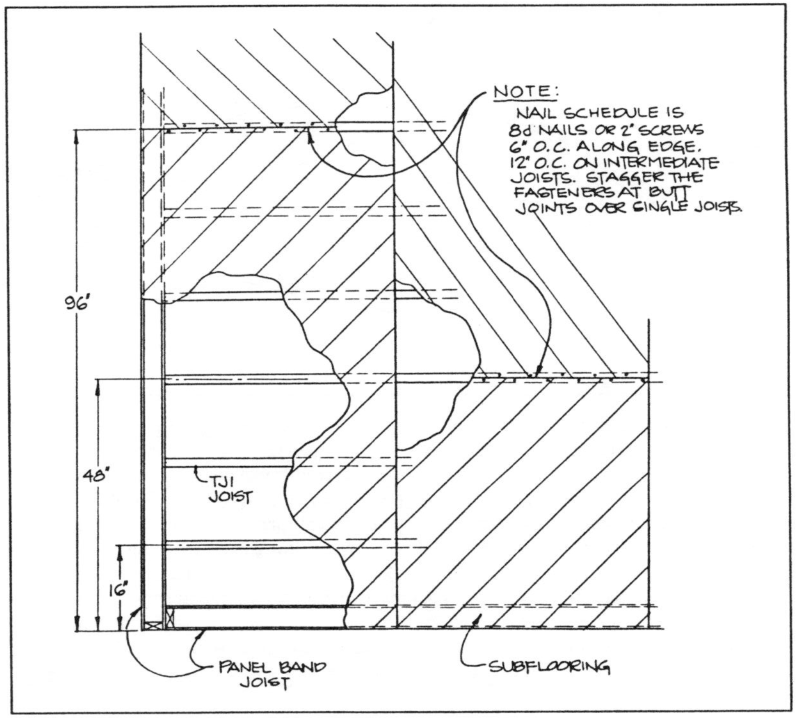

Figure 8. Installing Subflooring. Offset 4x8 sheets of subflooring and secure with construction adhesive and nails or screws.

IV. WALL PANELS — ASSEMBLY AND ERECTION

The Structurewall™ panels as delivered need to be assembled into wall elevations as shown in the panel cut-out drawings.

To start panel installation, organize the panels for the first long wall, whose outer skin has been attached to the deck/band panel. Lay the panels flat on the deck, outer skin up, to match the panel drawings as shown in **Figure 10**. Leave a 1" gap between panels. With the panels resting flat on the deck, the inner surface of panels are **down**. Set the panel bottoms against the attached bottom spline to help align the panels. Insert all 5/8 x 3" inner splines (those on the bottom side of the panels) at panel seams. Be sure that splines do not intrude into 1-1/2" rout at top and bottom of panel. Place a continuous bead of expanding foam sealant into the foaming groove between the spline routs, inset the 5/8 x 3 outer splines (upper side of panels) and slide the panels together.

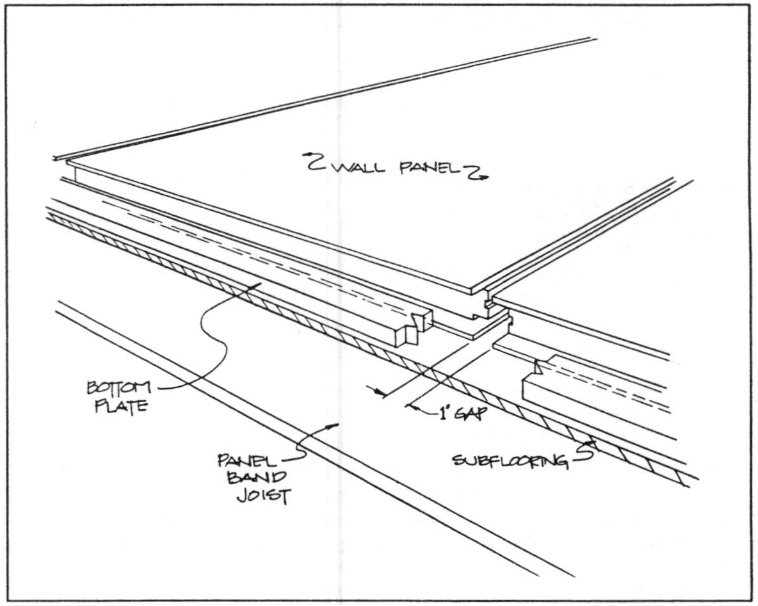

Figure 10. Panel Layout for First Wall. Lay out panels for a wall on the deck. Foam and join panels before tilting wall up into position on bottom spline.

Panel joints are usually made with dual 5/8 x 3" plywood splines as described above and shown in **Figure 11**. To prevent moisture migration through the wall, the joint must be sealed with expanding foam sealant. A specialized foaming groove has been routed into each panel edge to hold this bead of sealant. The bead of foam is applied just before panels are joined together, as described above, and the curing foam expands into the adjoining panel groove to seal the panels together.

In some situations, the plans will call for stronger spline joints between panels, as shown in

4. Install Bottom Splines (First Floor Walls)

Once the floor deck is on, 2x4 bottom splines (bottom plates) are secured around the full perimeter. The splines should be secured to the deck and band panel around the perimeter, setting the outer edge of the spline 1/2" in from the edge of the deck so that the outer surface of the wall panels will be flush with the deck and band panel.

Use a scrap of 1/2" wood as a gauge when you position the 2x4s. A bead of adhesive under the bottom spline is required. Use 16d nails, spaced 6" o.c. in two staggered rows to secure the bottom spline to the sill as shown in **Figure 9**.

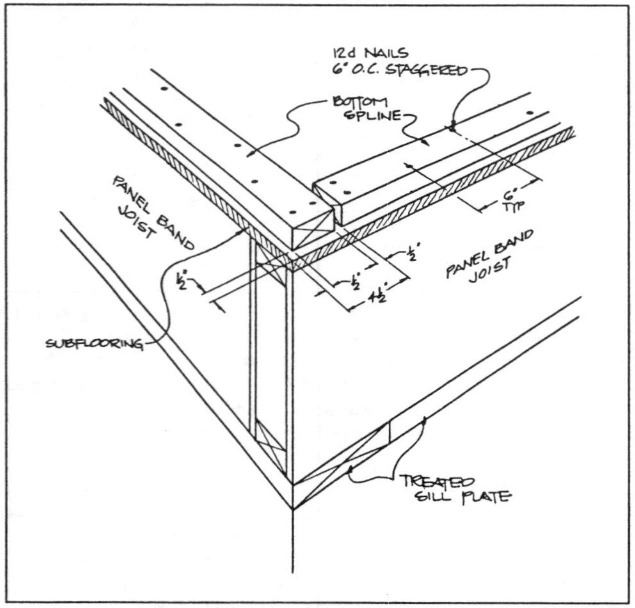

Figure 9. Securing Bottom Splines to Sill. 2x4 bottom splines are secured so that the wall panels will fit over them and be snug against the deck. Caulk underneath the bottom splines to ensure a tight seal.

Corner lapping of the 2x4 bottom splines must be done in the same manner as the wall panels which fit over them (see panel elevation key plan). The shorter spline must be held back 1/2" from meeting the longer spline to allow the side wall inner skin to be set into the corner (see **Figure 9**). Set the longer splines first (those extending all the way to the corner). Try to set butt splices in this bottom spline so that they do not coincide with panel splices. Do not set shorter bottom splines until the longer walls have been tilted in place. This allows a flat platform for assembling the longer panels. Generally, panels are joined together on the deck, then tilted up into position onto the bottom spline that has been installed shortly before erection. The two long walls are erected first, followed by the end (gable) walls.

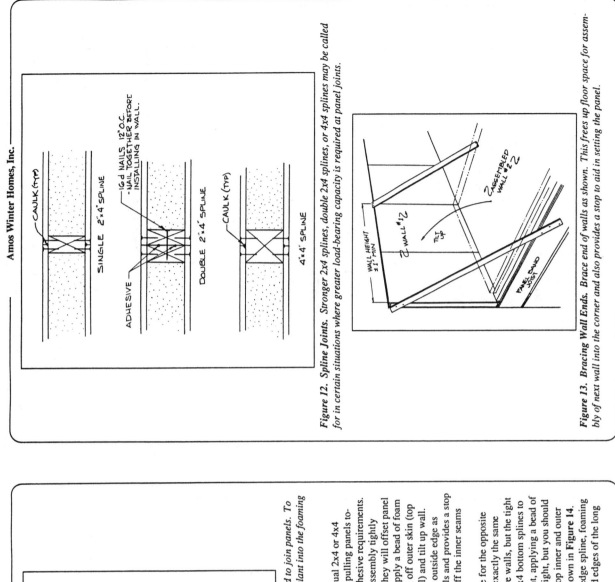

Figure 12. Spline Joints. Stronger 2x4 splines, double 2x4 splines, or 4x4 splines may be called for in certain situations where greater load-bearing capacity is required at panel joints.

Figure 13. Bracing Wall Ends. Brace end of walls as shown. This frees up floor space for assembly of next wall into the corner and also provides a stop to aid in setting the panel.

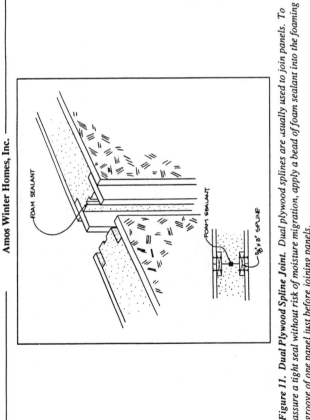

Figure 11. Dual Plywood Spline Joint. Dual plywood splines are usually used to join panels. To assure a tight seal without risk of moisture migration, apply a bead of foam sealant into the foaming groove of one panel just before joining panels.

Figure 12. Full-width routs are made in panels to the required depth for 2x4, dual 2x4 or 4x4 splines. Embed these splines into routed grooves with foam sealant just before pulling panels together, and secure with 8d nails as shown. Refer to **Figure 12** for caulk and adhesive requirements.

With truck straps and come-alongs (or equivalent apparatus), pull the wall assembly tightly together and install top and edge splines. With the top spline, stagger joints so they will offset panel seams. The 2 x4 edge splines should run from bottom rout to the top spline. Apply a bead of foam sealant into the rout for both top and edge splines before inseting splines. Nail off outer skin (top side of 2x4 panels) to installed splines per nailing schedule (8d at 8" o.c. typical) and tilt up wall. Brace wall as required to keep it straight and plumb. Brace end of walls on the outside edge as shown in **Figure 13**. This allows room on deck for assembly of gable end walls and provides a stop in tilting up these panels. With the panel in position, plumb and straight, nail off the inner seams with 8d nails 8" o.c.

Once the first long wall is up and braced in position install the bottom spline for the opposite long wall, then lay out the panels, join them and raise the wall into position in exactly the same manner. The end walls are also joined on the deck and raised into place as entire walls, but the tight spacing between long walls makes the erection a little different. First secure 2x4 bottom splines to the deck/band panel. Lay out the panels against the bottom spline for alignment, applying a bead of foam sealant between panels, as described above. The last panel will be quite tight, but you should be able to force it in. After all the panels are in place on the deck, slide in the top inner and outer plywood splines from the top of the wall (toward the center of the house), as shown in **Figure 14**. Then nail off the outer splines (top side of wall) and install the top spline and edge spline, foaming the routed groove first. Next apply two beads of adhesive along the waferboard edges of the long

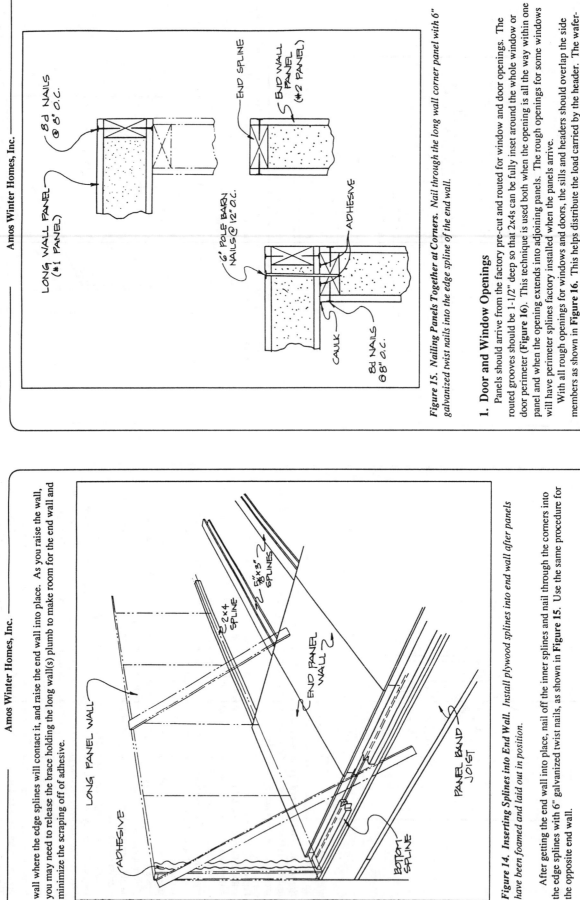

Figure 15. Nailing Panels Together at Corners. Nail through the long wall corner panel with 6" galvanized twist nails into the edge spline of the end wall.

1. Door and Window Openings

Panels should arrive from the factory pre-cut and routed for window and door openings. The routed grooves should be 1-1/2" deep so that 2x4s can be fully inset around the whole window or door perimeter (**Figure 16**). This technique is used both when the opening is all the way within one panel and when the opening extends into adjoining panels. The rough openings for some windows will have perimeter splines factory installed when the panels arrive.

With all rough openings for windows and doors, the sills and headers should overlap the side members as shown in **Figure 16**. This helps distribute the load carried by the header. The waferboard should be secured to the framing around rough openings from both sides with 8d nails or 2" screws spaced every 8".

wall where the edge splines will contact it, and raise the end wall into place. As you raise the wall, you may need to release the brace holding the long wall(s) plumb to make room for the end wall and minimize the scraping off of adhesive.

Figure 14. Inserting Splines into End Wall. Install plywood splines into end wall after panels have been foamed and laid out in position.

After getting the end wall into place, nail off the inner splines and nail through the corners into the edge splines with 6" galvanized twist nails, as shown in **Figure 15**. Use the same procedure for the opposite end wall.

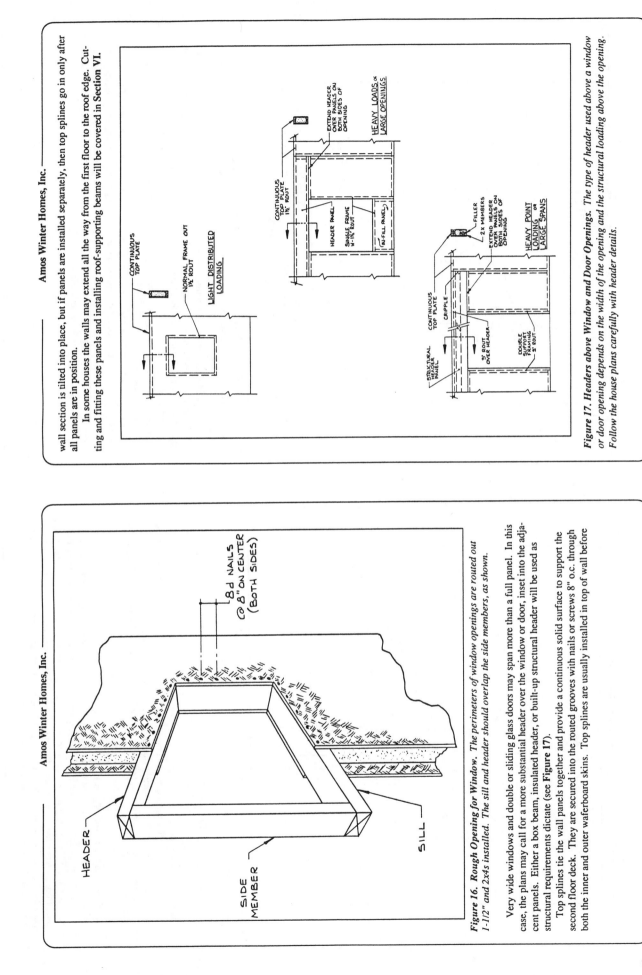

Amos Winter Homes, Inc.

wall section is tilted into place, but if panels are installed separately, then top splines go in only after all panels are in position.

In some houses the walls may extend all the way from the first floor to the roof edge. Cutting and fitting these panels and installing roof-supporting beams will be covered in **Section VI**.

CONTINUOUS
TOP PLATE

NORMAL FRAME OUT
1¼" ROUT

LIGHT DISTRIBUTED
LOADING

EXTEND HEADER
OVER PANELS ON
BOTH SIDES OF
OPENINGS

HEAVY LOADS or
LARGE OPENINGS

CONTINUOUS
TOP PLATE 1¼" ROUT

HEADER PANEL

SINGLE FRAME
W-1¼" ROUT

IN-FILL PANEL

FILLER
2 x MEMBERS

EXTEND HEADER
OVER PANELS ON
BOTH SIDES OF
OPENINGS

HEAVY POINT
LOADING or
LARGE SPANS

CONTINUOUS
TOP PLATE

CRIPPLE

5" ROUT
OVER HEADER

STRUCTURAL
HEADER PANEL

DOUBLE
SUPPORT
FRAMING
5" ROUT

Figure 17. Headers above Window and Door Openings. The type of header used above a window or door opening depends on the width of the opening and the structural loading above the opening. Follow the house plans carefully with header details.

Amos Winter Homes, Inc.

8d NAILS
@ 8" ON CENTER
(BOTH SIDES)

HEADER

SIDE
MEMBER

SILL

Figure 16. Rough Opening for Window. The perimeters of window openings are routed out 1-1/2" and 2x4s installed. The sill and header should overlap the side members, as shown.

Very wide windows and double or sliding glass doors may span more than a full panel. In this case, the plans may call for a more substantial header over the window or door, inset into the adjacent panels. Either a box beam, insulated header, or built-up structural header will be used as structural requirements dictate (see **Figure 17**).

Top splines tie the wall panels together and provide a continuous solid surface to support the second floor deck. They are secured into the routed grooves with nails or screws 8" o.c. through both the inner and outer waferboard skins. Top splines are usually installed in top of wall before

Amos Winter Homes, Inc.

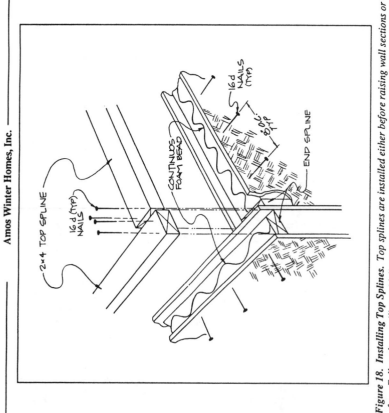

Figure 18. Installing Top Splines. Top splines are installed either before raising wall sections or after. Follow these nailing guidelines.

V. SECOND FLOOR DECK

1. Installing Beams

As the first floor walls are going up, you must consider how supporting girders or beams will be installed. Depending on the house design and size, there may be only purlin beams to support roof panels, or there may be girders to support second-floor joists as well. With either type, installation is basically the same.

Beam Pockets at the Top of a Panel Wall

The beam ends are set into **beam pockets** in the wall panels. How these beam pockets are made and how beam ends are prepared and set into place depends on where the pockets are located in a panel. If the beam pocket is at the top of a wall panel — as is common with second-floor girders spanning the width of a house — the pocket is open at the top, as shown in **Figure 20**. The beam pocket should be pre-cut and routed out to allow the beam end with special reinforcing scabs to be dropped down into it from above.

Amos Winter Homes, Inc.

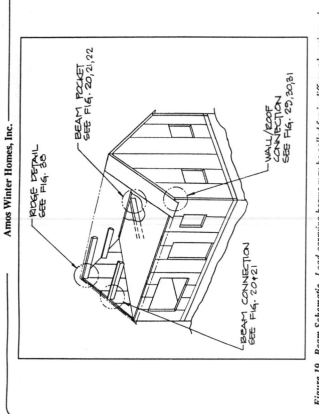

Figure 19. Beam Schematic. Load-carrying beams may be called for in different locations, depending on the structural requirements of the house. Beams are set into beam pockets in the wall panels which distribute the load into the wall panel skins.

If the beam pocket does not fall on a panel joint, then foam is routed out to a depth of 1-1/2" on both sides and the bottom as shown in **Figure 20**. 2x4 scabs are secured to the beam ends with two beads of construction adhesive and two offset rows of 16d nails 2" o.c. After the scabs are secured to the beam ends, apply a bead of expanding foam sealant into the routed grooves of the beam pocket and set the beam into position from above. Once in place, nail through the waferboard skin into the scabs from both the inside and out with 8d nails 2" o.c. as shown in **Figure 20**. Also nail through the outer waferboard skin into the end grain of the beam with 16d nails 2" o.c. in two staggered rows.

If the beam pocket aligns with a panel joint, as shown in **Figure 21**, it is not routed out for a 2x4 scab at the bottom, only on the two sides. The panel splines extend up to the bottom of the beam pocket and help support the beam. In some cases, heavier splines rather than the dual 5/8 x 3" plywood splines will be called for in panel joints under beam pockets. Such splines could be 2x4s, dual 2x4s or 4x4s, depending on the structural loading conditions. To fully carry the load from the beam, closer nail spacing may be called for than usual for securing panels into the spline(s). Be sure to follow Amos Winter Homes specifications carefully.

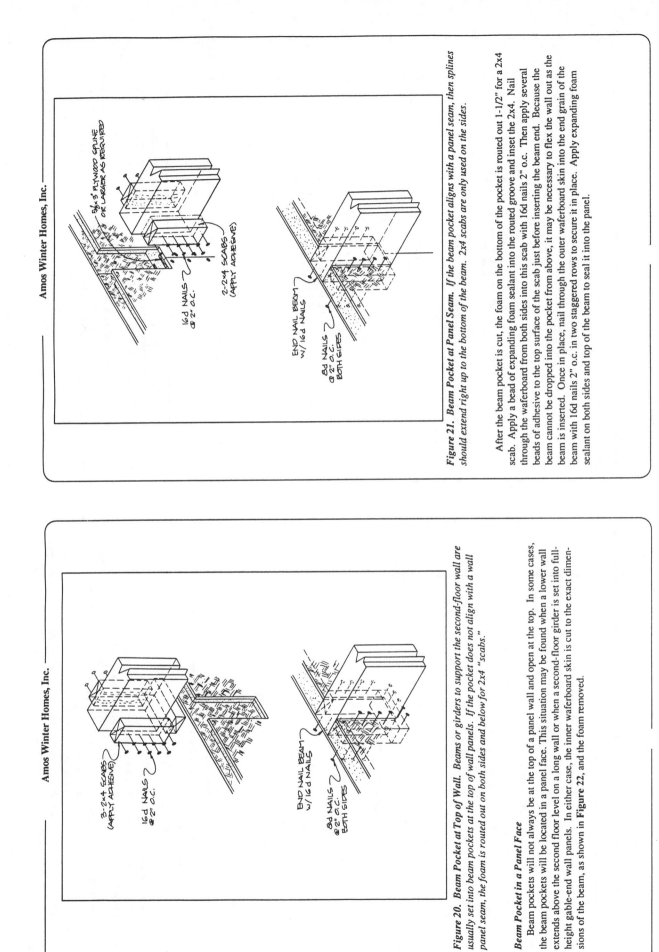

Figure 21. Beam Pocket at Panel Seam. *If the beam pocket aligns with a panel seam, then splines should extend right up to the bottom of the beam.* 2x4 scabs are only used on the sides.

After the beam pocket is cut, the foam on the bottom of the pocket is routed out 1-1/2" for a 2x4 scab. Apply a bead of expanding foam sealant into the routed groove and inset the 2x4. Nail through the waferboard from both sides into this scab with 16d nails 2" o.c. Then apply several beads of adhesive to the top surface of the scab just before inserting the beam end. Because the beam cannot be dropped into the pocket from above, it may be necessary to flex the wall out as the beam is inserted. Once in place, nail through the outer waferboard skin into the end grain of the beam with 16d nails 2" o.c. in two staggered rows to secure it in place. Apply expanding foam sealant on both sides and top of the beam to seal it into the panel.

Figure 20. Beam Pocket at Top of Wall. *Beams or girders to support the second-floor wall are usually set into beam pockets at the top of wall panels.* *If the pocket does not align with a wall panel seam, the foam is routed out on both sides and below for 2x4 "scabs."*

Beam Pocket in a Panel Face

Beam pockets will not always be at the top of a panel wall and open at the top. In some cases, the beam pockets will be located in a panel face. This situation may be found when a lower wall extends above the second floor level on a long wall or when a second-floor girder is set into full-height gable-end wall panels. In either case, the inner waferboard skin is cut to the exact dimensions of the beam, as shown in **Figure 22**, and the foam removed.

Doubled or tripled joists may be called for as girders and at stair or masonry penetrations. All multiple joist situations require the members to be glued and nailed together as per manufacturer's recommendations. "Laminated veneer lumber" joists are generally used for multiple joists. Joist

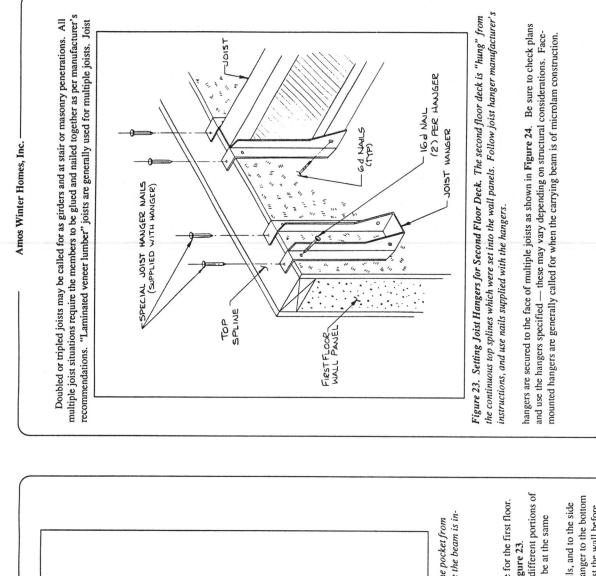

Figure 23. Setting Joist Hangers for Second Floor Deck. The second floor deck is "hung" from the continuous top splines which were set into the wall panels. Follow joist hanger manufacturer's instructions, and use nails supplied with the hangers.

hangers are secured to the face of multiple joists as shown in **Figure 24.** Be sure to check plans and use the hangers specified — these may vary depending on structural considerations. Face-mounted hangers are generally called for when the carrying beam is of microlam construction.

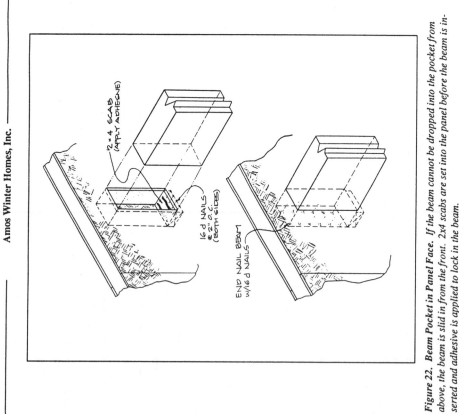

Figure 22. Beam Pocket in Panel Face. If the beam cannot be dropped into the pocket from above, the beam is slid in from the front. 2x4 scabs are set into the panel before the beam is in-serted and adhesive is applied to lock in the beam.

2. Installing Joists

Joists for the second floor are installed in a much different manner than those for the first floor. Nail joist hangers into the top spline of the first floor wall panels as shown in **Figure 23.** Refer to the house plan to find the proper joist spacing. The joist spacing in different portions of the floor may vary depending on the span. The top of the installed joists should be at the same height as the top of the wall panels and top splines.

Hangers are secured both to the top of the spline with special joist hanger nails, and to the side (through the waferboard) with 16d nails. Use two 6d nails to connect the joist hanger to the bottom flange of the joist (one on each side). The joist hanger must be pushed up against the wall before installing these nails.

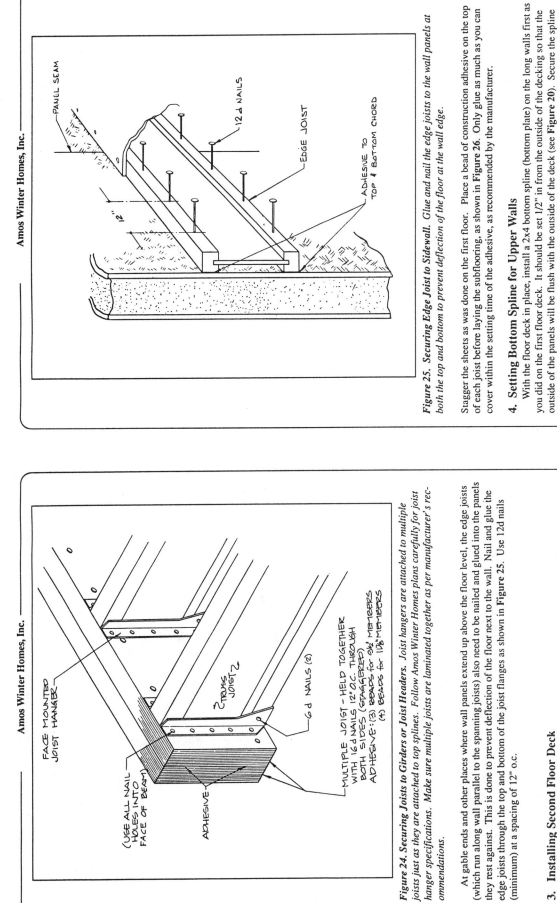

Figure 25. Securing Edge Joist to Sidewall. Glue and nail the edge joists to the wall panels at both the top and bottom to prevent deflection of the floor at the wall edge.

Stagger the sheets as was done on the first floor. Place a bead of construction adhesive on the top of each joist before laying the subflooring, as shown in **Figure 26**. Only glue as much as you can cover within the setting time of the adhesive, as recommended by the manufacturer.

4. Setting Bottom Spline for Upper Walls

With the floor deck in place, install a 2x4 bottom spline (bottom plate) on the long walls first as you did on the first floor deck. It should be set 1/2" in from the outside of the decking so that the outside of the panels will be flush with the outside of the deck (see **Figure 20**). Secure the spline with adhesive and 16d nails or 3" screws, 6" o.c. in two staggered rows.

Figure 24. Securing Joists to Girders or Joist Headers. Joist hangers are attached to multiple joists just as they are attached to top splines. Follow Amos Winter Homes plans carefully for joist hanger specifications. Make sure multiple joists are laminated together as per manufacturer's recommendations.

At gable ends and other places where wall panels extend up above the floor level, the edge joists (which run along wall parallel to the spanning joists) also need to be nailed and glued into the panels they rest against. This is done to prevent deflection of the floor next to the wall. Nail and glue the edge joists through the top and bottom of the joist flanges as shown in **Figure 25**. Use 12d nails (minimum) at a spacing of 12" o.c.

3. Installing Second Floor Deck

With the second-floor joists in place, the subfloor is next installed. Use the subfloor layout from the second floor framing plan (note starting point for placing subfloor sheets); 3/4" tongue-and-groove waferboard is most common. As with the first floor deck, lay the sheets of flooring perpendicular to the joists and flush with the outside of the wall or covering the edge joists (whichever situation exists).

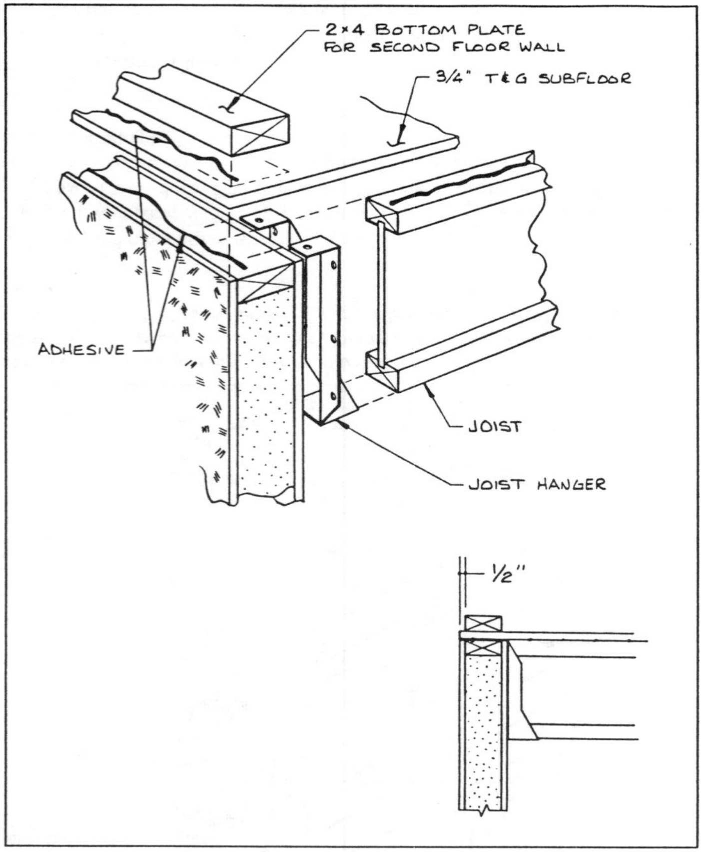

be bent so that the joist hangers can hang vertically (see Figure 31, page 37).

Gable-end wall panels often support laminated beams which carry much of the roof load as shown in **Figure 19** (page 25). These beams are installed in exactly the same way as they were for second floor girders, described previously. Because the beam pockets for roof beams are always located at the top of wall panels, the beams can be dropped into place from above. If supporting posts are called for in the plans, install them as specified.

There are generally three laminated beams installed in this manner: two purlin beams in mid-span and one ridge beam at the roof peak. There may be additional roof beams, depending on the house design, or there may not be a beam at the ridge. If a ridge beam is used, it is cut to match the roof slope on both sides with a 1" flat spot at the center on top. Purlins are cut to match the roof slope on one side with a 2" flat spot left on top.

For ease on the construction site, laminated roof beams should be set into place with a crane and one man at each gable end peak (**Figure 27**). The 2x4 scabs should be attached and all prep work should be done on the beam pockets before the beams are hoisted into place. Any joist hangers required on the purlins should be set before the beams are hoisted onto the roof. Refer to the framing plan.

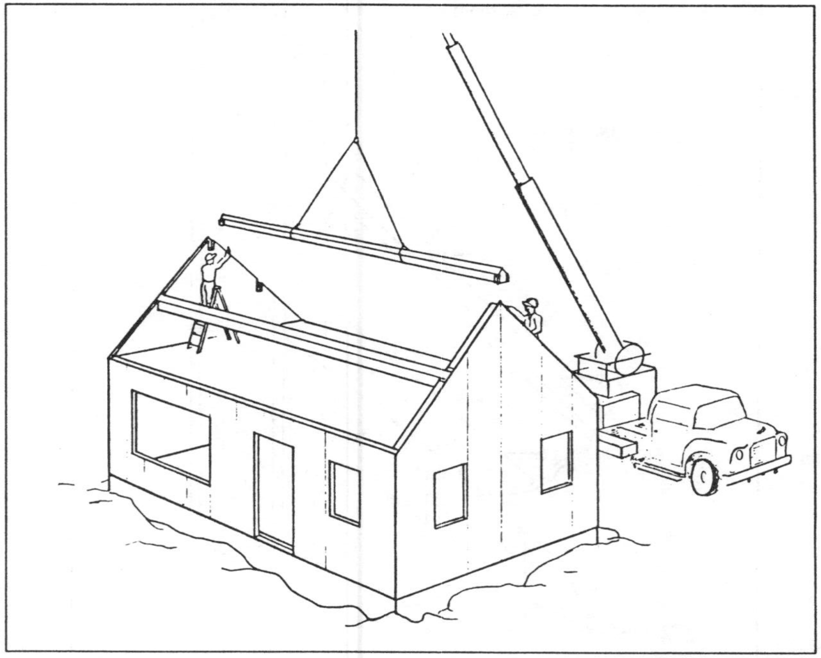

Figure 27. Setting Roof Beams. Beams are most easily installed with a crane. Finish all the prep work (securing scabs, installing joist hangers, etc.) before the crane arrives to reduce idle crane time.

Figure 26. Laying Second Floor Deck. The second floor decking extends all the way to the outside of the wall panels to fully tie the walls together. Apply construction adhesive as shown, both on the top spline and joists. Once decking is installed, the bottom splines for upper walls are secured (use the same order of assembly as with the first floor). The bottom splines should be set 1/2" in from the outside edge of the decking.

VI. INSTALLING SECOND-STORY WALL PANELS AND ROOF BEAMS

The same procedures are used here as for the first story walls (see **Section IV**) although the tops of the panels are often specially cut to match the roof slope. Cap all wall panels with 2x4 top splines or beveled splines as specified. If an attic floor is called for at this location, install joist hangers and joists as discussed for the second floor except that the joist hanger brackets will need to

1. Install Temporary Braces Between Roof Beams

Before installing roof panels, the roof beams must be braced and supported to prevent movement or deflection during installation of roof panels. To prevent the centers of the roof beams from spreading or pushing in while under unequal pressure during installation of roof panels, temporary bracing must be installed as shown in **Figure 28**. This brace has excellent strength both in compression and tension. Bracing should no be spaced no more than 12' o.c. Once final interior framing is completed, the brace(s) can be removed.

Figure 28. Temporary Bracing for Purlin and Ridge Beams. Temporary bracing for purlins is required while roof panels are installed to prevent spreading or movement. Bracing is removed after interior partition walls have been framed in.

2. Install Custom-cut Bottom Spline for Roof Panels

There are two different ways to secure roof panels at the eaves. Follow Amos Winter Homes plans carefully. With steep roof pitches (over 10:12, generally), the bottom edges of roof panels may fit into specially cut bottom splines which are secured to the attic subfloor as shown in **Figure 26**. Because this bottom spline is used for a panel installed at an angle, it is custom-cut for the precise roof angle in the plans.

Install the bottom roof spline so that the inner skins of the wall and roof panels will line up. With a floor deck, the spline will be secured on top of the subflooring. The roof spline will be cantilevered over the wall panel somewhat, the amount dependent on the roof pitch.

Secure the bottom roof spline into the attic subfloor and/or top spline of the wall panels with construction adhesive and 16d nails 6" o.c., in two staggered rows.

If a roof with a large overhang or roof pitch less than 10:12 is needed, a different method is used for joining roof and wall panels at the eave. With this technique, shown in **Figures 30 and 31**, the roof panel rests fully on the top spline of the wall panel, which is cut at a bevel matching the pitch of the roof.

A specially cut 2x6 (with parallelogram cross-section) is used as the top spline for the wall panels (an identical custom-cut 2x6 is used as the end spline of a plumb-cut roof panel). To accept this top spline, the wall panels require special routing (they should arrive pre-routed). Secure roof panels with both long twist nails and adhesive. For 4-1/2" roof panels, use 6" twist nails 12" o.c. set through the roof panel into the top spline. With 5-1/2" roof panels, use 8" twist nails. Apply two beads of construction adhesive between the top spline and roof panel before nailing.

With cathedral ceiling applications, temporary blocks of wood can be used to hold the roof panels in place during installation as shown in **Figure 30**. See the roof panel drawings or section views for locations of such blocks. Remove blocks after the assembly is completed and the glue has set.

Figure 29. Installing Bottom Spline for Roof Panels. With roof pitches steeper than 10:12, a specially cut bottom spline is used at the eaves to secure the roof panels to the top floor deck or wall.

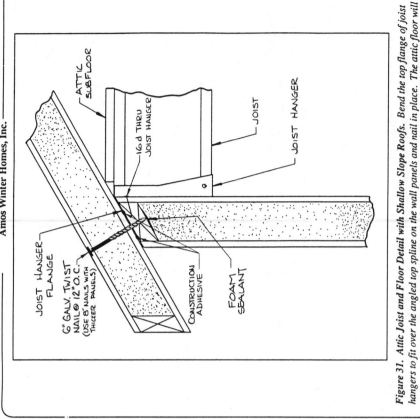

Labels in figure: ATTIC SUBFLOOR; 16 d THRU JOIST HANGER; JOIST; JOIST HANGER; JOIST HANGER FLANGE; 6" GALV. TWIST NAIL @ 12" O.C. (USE 8" NAILS WITH THICKER PANELS); CONSTRUCTION ADHESIVE; FOAM SEALANT

Figure 31. Attic Joist and Floor Detail with Shallow Slope Roofs. Bend the top flange of joist hangers to fit over the angled top spline on the wall panels and nail in place. The attic floor will extend above the wall-roof intersection slightly.

4. Securing the First Roof Panel

Frequently, there will be two courses of panels on each side of the roof. The lower course will span from the eave to the purlin beam, and the upper course will span from the purlin to the ridge beam (on smaller roofs, single panels will span the whole roof slope). Set all the lower panels first, on both sides of the roof. Start at one end and move along it, securing panels one by one.

The first panel, which will have a two-by rout in the outer and lower edges, is lined up with the gable end wall, either overhanging or flush as called for in the plans **(Figure 33)**. Apply two beads of adhesive to the top splines of the gabled end and beveled side walls and one bead on the purlin bevel. Secure the panel with 6" twist nails 12" o.c. as shown in the illustration. When thick panels (5-1/2") rather than standard panels (4-1/2") are being used for the roof, use 8" rather than 6" twist nails.

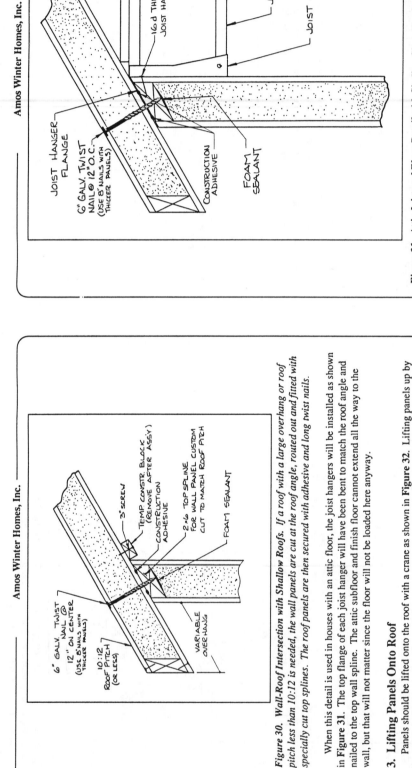

Labels in figure: 3" SCREW; TEMP. CONSTR. BLOCK (REMOVE AFTER ASS'Y); CONSTRUCTION ADHESIVE; 2x6 TOP SPLINE FOR WALL PANEL CUSTOM CUT TO MATCH ROOF PITCH; FOAM SEALANT; 6" GALV. TWIST NAIL @ 12" ON CENTER (USE 8" NAILS WITH THICKER PANELS); 10:12 ROOF PITCH (OR LESS); VARIABLE OVER HANG

Figure 30. Wall-Roof Intersection with Shallow Roofs. If a roof with a large overhang or roof pitch less than 10:12 is needed, the wall panels are cut at the roof angle, routed out and fitted with specially cut top splines. The roof panels are then secured with adhesive and long twist nails.

When this detail is used in houses with an attic floor, the joist hangers will be installed as shown in **Figure 31**. The top flange of each joist hanger will have been bent to match the roof angle and nailed to the top wall spline. The attic subfloor and finish floor cannot extend all the way to the wall, but that will not matter since the floor will not be loaded here anyway.

3. Lifting Panels Onto Roof

Panels should be lifted onto the roof with a crane as shown in **Figure 32**. Lifting panels up by hand or with hand winches is not recommended. A crane can set panels on the roof quickly, accurately and safely.

To lift panels onto the roof, drill a hole through each, offset slightly from center (toward the top end of the panel and somewhat to the side), and insert an eye bolt, as shown in **Figure 32**. The bolt should penetrate a section of 2x6 extending the width of the panel, and be secured on the bottom with a washer and nut. Use a 5/16" or larger eye bolt. It is very important to note that the bolt or attachment may fail. **Under no circumstances should anyone get underneath a panel being hoisted onto the roof!**

Splines should be installed in routs just before panel seams are foamed and butted together. After final positioning attach both skins to splines with 6d gun nails or 1-1/2" - 2" screws at 6" o.c. Alternately, splines can be pushed in after the panels have been foamed and butted together. With this technique, slide the splines in soon after joining panels, before the foam has begun to harden.

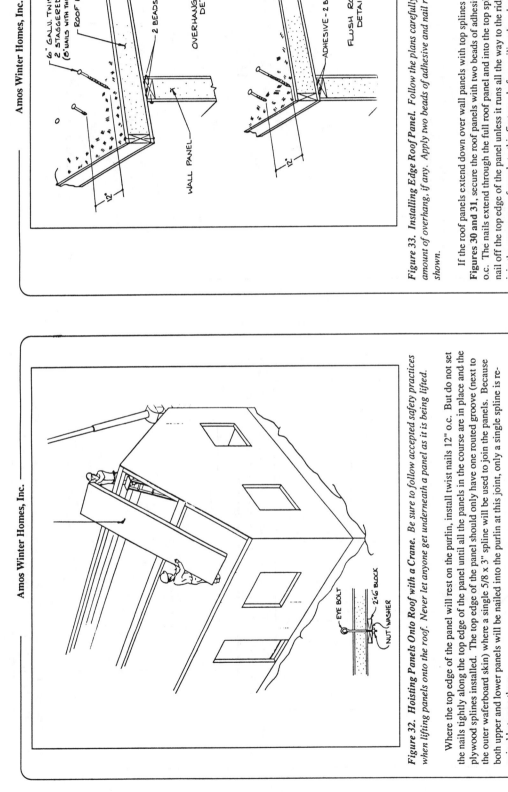

Figure 32. Hoisting Panels Onto Roof with a Crane. Be sure to follow accepted safety practices when lifting panels onto the roof. Never let anyone get underneath a panel as it is being lifted.

Where the top edge of the panel will rest on the purlin, install twist nails 12" o.c. But do not set the nails tightly along the top edge of the panel until all the panels in the course are in place and the plywood splines installed. The top edge of the panel should only have one routed groove (next to the outer waferboard skin) where a single 5/8 x 3" spline will be used to join the panels. Because both upper and lower panels will be nailed into the purlin at this joint, only a single spline is required between them.

At the bottom of the roof panel, the method of attachment depends on how the framing was done (refer back to **Figures 29, 30 and 31**). If the bottom of the roof panel fits into a bottom roof spline, attach this beveled 2-by spline to the deck or top wall spline with 16d nails at 6" o.c. in 2 staggered rows with 2 beads of adhesive. Nail through the outer waferboard skin into both the bottom roof spline and top wall spline using 16d nails 6" o.c. as shown in **Figure 34**. If possible, also nail through the inner waferboard skin into the bottom spline (from inside the house) with 8d nails 8" o.c. This may not be possible if there is a floor at the wall-roof intersection (predominantly used for the bow cape).

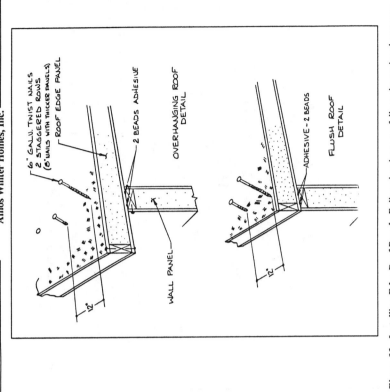

Figure 33. Installing Edge Roof Panel. Follow the plans carefully to determine the proper amount of overhang, if any. Apply two beads of adhesive and nail roof panel to the wall panel as shown.

If the roof panels extend down over wall panels with top splines cut at an angle as shown in **Figures 30 and 31**, secure the roof panels with two beads of adhesive and 6" or 8" twist nails 12" o.c. The nails extend through the full roof panel and into the top spline in the wall panel. Do not nail off the top edge of the panel unless it runs all the way to the ridge. This will make it easier to join the upper row of panels to this first row before nailing them both to the purlin.

5. Installing Other Roof Panels

Subsequent panels are installed in just the same manner. Install the 5/8 x 3" splines into the grooves in the first panel. Just before sliding the two panels together, apply a bead of foam sealant into the foaming channel between the splines as shown in **Figure 35**.

Panels are drawn tightly together with a come-along or ratcheting truck tie-down strap. Pull the panels together before securing them to the purlins, wall panels or splines at the joints. Follow this procedure with each roof panel being installed.

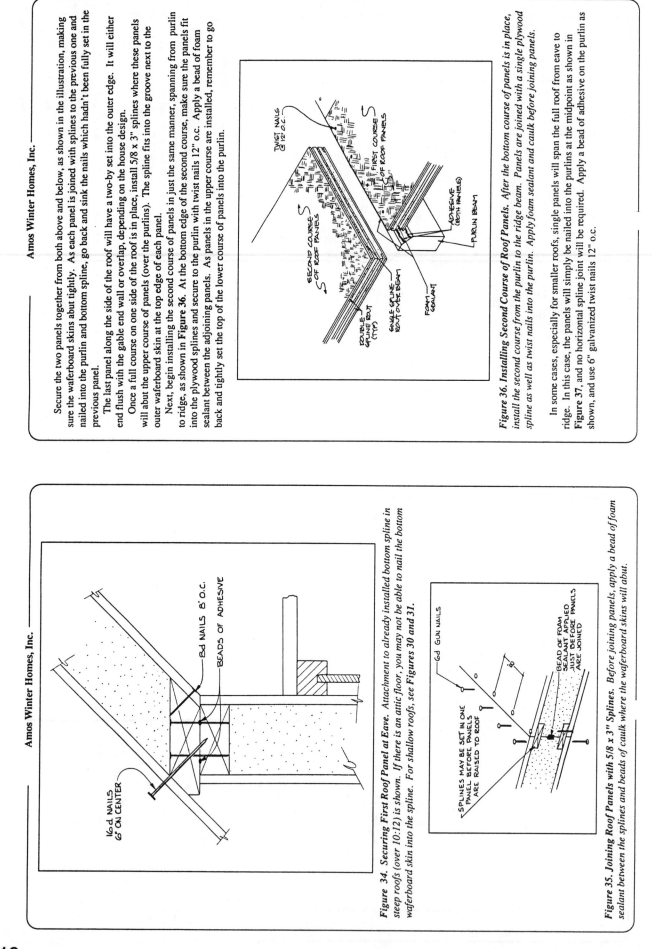

Secure the two panels together from both above and below, as shown in the illustration, making sure the waferboard skins about tightly. As each panel is joined with splines to the previous one and nailed into the purlin and bottom spline, go back and sink the nails which hadn't been fully set in the previous panel.

The last panel along the side of the roof will have a two-by set into the outer edge. It will either end flush with the gable end wall or overlap, depending on the house design.

Once a full course on one side of the roof is in place, install 5/8 x 3" splines where these panels will abut the upper course of panels (over the purlins). The spline fits into the groove next to the outer waferboard skin at the top edge of each panel.

Next, begin installing the second course of panels in just the same manner, spanning from purlin to ridge, as shown in **Figure 36**. At the bottom edge of the second course, make sure the panels fit into the plywood splines and secure to the purlin with twist nails 12" o.c. Apply a bead of foam sealant between the adjoining panels. As panels in the upper course are installed, remember to go back and tightly set the top of the lower course of panels into the purlin.

Figure 36. Installing Second Course of Roof Panels. After the bottom course of panels is in place, install the second course from the purlin to the ridge beam. Panels are joined with a single plywood spline as well as twist nails into the purlin. Apply foam sealant and caulk before joining panels.

In some cases, especially for smaller roofs, single panels will span the full roof from eave to ridge. In this case, the panels will simply be nailed into the purlins at the midpoint as shown in **Figure 37**, and no horizontal spline joint will be required. Apply a bead of adhesive on the purlin as shown, and use 6" galvanized twist nails 12" o.c.

Figure 34. Securing First Roof Panel at Eave. Attachment to already installed bottom spline in steep roofs (over 10:12) is shown. If there is an attic floor, you may not be able to nail the bottom waferboard skin into the spline. For shallow roofs, see Figures 30 and 31.

Figure 35. Joining Roof Panels with 5/8 x 3" Splines. Before joining panels, apply a bead of foam sealant between the splines and beads of caulk where the waferboard skins will abut.

beam to ensure a tight fit when the opposite roof panel is installed. Alternatively, you can leave an intentional gap and fill it after panels on both sides of the roof are installed. Use foam sealant or caulk depending on the size of the gap

When the roof is fully enclosed, coat each panel joint with roofing cement to keep moisture out until the finish roofing is installed. Moisture will not affect the structural properties of the waferboard, but it will cause the edges to swell, creating an uneven roof surface.

In some cases, there will be no ridge beam, so roof panels will have to meet at the peak without support. In this case, the panels are joined at the peak as shown in **Figure 39**. Along one side of the roof, specially cut two-by splines are inserted into routed grooves at the top edge of panels, foamed and nailed into place from above and below. Beveled splines for the other roof side are attached to those of the first side with 2 rows of adhesive and 16d nails at 6" o.c. in two staggered rows. When the final roof panels are installed, the upper routed edge (with bead of foam), must first engage the beveled plate at the ridge. The panel bottom must pivot downward so that the top groove fits around the the ridge spline and the bottom of the panel rests on the purlin (bead of adhesive on purlin, foam sealant in foaming groove). The panel is now pulled sideways, to close the joint (foamed) with the adjacent panel. A 4' section of plywood spline is hammered into the seam over the purlin. Attachment to purlin is as before: 12" o.c. for each panel with 6" or 8" nails, depending on panel thickness.

Figure 39. Joining Panels at Ridge Without Ridge Beam. Specially cut splines are inserted into the top edges of panels. Once these splines have been installed, the panels are joined with adhesive and 16d nails, angled through the waferboard and into the splines.

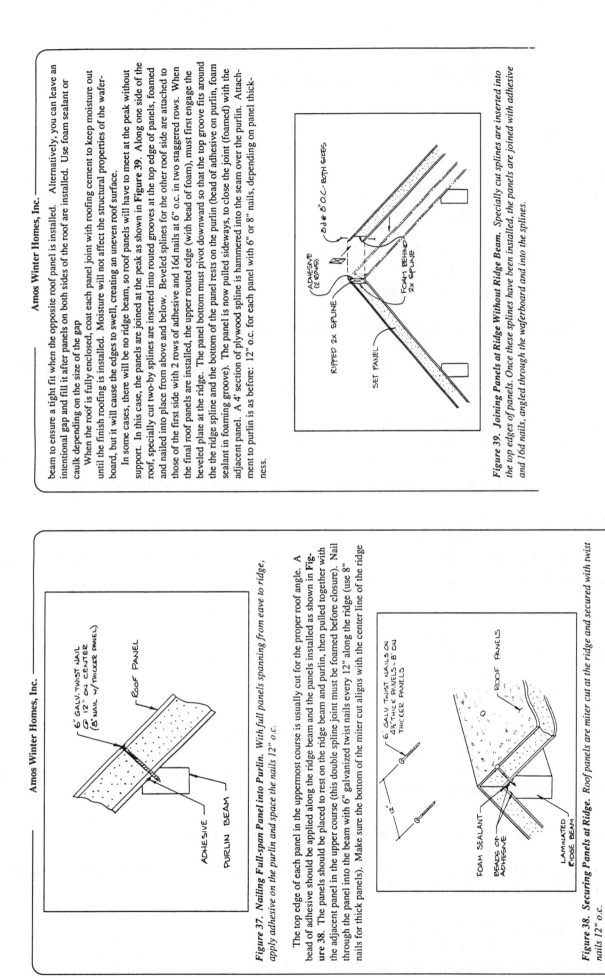

Figure 37. Nailing Full-span Panel into Purlin. With full panels spanning from eave to ridge, apply adhesive on the purlin and space the nails 12" o.c.

The top edge of each panel in the uppermost course is usually cut for the proper roof angle. A bead of adhesive should be applied along the ridge beam and the panels installed as shown in **Figure 38**. The panels should be placed to rest on the ridge beam and purlin, then pulled together with the adjacent panel in the upper course (this double spline joint must be foamed before closure). Nail through the panel into the beam with 6" galvanized twist nails every 12" along the ridge (use 8" nails for thick panels). Make sure the bottom of the miter cut aligns with the center line of the ridge

Figure 38. Securing Panels at Ridge. Roof panels are miter cut at the ridge and secured with twist nails 12" o.c.

SOURCES FOR "EARTH-FRIENDLY" BUILDING PRODUCTS

SHEATHING

Amoco Foam Products, 400 Northridge Rd., Atlanta, GA 30350
          800-241-4402   404-587-0535
Foam insulation sheathing made from recycled plastic

Homosote Co., Box 7240, W. Trenton, NJ 08628
          609-883-3300
A variety of sheathing products made from 100% recycled newsprint cellulose.

Huebert Fiberboard, Inc., P.O. Box 167, Boonville, MO 65233
          816-882-2704
Two wood-fiber roof insulation boards made from 15% recycled magazines and newspapers, and 85% waste mill wood chips.

Oregon Strand Board Co., 34363 Lake Creek Dr., Brownsville, OR 97327
          800-533-3374   503-466-5177
Sheathing consisting of several veneers of Douglas Fir and two thick inner layers of reconstituted wood fiber that are bonded together, creating a solid-core sheathing that is strong and durable.

Simplex Products Division, P.O. Box 10, Adrian, MI 49221
          517-263-8881
Insulating roof sheathing made from several plies of wood fiber, chemically- treated for water resistance and then pressure laminated for strength and stability.

Weyerhaeuser Co., Box 1645, Tacoma, WA 98477
          800-458-7180
Sheathing made from fast growing trees which are flaked and bonded with waterproof adhesive.

ROOFING MATERIALS & SYSTEMS

American Cem-Wood Products, P.O. Box C, Albany, OR 97321
          503-928-6397
Cemwood Shakes and Permatek shakes composed of roughly 2/3 portland cement and 1/3 wood fiber derived from waste sawmill chips.

CertainTeed Corp., P.O. Box 860, Valley Forge, PA 19482
          800-345-1145   215-341-7000
Variety of organic felt-based shingles that incorporate recycled paper and recycled waste slag with a resulting 20% to 25% recycled content.

Classic Products, P.O. Box 701, Piqua, OH 45356
          800-543-8938   513-773-9840
Rustic Shingle aluminum roofing made from recycled beverage-can aluminum.

Eternit, P.O. Box 679, Blandon, PA 19510
          215-926-0100
Fiber-cement composite roofing slates made from portland cement and wood fiber cellulose.

FibreCem Corporation, Box 411368, Charlotte, NC 28241
          800-346-6147   704-527-2727
Non-asbestos fiber-cement composite roofing slates made from portland cement, cellulose fibers, silica, and other additives.

Georgia Pacific, 133 Peachtree St. N.E., Atlanta, GA 30303
          800-447-2882
A variety of asphalt organic shingles with recycled waste paper used in the base.

Gerard Roofing Technologies, P.O. Box 9459, Brea, CA 92622
          714-529-0407
Roofing tiles and shakes with a base of pre-painted galvanized or galvalume steel and a coating of graded stone granules.

James Hardie Bldg. Products, 26300 LaAlameda #400, Mission Viejo, CA 92691
          800-426-4051   714-582-0731
Hardishake fiber cement composite roofing slates with a wood shake texture.

Masonite Corp., 1 South Wacker Drive, Chicago, IL 60606
          800-446-1649
Shingles made from wood fibers, bonded together under heat and pressure to form a single more dense and durable than natural wood.

Maxitile, Inc., 4153 L.B. McLeod Road, Orlando, FL 32811
          407-649-7178
Maxitile composite roofing consisting of portland cement, silica and cellulose fiber.

Metal Sales Manufacturing, 22651 Industrial Blvd., Rogers, MN 55374
          800-328-9316
Stile tile-like metal roofing panels with a base of hot-dipped galvanized steel.

Nailite International, 1251 Northwest 165th Street, Miami, FL 33169
          800-328-9018   305-620-6200
Shake roofing panels made from recycled plastic and virgin resins provided by General Electric.

RTS Company, 1805 Newton Avenue, San Diego, CA 92113
          800-879-8382
Nine different roofing systems consisting of steel or aluminum shingles.

Supradur, P.O. Box 908, Rye, NY 10580
          800-223-1948   914-967-8230
Fiber-cement composite roofing shingles available in slate, shake and traditional styles.

SIDING & TRIM

Abitibi-Price Corporation, Building Products Division, Troy, MI 48084
          800-521-4250
Molded hardboard siding products including panels, lap siding and simulated shake siding.

Eternit, P.O. Box 679, Blandon, PA 19510
          215-926-0100
Asbestos-free, fiber-cement building products used for fascias, facades and interior walls.

FibreCem Corporation, Box 411368, Charlotte, NC 28241
          800-346-6147   704-527-2727
Non-asbestos fiber-cement building panels and HandiBoard Lap Siding.

Georgia Pacific, 133 Peachtree St. N.E., Atlanta, GA 30303
          800-447-2882
Exterior and interior trim is a high resin, high temperature cured all-wood fiber composite.

James Hardie Bldg. Products, 26300 LaAlameda #400, Mission Viejo, CA 92691
          800-426-4051   714-582-0731
Asbestos-free fiber-cement products made of portland cement, ground sand and cellulose fiber.

Louisiana Pacific, 111 S.W. 5th Ave., Portland, OR 97204
          503-221-0800
Lap and panel siding, exterior trim, and soffit panels consisting of oriented strand board with a finished weather-proof surface.

Masonite Corp., 1 South Wacker Drive, Chicago, IL 60606
          800-446-1649
A variety of hardboard siding products.

Oregon Strand Board Co., 34363 Lake Creek Dr., Brownsville, OR 97327
          800-533-3374   503-466-5177
Lap siding consisting of three veneers of Douglas Fir and two thick inner layers of reconstituted wood fiber that are bonded together, creating a solid-core siding that is strong and durable.

Temple-Inland Forest Products, P.O. Drawer N, Diboll, TX 75941
          800-231-6060   409-829-5511
Engineered wood trim product made from wood chips that are refined into individual fibers, and formed under heat and pressure into a uniformly dense material.

INTERIOR WALLS & CEILINGS

Contact Lumber, 1881 S.W. Front Ave., Portland, OR 97201
          800-547-1038
A variety of jamb, moulding and other trim products made from thin veneers of finish wood laminated over a core of finger-jointed lumber.

Coverage Inc., P.O. Box 8498, Warwick, RI
401-738-1197
Textured wallpaper that is made from 66% recycled paper and 32% Srecycled woodchips.

Domtar Gypsum, P.O. Box 543, Ann Arbor, MI 48106
313-930-4700
Gypsum board containing various percentages of recycled scrap wallboard and byproduct gypsum reclaimed from the emissions of fossil-fueled factories and chemical production facilities.

Evanite Fiber Corp., P.O. Box E, Corvallis, OR 97333
503-753-1211   503-629-0860
Hardboard made from waste wood such as pallets and construction debris which is chipped, mixed with sawdust and plywood manufacturing waste, and heat-pressurized to form a solid panel.

Highland American Corp., P.O. Box 4340, East Providence, RI 02914
401-438-4990
A solid gypsum fiber board made from cellulose fiber (which consists of 95% post-consumer newsprint) and gypsum.

Louisiana Pacific, 111 S.W. 5th Ave., Portland, OR 97204
503-221-0800
Fiber-reinforced gypsum panels made from several layers of gypsum, perlite and cellulose fiber from recycled newsprint and telephone directories.

Meadowood Industries, Inc., 33242 Red Bridge Road, Albany, OR 97321
503-259-1303
Meadowood wall and ceiling board made from ryegrass straw - an agricultural byproduct.

Panterre America, Inc., 2700 Wilson Blvd., Arlington, VA 22201
703-247-3160
Panels made by heating and compressing a mixture of waste paper and agricultural fibers such as straw, rice hulls, or peanut shells.

Schenk, 290 Interstate N. Pkwy., Suite 190, Atlanta, GA 30339
404-953-6486
Fiber gypsum board consisting of cellulose (from newsprint and magazines), gypsum and perlite.

CARPET PADS OR BOARDS

Chris Craft Industrial Products, Inc., P.O. Box 70, Waterford, NY 12188
518-237-5850
A variety of carpet padding made from reclaimed and recycled fibers including jute, hemp, acrylics and cotton.

Dodge-Regupol, P.O. Box 989, Lancaster, PA 17603
800-322-1932   717-295-3400
Carpet underlayment made from 100% recycled tire rubber.

Homosote Co., Box 7240, W. Trenton, NJ 08628-0240
609-883-3300
Carpet underlayments made from 100% recycled newsprint cellulose.

RB Rubber Products, 904 E. 10th Ave., McMinnville, OR 97128
800-525-5530
Rubber matting made from 100% recycled waste tire rubber.

FLOOR COVERINGS

Albany Woodworks, P.O. Box 729, Albany, LA 70711
504-567-1155
Reused Longleaf heart pine wood flooring milled from dismantled pre-1900 buildings throughout the Southeastern United States.

Coastal Millworks, 1335 Marietta Blvd. N.W., Atlanta, GA 30318
404-351-8400
Resawn Pre-1900 Antique Heart Pine structural beams, reclaimed from non-historial structures slated for demolition.

Conklin's Authentic Antique Barnwood, R.D. #1 Box 70, Susquehanna, PA 18847
717-465-3832
Pine, Hemlock, Chestnut and Heart Pine flooring made from remilled antique beams.

Goodwin Lumber, Route 2, Box 119-AA, Micanopy, FL 32667
800-336-3118   904-466-0339
Flooring, dimensional lumber and beams milled from virgin heart pine logs reclaimed from riverbeds in the South.

Joinery Co., P.O. Box 518, Tarboro, NC 27886
919-823-3306
Flooring made from reused antique longleaf heart pine remilled from timbers salvaged during demolition of "Early American" buildings.

Tiresias, Inc., P.O. Box 1864, Orangeburg, SC 29116-1864
803-534-8478 800-553-8003
Flooring made from reused antique heart pine remilled from timbers salvaged during demolition of "Early American" buildings.

Carlisle Tire & Rubber Co., P.O. Box 99, Carlisle, PA 17013
717-249-1000
Softpave resilient tiles molded from recycled tires and a rubber binder.

Dodge-Regupol, P.O. Box 989, Lancaster, PA 17603
800-322-1932   717-295-3400
Natural cork flooring and recycled rubber EVERLAST flooring.

Durable Mat Company, P.O. Box 290, Norwalk, OH 44857
800-537-1603   419-668-8138
A variety of floor tiles and mats made from recycled rubber from truck tires.

Forbo North America, P.O. Box 32155, Richmond, VA 23294
800-233-0475   804-747-3714
Linoleum flooring made from softwood powder, linseed oil, pine tree resins, cork, chalk, and a jute backing.

GTE Products Corp., 1 Jackson Street, Wellsboro, PA 16901
717-724-8200
Prominence ceramic floor tiles made chiefly from waste glass produced in GTE's lightbulb manufacturing division.

Hendricksen Flooring, 8031 Mill Station Road, Sebastopol, CA 95472
707-829-3959
Natural linoleum and cork flooring and carpets made from natural Sisal, Coir fibers, and seagrass.

Image Carpets, P.O. Box 5555, Armuchee, GA 30105
404-235-8444
Carpets with 100% recycled PET plastic fibers (soft drink and ketchup bottles) as carpet face fibers.

Stoneware Tile Company, 1650 Progress Dr., Richmond, IN 47374
317-935-4760
Durable, glass bonded tiles that are made from recycled auto windshield glass.

Summitville Tiles, Inc.,, Summitville, OH 43962
216-223-1511
Four styles of impervious glazed porcelain pavers made from a byproduct of feldspar mining.

Syndesis Studio, 2908 Colorado Ave., Santa Monica, CA 90404
213-829-9932
Solid pre-cast lightweight cement-based Syndecrete products made to custom order.

LANDSCAPING & PATIO/DECK BUILDING MATERIALS

Carrysafe, 361 Bluff City Blvd., Elgin, IL 60120
800-231-9721   312-523-1366
Plastic planking from recycled high density polyethelene plastic derived from milk jugs.

Environmental Plastics, Inc., 4981 Keelson Dr., Columbus, OH 43232
614-861-2107
Plastic lumber manufactured from recycled plastics and regrind vinyls.

Replas Products, 411 B Southgate Court, Mickleton, NJ 08056
609-423-2607
Many various products made from recycled plastic.

Rivenite Corporation, 6121 Highway 98 North, Lakeland, FL 33809
        813-858-8299
Rivenite composite lumber made from recycled wood fibers and scrap plastics.

COMPLETE HOUSE SYSTEMS

Mansion Industries Inc., P.O. Box 2220, City of Industry, CA 91746
        818-968-9501   800-423-6589
Manufactures ENVIROCOR panels from waste agricultural fibers.

Solar Survival Architecture, P.O. Box 1041, Taos, NM 87571
        505-758-9870
Earth-sheltered, adobe houses using recycled tires, cans and bottles as substrate for walls.

Stone Container Corporation, 2021 Swift Drive, Oak Brook, IL 60521
        312-574-9550
Low-cost housing units made from corrugated fiberboard panels assembled with bolts.

WALL FRAMING

Alpine Structures Incorporated, P.O. Box 1006, Oxford, NC 27565
        800-672-2326
Structural I-joists, engineered ASI headers, and Timbermax laminated veneer lumber.

Bellcomb Technologies, Inc., 70 N. 22nd Ave., Minneapolis, MN 55411
        612-521-2425
Building system using a series of interlocking kraftpaper honeycomb panels.

Bohemia Inc., P.O. Box 277, Saginaw, OR 97472
        800-999-2326
Adhesive-laminated beams, columns and headers.

Boise Cascade Corporation, P.O. Box 50, Boise, ID 83728
        800-237-4013
I-Joist consisting of a finger-jointed plywood web between laminated veneer flanges.

Champion International Corporation, P.O. Box 1593, Tacoma, WA 98401
        206-572-8300
A complete line of finger-jointed lumber.

Georgia Pacific, 133 Peachtree St. N.E., Atlanta, GA 30303
        800-447-2882
Laminated veneer beams and headers, and wood I-beams and I-joists consisting of plywood webs and 2 ft by 4 ft lumber.

Jefferson Lumber Company, P.O. Box 696, McCloud, CA 96057
        916-235-0609
Timbers, beams and lumber milled from timbers reclaimed from old buildings.

P & N Recycling, 140 Mariposa Terrace, Medford, OR 97504
503-772-4132   916-987-0697
Recycled dimensional lumber from dismantled structures-including old lumber mills.

Standard Structures Inc., P.O. Box K, Santa Rosa, CA 95402
707-544-2982
Engineered wood products including ssl Joists, finger-jointed and laminated framing lumber.

Tecton Laminates, 2700 Pinegrove Ave. #43, Port Huron, MI 48060
800-825-8720   313 385-8809
Laminated lumber beams and headers.

Trus Joist Corp., P.O. Box 60, Boise, ID 83707
208-375-4450
Laminated veneer lumber, and I-joists with flanges, and plywood or oriented strand board webs.

Unadilla Laminated Products, 32 Clifton St., Unadilla, NY 13849
607-369-9341
Structural glued laminated columns, trusses, arches, purlins, and beams.

Willamette Industries, P.O. Box 68, Tualatin, OR 97062
503-692-5410
Joists consisting of machine stress rated (MSR) lumber flanges joined to oriented strand board web using finger joints.

MISCELLANEOUS

ADO Products, 7357 Washington Ave., Edina, MN 55439
612-943-2190
Attic ventilation chutes made from recycled high-density polyethylene.

A.E.R.T. Inc., P.O. Box 172, Junction, TX 76849
915-446-3864
A composite material comprised of recycled wood fiber and recycled polyethylene.

American Standard, Box 6820, 1 Centennial Plaza, Piscataway, NJ 08855
800-821-7700 ext. 4023   201-980-3000
Bathtubs and whirlpools manufactured with a porcelain enameled surface with an enameling grade metal and structural composite material.

Aquapore Moisture Systems, 610 South 80th Ave., Phoenix, AZ 85043
602-936-8083
Moisture Master soaker hoses made from recycled tire rubber.

Catrel USA, Raritan Plaza II, CN 3106, Edison, NJ 08818
201-225-4849
Recycling and conversion of municipal solid waste into building material products.

Cunningham Brick Co., Route 2, Cunningham Brick Rd., Thomasville, NC 27360
919-472-6181
Brick Nuggets made from reprocessed oil contaminated soils.

Earth Products Intl., 5750 W. 95th Street, #124, Overland Park, KS 66207
913-642-7001
Building materials and products made mostly from dirt.

Glass Aggregate Corp., 1085 Oakleigh Road N.W., Grand Rapids, MI 49504
616-791-0793
A totally self-contained underdrain unit, consisting of a geotextile non-woven fabric sleeve filled with crushed, recycled glass.

Hexagon Honeycomb Corp., 7980 Clayton Rd., #201, St. Louis, MO 63117
314-647-0701
Structural kraft paper honeycomb core material for commercial applications.

International Honeycomb, 9700 Bell Ranch Dr., Santa Fe Springs, CA 90670
800-323-9163   213-944-0052
Manufacturers of kraft paper honeycomb core material suitable for panel fabrication.

Mandish Research International, 5055 State Road 46, Mims, FL 32754
407-267-2561
Precast lightweight concrete products made with recycled fiberglass, plastic, or old tires.

Maryland Clay Products, 7100 Muirkirk Road, Beltsville, MD 20705
301-792-0444   301-953-2214
Paving bricks that incorporate oil-contaminated soil in their composition.

Maze Nails, 100 Church St., Peru, IL 61354
815-223-8290
A complete line of nails made from recycled steel.

Medite Corporation, P.O. Box 4040, Medford, OR 97501
503-773-2522
Formaldehyde-free medium density fiberboard.

Neutralysis, 550 Frontage Road Suite 291, Northfield, IL 60093
312-441-9444
Non-toxic concrete aggregate made from municipal waste.

Phoenix Scientific, 3670 N. High St., Columbus, OH 43214
614-267-0100
Paving bricks made from municipal incinerator ash.

Plastic Tubing Incorporated, Box 878, Roseboro, NC 28382
919-525-5121
Septic tank pipe and fittings made from recycled HDPE plastic.